*Guy Lyon Playfair*

# MEDICINE, MIND & MAGIC

O, she's warm!
If this be magic, let it be an art
Lawful as eating.

Shakespeare, *The Winter's Tale*

AQUARIAN

THE AQUARIAN PRESS
Wellingborough, Northamptonshire

First published 1985 by Jonathan Cape Ltd.
First trade paperback edition 1987

© GUY LYON PLAYFAIR 1987

British Library Cataloguing in Publication Data

Playfair, Guy Lyon
Medicine, mind and magic.
1. Psychical research
I. Title
133      BF1031

ISBN 0-85030-588-8

*The Aquarian Press is part of the
Thorsons Publishing Group*

Printed and bound in Great Britain

# Contents

# Acknowledgments

For permission to quote copyright material, I would like to thank Dr E. J. Dingwall, Professor Alister Hardy, Dr Ainslie Meares, Dr Howard Miller, Dr Richard Newman, Dr Bernauer W. Newton, Dr Loren Parks and Colin Wilson.

My thanks are also due to the librarians and staff of the Science Museum Library, the British Society of Medical and Dental Hypnotists, the Society for Psychical Research, the College of Psychic Studies and the Brompton Library.

I am most grateful for help received in many forms from Michael Barnes, Kenneth J. Batcheldor, Tony Bloomfield, David Bolt, Nicholas Clark-Lowes, Anthony Colwell, Joe Cooper, Dr Alan Gauld, Dr Brian Inglis, Barbara Ivanova, Marcus McCausland, Dr Crisetta MacLeod-Morgan, Eleanor O'Keeffe, Professor J. H. L. Playfair, Dr Lee Pulos, Glen Rein, Dr Stanley Rose, Dr Carl Sargent, David St Clair, Tania Schmoeller and Larissa Vilenskaya, in addition to those named above and to a number of sources who have asked to remain anonymous.

G.L.P.

# Part I

# MEDICINE

# Miracle at East Grinstead

The patient was a horrible sight. His whole body, apart from his face, neck and chest, was covered by a black substance that bore no resemblance to normal skin. As he was being wheeled into the operating theatre in the Queen Victoria Hospital, East Grinstead, the anaesthetist noted 'large warty excrescences' five millimetres wide all over the legs and feet, while the hands were enveloped in 'a rigid horny casing' that had cracked and become chronically infected.

'To the touch,' he wrote later, 'the skin felt as hard as a normal finger-nail, and was so inelastic that any attempt at bending resulted in a crack in the surface, which would then ooze blood-stained serum.' In fact, the patient could hardly move without causing painful fissures to appear in the grotesque armour-plating he had worn all his life.

He was sixteen years old. His name has not been made public, so I will call him John. He was suffering from what is known as fish-skin disease; a misleading term, for the vile black substance that covered most of his body had none of the functional beauty of real fish skin. He had been born with it, and it had become thicker and darker throughout his life, during which he had been in and out of several hospitals without being cured. At school, he had been treated like an outcast because of his unpleasant appearance and equally unpleasant smell. Not surprisingly, he was shy and withdrawn, and his chances of leading a normal life seemed minimal.

The Queen Victoria Hospital had a worldwide reputation for its plastic surgery department, where Sir Archibald McIndoe and his team had worked wonders on the shattered bodies of pilots shot down during the Battle of Britain. Now, the plastic surgeons were going to see what they could do for John, and on 25 May 1950 they

*Medicine, Mind, and Magic*

set to work on him, starting with the palms of his hands. If these could be restored to normality by skin transplants, John could at least do manual work, which he had been unable to do previously without considerable pain.

They scraped the black mess off both his palms, and transplanted some skin from his chest. The operations did not succeed; a month later the newly-grafted skin had thickened and turned black, and a second attempt was equally unsuccessful. Sir Archibald McIndoe himself had a look at the patient, and agreed with his colleagues that there was no reason to suppose that they could do anything more for him. We can safely assume that this meant the end of the road for the poor boy. Plastic surgery was his last hope, and if the world's most celebrated team of plastic surgeons felt obliged to give up, John and his parents would have to accept the inevitable. He was incurable.

Then, in February 1951, the anaesthetist had an idea.

'Why don't you treat him with hypnosis?' he asked one of the surgeons. 'It's very good for cases like this.'

The anaesthetist was Dr Albert A. Mason, a senior registrar who was also a skilled hypnotist. Among his successful cases had been several involving the removal of warts by suggestion under hypnosis, and as far as he was concerned, John's case looked like one of multiple warts. If one wart could be removed by hypnosis, why not a million of them?

The surgeon was not amused. He was already very annoyed that John's skin grafts were not taking.

'He turned round and looked at me rather sourly,' Mason recalled later, 'and said "Why don't you?", and walked out of the theatre.' None of those concerned can have had any idea that medical history was about to be made.

Mason duly hypnotised John, told him that the warts were going to fall off his left arm, and asked him to come back the following week.

'About five days later', Mason reported, 'the horny layer softened, became friable, and fell off.' Underneath it was what appeared to be normal skin. After another five days, John's arm was 'completely clear from shoulder to wrist'. He was referring only to his patient's left arm. The right one was as black as ever.

Feeling rather pleased with himself, Mason took John along to show him to the surgeon. 'Well,' he said, 'I told you warts did very well with hypnosis.'

The surgeon's jaw dropped. 'Jesus Christ!' he exclaimed. 'Do you know what you've done?' (These are his exact words as recalled by Dr Mason.)

'No,' Mason replied. 'What?'

'This', said the surgeon, 'is a case of congenital ichthyosiform erythrodermia of Brocq. Now go into the library and look it up.'

Mason did so, and was astonished to find that ichthyosis, as it is commonly known, is not only congenital, meaning that John had been born with it, but also structural and organic. This meant that John's skin had no oil-forming glands that would enable its outer layers to flake off and renew themselves. His black armour-plating would just go on building up. In the opinion of one of Britain's leading medical hypnotists, Dr Stephen Black: 'This is an appalling and entirely disfiguring condition, and normally remains with the patient throughout life – which is apt to be short.' It had been considered incurable since 1904.

'For something like this to change is really as unbelievable as for a club foot to change,' Mason said. But it had changed.

He told his colleague what he had found in the library.

'Well,' said the surgeon, 'you'd better have an explanation, because we're presenting (John) at the Royal Society of Medicine in two days.'[1,2]

Mason did not have an explanation, and nor did anybody else. Some of the doctors who attended the demonstration at the Royal Society were profoundly impressed. Dr Ray Bettley was surprised that such a case should respond to any kind of treatment. 'That it should respond to hypnotic suggestion', he said, 'demands a revision of current concepts of the relation between mind and body.' Dermatologist Dr Kathryn Cohen was 'astounded by the changes wrought in the patient's skin'. John's cure, she said, was 'unprecedented and inexplicable'.

One doctor made a gallant attempt to explain it. 'We must suppose', he said, 'that the hypnotic suggestion acts locally in some such way by soothing or accentuating the psychical trauma, whatever that may be.' Another doctor said he was not surprised by the cure, since ichthyosis was just another allergy, to which Dr Cohen retorted that nobody knew exactly what an allergy was in the first place. (The original definition by Von Pirquet, the Viennese doctor who coined the word in 1906, was 'an acquired specific altered capacity to react' by body tissue.)[3]

Even Stephen Black, who carried out a good deal of research into hypnosis and allergy in the 1960s (some together with Mason), could only speculate that 'allergy, or something very like it, is still as good a guess as anything else' to describe ichthyosis.[4] It seemed clear that nobody had any idea what Mason had really done. The editor of the *British Medical Journal* commented on 'the need for further basic scientific work on the relation between the mind and the skin', while a *BMJ* reader predicted that Mason's case 'may well open up a new province in pathology and therapeutics'.

Now the story becomes considerably more complicated. After his initial and immediate success with John's left arm, Mason carried on his treatment, starting with the right arm and moving on to the legs and finally the trunk. He was eventually able to report an improvement in each area, ranging from 50 per cent on the legs and feet (which had previously been 'completely and heavily covered' by the black armour) to 95 per cent on the arms and complete clearing of the palms, although the fingers were 'not greatly improved'. So far, so good.

A year later, Mason was delighted to find that John's mental state had changed as dramatically as had that of his skin. He had become 'a normal happy boy' and had found a job as an electrician's assistant. Although all areas of his skin had not cleared entirely, there had been no relapse in the successful treated parts. After a further three years the situation was much the same. The cure was not total but, as far as it went, it seemed to be permanent.

Mason then asked John if he would like him to try to clear up the remaining black patches. John agreed, but the experienced hypnotist found to his bewilderment that his star patient had become 'totally unhypnotisable'. He even seemed rather frightened by the idea of being hypnotised. Mason decided 'to leave well alone'.

He then went on to tackle a further eight cases of congenital ichthyosis. These were not reported until 1961, when he wrote to the *British Medical Journal* announcing that every one of them had been a complete failure. 'Why one case responded and the others did not still remains a mystery,' he commented. In the same year, however, an Oxford general practitioner, Dr C. A. S. Wink, published an account of his successful treatment of two similar cases – two little sisters aged seven and five. Like Mason, he had worked on one part of the body at a time, and had also failed to bring about total clearing although there had been considerable improvement in each case.[5,6]

Mystery was being added to mystery. Why should a hypnotist succeed with one patient, then fail with eight others? Why should he be unable to hypnotise his original patient four years later? Why should Wink succeed with *two* patients? Why should some parts of the body respond to suggestion under hypnosis more than others? Above all, why on earth should any part of the body respond at all? As Mason himself put it, referring to ichthyosis and a couple of other skin diseases that he had managed to treat successfully: 'When one considers that these conditions are caused by a congenital *absence* of certain dermal tissues, one can only conjecture wildly as to why they should respond to anything.'

He went on to conjecture very modestly and cautiously, going out of his way to thank John for recovering from a 'hitherto incurable disease ... thereby making me believe that I had "power" and so causing me to spend ten years disproving this belief'. His original conclusion was that either there was a psychological factor in the cause of ichthyosis, or else it was possible to influence a congenital organic condition by psychological means. Or, of course, it could be a combination of both.[7]

Recalling the original case in 1982, thirty years after the event, by which time he had moved to California, become a psychoanalyst, and given up hypnotism altogether, Mason was still mystified. 'I suppose it means that potentially anything can be done, since we have the embryonic possibilities within our skin.' He assumed that there must have been 'tiny remnants of glands' in John's body that had somehow come to life under the stimulus of suggestion under hypnosis. 'But', he added, 'the stimulus for such a profound change must be equally profound.'

True, no doubt, but what was the stimulus? Did it come from the patient or the hypnotist? If it came from John, why did it work the first time and on several subsequent occasions, only to fail four years later? If it came from Mason, the same questions arise. We can rule out the possibility that he had lost the knack, for he subsequently published several cases of successful treatment of other conditions. Anyway, good hypnotists tend to get better at their job, helped by the increasing confidence that comes with experience. They do not suddenly forget how to do it.

Having asked so many questions, I will now try to answer at least one, not by wild conjecture, but by drawing attention to some features of the original case that have not been mentioned in any comments on it, including Mason's, that I have been able to find.

When Mason first saw John, he thought he was looking at a case of multiple warts. This was quite a reasonable assumption. Ichthyosis is fortunately a rare disease, and many doctors never come across it at all. He knew he could cure warts by hypnotic suggestion, so there was no reason why he should not be able to cure millions of them. He had complete confidence. He had also been given a considerable stimulus when his surgeon colleague had told him to go ahead and cure the patient himself. This was a direct challenge, and it is well known that on such occasions people often find themselves doing things they did not know they could do, such as making an effective speech in public or performing 'superhuman' feats of physical strength.

Mason found out what John's disease really was, and that it was supposed to be incurable, only after he had already begun to cure it. It must be rather unsettling to find out that you have just done something that is supposed to be impossible, especially if you do not understand how you did it. Mason's original total confidence must have begun to falter, if only at a very deep unconscious level, until it eventually fell to the point where he could not even get his patient into the hypnotic state. In 1955 he was dealing with the same disease and the same patient as in 1951. The only thing that had changed was the state of his own mind.

Dr Wink, unlike Mason, did know that his patients had ichthyosis and not warts. He also knew something Mason had not known in 1951 – that ichthyosis could be cured by suggestion under hypnosis. So he too had confidence in his own ability, though for a very different reason. It is important to remember that Mason mentioned his eight failures only *after* Wink had published his own case. If Wink had known about these earlier, his level of confidence must surely have been lowered. It is becoming evident that the confidence-level of the hypnotist is a crucial factor in a successful cure. Indeed, in a recent book written by and for medical hypnotists, we find the following (with emphasis in the original): 'Suggestions must be given in a positive and dogmatic way, *there must be no doubt in the hypnotist's voice (or mind) that the improvement suggested will be achieved.*'[8]

How, it will be asked, can a hypnotist's mind be expected to be free from doubt if he is trying to do something that has not been done before? Dr Wink made a revealing comment in this context. 'In most cases', he wrote in his report, 'emphatic and optimistic assertions of cure by hypnosis remain indefensible so long as the outcome is in fact uncertain.' On the other hand, he added, to make cautious suggestions is 'to spike one's own guns by undermining the authority behind one's suggestion'.

The second statement is undoubtedly true. The first is a matter of opinion, and I cannot help suspecting that Mason's 1951 case would not have been successful if he had known what it was he was trying to cure. He might even not have attempted it. Who can tell how many other 'incurable' conditions are as incurable as is generally assumed?

The cases mentioned above are not the only ones in recent years in which hypnotically-induced cures have taken place that can be described as miraculous – not implying the intervention of any supernatural agency, but in my dictionary's other sense of 'exciting admiring awe'.

The work of Dr Dabney Ewin of Tulane University in New Orleans certainly excites my admiring awe. In the casualty ward of the hospital where he is an associate professor of surgery, he uses hypnosis not as a last resort, but as a first resort, in the emergency treatment of burns. Indeed, the success of his daring method seems to depend on how soon his patients can get to him after their accidents.

When we burn ourselves, two quite separate things happen. First, the area involved is damaged by the heat. This happens immediately, but there is then an 'inflammatory response' from the body that leads to swelling, inflammation and pain. This reaction can take up to twenty-four hours to have its full effect, and it seems there is a time-lag before the original stimulus-message is sent from the site of the wound. Ewin takes advantage of this.

'If you can get to them within the first two hours, before the response has been released, you can block the response and, in effect, have them react as though they had not been burned,' he explained in a 1982 interview. He then produced photographs of the damage done to a patient's arm after an explosion of acetylene – which burns at 3,000 degrees Centigrade. Within an hour of the accident, he had hypnotised the man, implanted the suggestion of feeling cool and comfortable, dressed the wound and sent him back to work. The following day, the skin was still charred, but there was no swelling, no infection, and above all no pain. The arm was completely healed in twelve days. There is, it seems, a place for hypnosis in the first-aid kit.[9]

There are obvious difficulties in carrying out controlled experiments to prove this. The researcher would need two identically-burned arms to work on, one of which would have to be left untreated. He is not likely to come across these by chance, so he would have to burn them deliberately. Any doctor who did such a thing today would probably be struck off the register for malpractice.

Yet it has been done, and the man who did it was Professor Joseph Delboeuf (1831–96) of the University of Liège, a member of the Belgian Royal Academy. The patient, named as Mademoiselle J., is thought to have been one of his servants. If so, she was a remarkably obedient one, and her suffering for the cause of science deserves to be remembered.

At seven o'clock one evening in 1887, Mademoiselle J. sat at a table and laid her bare arms upon it. Delboeuf heated an iron bar eight millimetres wide until it was red hot. He then calmly proceeded to brand the woman by laying the bar down so that it rested on both her arms, suggesting as he did so that she would feel pain only in her left arm. This, not surprisingly, she did.

He then bandaged both arms, and on removing the bandages the following morning he found a clearly outlined stripe of exactly the same width as the bar on the right arm, with no sign of swelling or inflammation. The left arm presented quite a different picture: the eight-millimetre stripe had expanded to three centimetres of inflamed blister. And it hurt, whereas the right arm did not. At least, this is what Delboeuf reported; we do not have Mademoiselle J.'s version of events.

A day later, the left arm was hurting even more, whereupon Delboeuf mercifully removed the pain by suggestion and, according to him, brought about rapid and successful healing of both arms. He concluded that just as a persistent belief in disease could actually cause it, an equally persistent non-belief could help it go away.[10]

In a considerably more humane experiment carried out in 1975, French psychiatrist Dr Léon Chertok showed that wounds can not only be healed by suggestion, but also caused by it. He managed to produce a handsome blister on the arm of a patient by placing a coin on it and suggesting that it was very hot, which it was not. An intriguing detail was that the patient reported feeling no sensation of heat at all, and yet her skin reacted as if something extremely hot had indeed come into contact with it – on the exact spot where the coin had been placed.

Whereas Ewin had managed to stop the nervous system from getting its message through, Chertok did just the opposite by persuading it to send a fake message without any conscious cooperation at all on the part of the patient. He saw this as 'irrefutable proof of the influence of the mind on physiological processes', and wondered why this was still not fully acknowledged 'in spite of the accumulation of data'.[11,12]

Some of the best data have been provided by Stephen Black, whose adventurous and scientifically impeccable research during the 1960s seemed to open up several new provinces in medical science. In one particularly interesting experiment, he managed to suppress the 'Mantoux reaction' to injections of tubercle bacillus in four subjects out of four by direct suggestion under hypnosis. Normally, if these injections are given to somebody who has had tuberculosis, there is an almost immediate reddening and swelling of the skin in response, which can be accurately measured. Black simply ordered his subjects 'not to react', and they did not, although the same four subjects had shown the normal Mantoux reaction when injected without hypnosis.[13]

Experiments like those I have mentioned involving suggestion and the skin are of special interest for the simple reason that the results are immediately visible, and so are not open to doubt. Chertok's coin test was filmed from start to finish, while Mason, Ewin and Black all have photographic evidence for their cases. Black even took biopsies, slicing pieces of skin from the arms of his long-suffering subjects and photographing them under a microscope. There can no longer be any doubt at all that the mind can influence the skin – for better or worse – to a very considerable extent, far more so than when we turn pale or blush. And if it can do this, might it not be able to influence other parts of the body to the same extent?

Before pursuing this question, here is some evidence of my own for a skin phenomenon I have witnessed at first hand.

Stigmata are physical symptoms, in the form of marks on the skin, of what is called hysterical conversion, whereby repressed feelings and impulses get 'converted' into real and visible effects. The best known example of this is an appearance of marks on the bodies of priests and nuns that resemble the wounds of the crucified Jesus.

It was in July 1975, and the body in question belonged to a very attractive teenage girl from the East End of London. Her father had died three months previously, at the age of forty, following what she believed to have been a hospital accident. Since then, she had been very depressed, and the fact that she did not get on with her mother only made things worse. She was now being looked after by her boyfriend and his very sympathetic family.

As we sat talking in the living-room, in broad daylight, the five of us present all saw a large red patch appear on the girl's bare arm, above the elbow. A drop of blood then oozed out, followed by the sudden appearance of five or six thin, straight red lines. These simply materialised out of the red patch as if the girl had been slashed with an invisible razor, though she apparently felt no pain. I managed to take two photographs while this was going on, and later that day similar marks appeared on her heel and on two places on her upper shin, all of which I also photographed. A particularly baffling detail was that the bleeding in each case stopped almost as soon as it started, some of the straight lines not bleeding at all.

Here was a plainly visible effect similar to those produced to order by Delboeuf and Chertok (and many others), although in this case nobody was suggesting anything, unless it was the unfortunate girl herself, and she was certainly not doing that on purpose. The emotional turmoil she was in as a result of her father's sudden death probably had a good deal to do with the appearance of her stigmata, but how an emotional state can convert itself into straight lines on the skin is a complete mystery. To label such a process 'conversion hysteria' explains nothing. This incident made me suspect that the force of suggestion may be at work in many more ways than we realise, with or without the help of a hypnotist.

What is hypnosis, anyway? Until very recently, nobody has been quite sure. One prominent American researcher, Dr Theodore X. Barber, has argued that there is in fact no such thing, and that since the phenomena we associate with what we call hypnosis are also to be found in other states of consciousness, there is no need for the word at all. It is certainly a misleading one. Although it comes from the Greek word for sleep, *hupnos*, the man who coined it (James Braid, 1843) was well aware that the hypnotic state is not the same as ordinary sleep. He saw hypnosis as a kind of 'nervous sleep' or partial suppression of the brain, 'a peculiar condition of the nervous system into which it can be thrown by artificial contrivance'.[14]

Stephen Black gave a more complete definition in 1969: 'Hypnosis is a sleepless state of decreased or altered consciousness which occurs in most animal phyla as a result of constrictive or rhythmic stimuli usually imparted by another organism and which may be distinguished from sleep by the presence of catatonia, relative awareness or increased suggestibility and in which direct contact is made with the unconscious mind in man.' It is the last ten words of that unwieldy sentence that may be the most important.[15]

The word *suggestion* is equally misleading. It often has a rather half-hearted connotation, as in 'Shall we go for a walk?', implying that the suggester does not really care one way or the other. Yet there is nothing half-hearted about suggestion as used in hypnosis. The Russian neurologist V. M. Bekhterev defined it in 1905 as 'the direct conveyance of ideas, emotions, or any other psychophysical conditions to another person's mind in such a way that his personal consciousness and his criticism are bypassed'.[16]

He was of course referring to the unconscious mind. This in turn was informally described by Dr Gilbert Maher-Loughnan, vice-chairman of the Hypnosis Section of the Royal Society of Medicine, in a 1982 interview as: 'the thing that controls our heartbeats, our blood pressure, our respiration – every function of the body'. He added: 'The use of hypnosis as I see it is to mobilise these unconscious processes and to further the improvement in whatever part of the autonomic nervous system, which is controlled by the unconscious, has gone out of order.'[17]

Now, if the unconscious mind controls *every* function of the body, and if suggestions can be made directly to it, it seems that we have here a fairly powerful technique, especially as it is well known that almost any suggestion tends to be accepted and carried out by the unconscious unless it has a very good reason not to do so. What, then, are the limits of this technique?

If somebody can interfere with the internal information system of somebody else merely by inserting the appropriate programme, thereby causing or suppressing blisters or renovating large areas of 'incurable' fish-skin, what else might be possible? Hypnosis may not be a panacea, or cure for all ills, but it is unquestionably a cure for some of them, including some very serious ones.

We might think that this undeniable fact has led to great efforts being made to research its full potential. If the mind can bring about cures, at almost no cost and with no side-effects, should we not study it as thoroughly as we study chemical and surgical techniques of attacking or invading the body? In a cost-conscious society, it makes no sense to ignore a harmless, inexpensive and very powerful technique that can easily be learned by almost anybody. Yet this is what the great majority of medical practitioners and researchers have been doing for two hundred years.

There had been 'an incredible lack of investigation' into the possible influences of mind on body, the American hypnotist Leslie LeCron wrote in 1952. Many cases had been reported in the past, he said, in which major diseases had been relieved by hypnotic suggestion after conventional medicine had been tried without success. 'It may be', he concluded, 'that the old-timers were right in their claims.'[18]

In 1986, a major newspaper announced that 'a pioneering medical hypnosis technique' had enabled a woman to have a 'miracle' baby after no less than four miscarriages. The reader was given the impression that hypnosis had been discovered the previous day. Thirty years earlier, the authors of the textbook already mentioned devoted two chapters to 'Hypnosis and Suggestion in Obstetrics', citing a dozen references and noting that 'accounts have also been published of women who have never been able to give birth to a viable foetus, in spite of several pregnancies, but who have been enabled to do so with the help of appropriate hypnotherapy.'[19]

'Hypnosis is the black sheep of the family of problems which constitute psychology,' according to psychologist Julian Jaynes, writing in 1976. 'It wanders in and out of laboratories and carnivals and clinics and village halls like an unwanted anomaly. It never seems to straighten up and resolve itself into the firmer properties of scientific theory.'[20]

This book is an attempt to help it do so. It is neither a history nor a manual of hypnosis. It is not an attack on conventional medicine. It is the record of a personal inquiry in which I look for answers to three questions: what is hypnosis, what are its limitations, and what are the implications of its full potential?

# 2

# Postponed Investigation

'And the Lord God caused a deep sleep to fall upon Adam, and he slept: and he took one of his ribs, and closed up the flesh instead thereof' (Genesis 2:21).

According to Dr Sydney van Pelt, a former president of the British Society of Medical Hypnotists, the Bible abounds with episodes, of which the above may be the first, that 'in the light of our present knowledge can be regarded as hypnotic'. So, as he shows, do the histories of most major civilisations. A bas-relief on a Theban tomb, for instance, shows 'a priest obviously in the act of hypnotising a patient'.

The Egyptians and the Greeks had their 'sleep temples'. Roman healers, according to Apuleius, would put their patients into trance and pass their hands over them. 'How if I stroke him slowly, so that he sleeps?' asks a character in Plautus's *Amphytrio*.

English and French monarchs from Edward the Confessor (1043–66) and François I (1515–47) have practised the 'royal touch', and numerous commoners have followed their example, one of the best known being the seventeenth-century Irishman Valentine Greatrakes. In Britain today, there are more than three thousand members of the National Federation of Spiritual Healers. There are few cultures anywhere in the world without a tradition of shamanism, medicine-men or witch-doctors, and it is still a matter of common belief that some people have the ability to influence both the minds and the bodies of others merely by making use of what Dr van Pelt calls 'this strange force that lies latent within mankind'.[1]

The man who tried to free this strange force from its occult associations and bring it into standard medical practice was Franz Anton Mesmer (1734–1815). 'Nature', he claimed, 'offers a universal means of curing and preserving mankind', and he did his best to explain how this universal means operated, using the accepted scientific language of his time.[2]

As he saw it, all living beings are immersed in a sea of fluid or ether through which they can interact by what he called 'animal magnetism'. Just as a mineral object could transfer its magnetic influence to another object, so could a human being concentrate the etheric fluid and channel it into the body of another person, thus transmitting a life-enhancing current. This was not an original idea; it can be traced back directly to van Helmont and Paracelsus in the sixteenth and fifteenth centuries respectively. Mesmer was merely the first working doctor to put it into practice on a large scale.

Like numerous other unorthodox healers before and since his time, Mesmer unquestionably obtained positive results in many cases, but without knowing what he was really doing. Much of the confusion that still surrounds his reputation is due to the fact that he practised several techniques at once without understanding any of them, or at least without explaining them in terms that make sense today. Let us try to sort them out.

First of all, he was a good old-fashioned hand-healer, one of those who feel instinctively that placing the hands on a sick body is good for it. This belief goes back to the father of medicine himself, Hippocrates, who taught in about 500 BC that the human hand has 'a singular property' that can remove 'aches and diverse impurities' from a patient's body. 'It is believed by experienced doctors', he (or one of his students) said, 'that the heat which oozes from the hand, on being applied to the sick, is highly salutary', and he also believed that just as some diseases are contagious, so is health. It can be 'implanted by certain gestures'.

Mesmer's pupil, the Marquis de Puységur, was a good deal more explicit than his teacher. It did not matter in the least, he wrote, if there was such a thing as animal magnetism or not. It was 'a hypothesis, and not a reality'. All the same, it could be helpful if the healer thought of his hands as poles of a magnetic field, and visualised a magnetic fluid running from one to the other, through the patient's body. The essential thing was to touch the patient on the appropriate spot, 'afin d'y occasionner la chaleur' (in order to cause heat there).[3]

This was not enough in itself. The healer needed 'the will to do good'. Puységur went so far as to say that 'animal magnetism is not the action of one body on another, but the action of thought on the body's vital principle'. The idea that the imagination can affect the physical body goes back at least to the eleventh-century Arab physician Avicenna, but Mesmer was the first to put it into practice in a strictly medical context on a large scale. This brings us to the psychological aspect of his work.

The atmosphere in his salon was more like that of a theatre than a doctor's clinic. The room was dimly lit, soft music was played, and patients sat in rows around a large wooden tub (*baquet*) filled with water, iron filings and bits of ground glass. They were actually tied together by a cord attached to the tub, sometimes also holding hands to form a human chain, or holding the angled rods that were stuck through holes in the lid of the tub. Mesmer and his assistants would stroll around waving metal wands, which they would point at individual patients while giving them a 'mesmeric' stare in the eyes and sometimes also laying their hands on them.

Thus, without speaking a word, Mesmer was also able to create an atmosphere of drama, mystery and very powerful general suggestion, and it is hardly surprising that the more suggestible of his patients would have violent emotional crises, as repressed material from their subconscious minds was suddenly released in what is now known as catharsis (from the Greek word for 'purge', or 'purify'), or abreaction, a kind of self-exorcism by reliving a disagreeable or 'traumatic' experience from the past.

It is quite wrong to think of suggestibility as a character weakness. It is, says William Sargant, 'one of the essential characteristics of being "normal"', and some patients 'may become so suggestible that they produce in all sincerity the symptoms which suit their psychiatrist's theories.' He adds wryly: 'If they change psychiatrists, they change symptoms.' This may well explain much of Mesmer's success with what we now call 'psychosomatic' complaints, or physical symptoms that result from mental states. In coming to see Mesmer, patients must have known roughly what to expect, and what was expected of them.

Much of Sargant's experience came from treating battle-shocked soldiers and airmen during World War 2, rather than delicate young ladies from Vienna or Paris, yet many of his observations are relevant to Mesmer's highly original form of group therapy. He found that the very act of creating a powerful state of emotion could in itself amount to a successful treatment. 'Any method which induces states of excitement leading to a suitable degree of exhaustion and consequent alteration in brain function can work miracles on its own', he writes, noting that faith healing 'rarely happens in a calm, rational atmosphere'.[4] The atmosphere in Mesmer's salon was anything but calm and rational, so it is not surprising that powerful emotions were created there.

As Sargant has shown in his classic study of brainwashing, the processes of sudden religious or political conversion and faith healing have a common factor, which he describes as 'the breaking up of old behaviour patterns and the emergence of new ones'. This can be done in many ways, whether by singing and dancing in groups to the point of total exhaustion and consequent 'spirit possession', or by relentless interrogation and disorientation of individuals. In each case, the brain can be made to perform something like a pole-shift just as the magnetic field of the earth does every million years or so and north becomes south. The brainwashed prisoner or religious convert is likewise turned upside-down, and starts to behave quite differently, becoming a 'born again' Christian, Moonie, or Communist, and both rejecting and denouncing his former beliefs with often astonishing zeal and sincerity.[5]

Not only the brain can be washed, it seems, but the whole body. Faith healing is body-washing. A new pattern of behaviour is imposed on it, sometimes instantaneously, so that it reverts to its former healthy state. In theory, this is as simple as programming a computer, but in practice it is far from simple. If it were, all disease would be instantly curable and medicine and surgery would be things of the past.

The problem lies in designing the programme and in persuading the brain to accept it. Unfortunately, we do not yet know enough about either end of the process, although there are plenty of clues scattered around, which I am trying to gather up here. All that can be said at this stage is that when the programme is designed properly, it slips easily into the brain and is carried out accordingly. When it is not designed properly, the brain has an annoying way of rejecting it, partially or wholly. To add to the confusion, it seems possible to design the correct programme entirely by mistake, as seems to have been the case with Dr Mason and his ichthyosis patient, and may also have been the case with *all* of Mesmer's successfully treated patients. Let us look more closely at some of the clues to be found in descriptions of his healing methods.

When treating individual patients, Mesmer would sit facing them so that his knees touched theirs. He would stare into their eyes, ordering them to fix their gaze on his, and he would then touch whatever part of the body needed healing. In this way he was making use of two of the most powerful and simple techniques for inducing a state of combined suggestibility and expectancy: staring and touching.

The power of the human eye is considerable. Whether or not it can stop charging tigers in their tracks, its potential effects, pleasant or unpleasant, are well known. I was once made acutely uncomfortable in a train by the piercing gaze of a rather sinister-looking man opposite me. I eventually offered him my newspaper, hoping that would distract him, only to be told politely that he was completely blind. On the other hand, nothing can be more stimulating than even a brief glance from an attractive member of the appropriate sex. Here again, all kinds of suggestions pop into the mind of the receiver, whatever the real intentions (if any) of the sender.

The early mesmerists found eye-fixation the easiest way to induce what we would now call a light hypnotic state, although James Braid discovered that staring at almost anything had the same effect. He used his metal lancet-case, holding it just above his patient's eye level, so that the eyes had to strain to keep it in view and thus tire more quickly. It was, Braid found, the restricting of the patient's vision that induced hypnosis, not the eyes of the hypnotist.

Although the word derived from Mesmer's name is still wrongly associated with the fictional Svengali-Trilby relationship, the domination of one will by another, Mesmer himself insisted that doctor and patient should be in a state of 'agreement between two wills, which might be called to be in rapport'. The easiest way to achieve this state must surely be to stare at patients and touch them.

The power of touch is just as effective as that of staring, in several obvious ways, and in others that it would take a psychologist to explain. The slightest accidental touch can convey the suggestion of a major threat. This may explain the sometimes violent over-reaction shown by people who are bumped into on the pavement, or who have their cars touched by the one behind, even when there is no visible damage. Yet in the healing context, touch can induce security and comfort to a much greater extent than eye-fixation. (Thanks to the efforts of New York nurse Dolores Krieger, 'therapeutic touch' has become a newly rediscovered part of nursing practice.)

From the evidence we have, then, there seems no doubt that Mesmer was a master of the art of suggestion. Before concluding that this was the only art of which he was a master, we should take a look at what he himself always insisted was his main implement – in fact, his only one; that mysterious animal magnetism. We should try to understand why he came to believe in it so firmly.

In 1768, when he was thirty-four and had been in practice for just two years, Mesmer was approached by Father Maximilian Hell, a Jesuit professor of astronomy at the University of Vienna and a great believer in the curative power of magnetism – mineral, not animal. He lent Mesmer some magnets, asking him to try them out on his patients, and as luck would have it, Mesmer had the ideal patient in his own house: his stepson's fiancée Franzl von Oesterlin, who had been suffering from a mysterious ailment for some time.

Mesmer duly applied the magnets to Franzl's body, with dramatic results. But, almost immediately, he found that he could have the same effect on the girl with his bare hands, moving them around in 'magnetic' passes that put the girl into a state of crisis from which she passed into deep sleep, to wake up apparently cured. Not unreasonably, Mesmer concluded that a similar force was at work whether he used magnets or hands. If mineral magnetism could cure, then so could human or animal magnetism. This must have seemed a perfectly plausible idea at the time, especially as healing by induced crisis was already being practised by another Jesuit, Father J. J. Gassner, whose patients would go into trances and convulsions as the result, he said, of divine intervention. All Mesmer had to do was combine the methods of his two Jesuit mentors, put them to work in a secular context, and wait for the patients to beat a path to his door, which they immediately did. This is not the behaviour of a charlatan, which Mesmer is still often accused of having been.

To confuse the issue somewhat, it is now known that magnetism can indeed heal, though not quite in the way Hell and Mesmer thought. The use of pulsed low-frequency magnetic fields, for example, is now a standard method of treating bone fractures. Does the following sound familiar?

The earth has a natural electromagnetic background, produced by the earth itself and by cosmic sources, and the age-old question as to whether this background can be detected by living organisms has now been answered in the affirmative – the earth's electromagnetic background is an important environmental factor for all living things ... The task now is nothing less than to develop a new biology in which electromagnetic energy receives the critical consideration and evaluation that it merits on the basis of present knowledge.[6]

Apart from the reference to electromagnetism, which was not discovered until after his death, this could have been written by Mesmer. It was in fact written in 1982, by two American orthopaedic surgeons, Robert O. Becker and Andrew A. Marino, and it shows that Mesmer's ideas (which were not entirely his own in any case) were not quite as wrong as they are sometimes assumed to have been. We *do* live in an 'etheric fluid' of natural electromagnetic radiation, caused by the interactions between solar and cosmic radiation and the earth's magnetic field, and as the *Great Soviet Encyclopedia* puts it: 'The cyclic variations in solar radiation affect the life processes of terrestrial organisms.' Heliobiology, the study of such variations and their biological effects, has been an officially recognised scientific discipline in the Soviet Union since 1968, although few Western scientists seem to have heard of it.

This is not to say, of course, that electromagnetism can be channelled from one person to another. We still know next to nothing about the physical mechanisms of hand-healing, and we cannot be sure that there are any. Even so, many modern healers still think in terms of transmitting some kind of universal vital force, prana, bioplasma or whatever, by the conscious exercise of their wills. This is all Mesmer claimed to be doing, and it is ironic that it was his theory rather than his practice that led to his downfall.

In 1784 Louis XVI (himself a practitioner of the royal touch) ordered an enquiry into animal magnetism. The appointed committee found that 'some great force' seemed to emanate from magnetisers, or mesmerists, and to have a beneficial effect on people. But it was not animal magnetism, just 'imagination'. A satisfied patient protested, with a nice touch of Gallic irony: 'If it is to illusion that I owe the health that I believe I enjoy, then let me make use of an invisible agent which does not exist, but which cures me.'

'To say, as the Commissioners did in 1784, and as many people do in 1967,' wrote Dr E. J. Dingwall in that year, 'that it is "all imagination" explains nothing. All it does is to postpone investigation.'[7]

Was it all imagination? One dissenting member of the 1784 commission thought not. This was the botanist Laurent de Jussieu, who felt that what needed investigation was not animal magnetism, but animal *heat*. The sudden manifestation of heat in the patient's body, to which Puységur drew attention, is still today one of the most commonly reported effects of the hand-healing process. I have felt it myself on several occasions, on the first of which it came as a complete surprise both to me and to the healer, so I cannot accept that it was due to my imagination or his suggestion. It was not gradually increasing heat such as you might expect from a bare hand on your abdomen, but a sudden and instant heat, as if I had been touched with a clothes iron. The healer, a young American being trained by Bruce MacManaway, was delighted when I told him what I felt. It was, he told me, the first time he had managed to induce heat, which he knew healers were supposed to do.

Another occasion was even more remarkable, at least to me. It was during a session with Matthew Manning, who was trying to help the nerve-deadness that had followed a slipped disc. He placed a hand on the back of my neck, whereupon I felt repeated pulses of intense heat, as if some electrical device were being switched on and off, although the healer's hand did not move. There was an immediate improvement in the sensitivity of my right hand, which four years later had not relapsed. There is no way, I am assured, that the ulnar nerve can be unblocked so rapidly. However, mine was.

Matthew Manning is one of several healers who have apparently been able to alter the behaviour of cells and enzymes in controlled laboratory experiments, even without any direct physical contact at all. It is becoming increasingly difficult to rule out the possibility that healers do in fact transmit something. The position is well summed up by Bruce MacManaway, with the precision and practical approach one would expect from a retired British Army officer: 'We may not understand the healing energy, but it appears to be available for human use.'[8]

A final word on Mesmer, from Professor Ronald E. Shor, a recognised authority on hypnotism: 'While untenable from the standpoint of objective scientific truth, Mesmer's powerful therapeutic theories were functionally, pragmatically true.'[9]

From Dr van Pelt: 'His only crime was that he endeavoured to place a mysterious power on a scientific basis for the benefit of humanity.'[10]

And from Vincent Buranelli, a modern biographer: 'Mesmer's tragedy was that he had the right facts and the wrong theory.'[11]

The first major advance in the medical use of mesmerism came when French doctors found they could use it to induce analgesia, or inability to feel pain. This was an important discovery, because it showed that a physical symptom common to many serious diseases could be suppressed entirely. How, when, and by whom this was first done remains unclear, but in 1829 Dr Jules Cloquet removed a breast tumour from a fifty-three-year-old woman without apparently causing her any pain at all. The benefits of this discovery, in the days before the introduction of chloroform and other anaesthetics, were potentially enormous. One can hardly imagine the agony of having a major operation, or even having a tooth pulled out, while remaining fully conscious. It is a wonder patients ever survived, and of course many did not.

Cloquet duly reported his feat to the French Academy of Medicine, only to be told that he had been fooled. His patient had only been pretending not to feel pain. Eight years later, a dentist named Oudet had much the same reception when he extracted a tooth painlessly after mesmerising his patient.

In 1843 Dr John Elliotson, one of the founders of University College Hospital in London, published 'Numerous Cases of Surgical Operations Without Pain in the Mesmeric State'. Four years later, a young Scottish surgeon named James Esdaile reported from India that he had performed no fewer than 315 major operations, including nineteen limb amputations, and several *thousand* minor ones using his own mesmeric technique. This did not involve either verbal suggestion or eye-contact, often being done to patients whose eyes were closed. Esdaile insisted that more than imagination was involved in his method. 'From all that has come under my observation,' he wrote, 'I am convinced ... that mesmerism *as practised by me* is a physical power exerted by one animal over another, under certain circumstances and conditions of their respective systems.'[12]

With evidence like that of Elliotson and Esdaile coming in, surely official attitudes had to change, at least in Britain? They did – for the worse. Elliotson was told to stop using mesmerism in his own hospital, whereupon he resigned after declaring:

> The Institution was established for the discovery and dissemination of truth. *We* should lead the public, not the public us. All other considerations are secondary. The sole question is whether the matter is the truth or not.

The medical journal *The Lancet* took note of the breakthrough in the war against human suffering, pioneered in Britain by Elliotson, in these words:

Mesmerism is too gross a humbug to admit of any further serious notice. We regard its abettors as quacks and impostors. They ought to be hooted out of professional society.

Elliotson, the chief abettor, was a pioneer in other fields. He introduced the stethoscope into Britain. (*The Lancet* did not approve of that either) and was using acupuncture (or hat-pins, as his critics complained) as early as the 1820s. Dr van Pelt considered him to be 'one of the most brilliant men in the history of British medicine'.[13]

Why, we might ask, did university authorities and editors of medical journals react as they did in the face of a promising new discovery? A plausible reason was given by Frank Podmore, a tough critic of anything that could be considered paranormal, or inexplicable in terms of accepted knowledge, in his study of the period:

The progress of science is frequently attained by a kind of dichotomy; any novel current of opinion appears by a kind of psychological induction to create a current of at least equal intensity in the reverse direction ... The deliberate negligence of the scientific world left the whole field to be cultivated by the visionary and the charlatan. The abundant crop of false beliefs and extravagant systems which flourish at the present time is the direct result of the apathy or obstinate incredulity shown by the physicians of two generations ago.[14]

He was writing in 1909, by which time Christian Science was spreading rapidly, to the dismay of Christians and scientists alike. (Its roots can be traced back directly to mesmerism, via the American practitioner Phineas Quimby.) Medical hypnotism was also enjoying a revival in both Britain and France; not all physicians had been apathetic or incredulous, in fact the British Medical Association had come out uncompromisingly in favour of it in an 1892 statement. There was a mass of published evidence from such doctors as Hack Tuke, Charles Lloyd Tuckey, J. Milne Bramwell and Bernard Hollander to support the BMA's view that it was a genuine phenomenon and 'frequently effective' as a therapeutic agent.

The 'negligence of the scientific world' towards hypnotism was remarkable. There was not a single controlled experiment involving it carried out anywhere in the world throughout the nineteenth century. It was kept going by individuals, not by academies or medical associations, and it never quite freed itself from its occult image. Indeed, this image was intensified by the numerous commercial stage hypnotists who were quick to exploit the more dramatic features of hypnosis and turn it into a degrading and dangerous public spectacle.

In France, the Royal Academy of Sciences decided in 1831 that animal magnetism (as it was still known) was worthy of being 'admitted within the sphere of the medical sciences'. It had of course already been there for more than fifty years, but only on an individual basis and not without considerable opposition. In both Britain and France, it seems to have survived by being passed from one doctor to another like an infectious disease. It was a visiting Swiss mesmeriser, for example, who first interested Braid in the subject, and it was Braid in turn who directly inspired Ambroise Liébeault, a modest doctor from Nancy who was to become one of the most successful and influential hypnotists of the century. His methods were developed by Émile Coué, whom José Silva has acknowledged as an important influence on his popular Mind Control method. Bramwell, who came from Esdaile's home town of Perth, was deeply impressed as a boy by his father's personal recollections of Esdaile, and by his prediction that 'some day, hypnotism will revolutionise the practice of medicine'.[15] The whole family tree of present-day hypnotists can be traced back directly to Mesmer.

It is often assumed that animal magnetism, or mesmerism, was no more than a primitive forerunner of hypnotism. As I shall show later, they are not the same thing at all, although some of the results of each may be similar. The main difference is that hypnotists use verbal suggestion, whereas mesmerists (who as we shall see are still around) say nothing at all. In each case, the patient's state of consciousness is altered, but not necessarily in the same way.

There is nothing new about verbal suggestion in itself. In the ancient Atharva Veda text, for instance, we find a mantra for the prevention of bleeding that could have come from a recent textbook on biofeedback: 'As though you were dammed by a great sea wall, by a lofty bank of gravel and sand, be still now and rest.' It probably sounds more hypnotic in the original Sanskrit.[16]

The introduction of verbal suggestion into mesmeric practice is usually credited to Father José de Faria, a Portuguese priest from Goa, who would stand in front of his subject and yell at the top of his voice 'SLEEP!' For all his lack of subtlety, Faria realised as early as 1814 that the subject's state of mind was of great importance, and by the end of the century specific verbal suggestion was a standard feature of hypnotism. By 1905, Auguste Forel was able to compile a long list of 'morbid conditions' that had been found to respond to suggestion under hypnosis. It included: pains of all description, especially headaches, neuralgia, sciatica and toothache; sleeplessness, functional and organic paralysis, chlorosis, menstrual problems, loss of appetite, all nervous digestive disturbance, constipation, some kinds of diarrhoea, dyspepsia, alcoholism, drug addiction, rheumatism, lumbago, stammering, seasickness, bed-wetting, chorea, hysterical disorders (including phobias) and 'bad habits of all kinds'.[17]

By the beginning of this century, then, it seemed that the prediction of Dr Bramwell (senior) had come true: hypnotism was about to revolutionise the practice of medicine. The reasons why it did not are far from easy to identify.

In 1952, the BMA issued a statement in its house organ, the *British Medical Journal*, giving the view of a special committee on hypnotism. 'This', the *BMJ* explained later, 'had been prepared because of frequent inquiries received by the Association on the subject, which at that time was receiving wide publicity, and which had received no consideration by the Association since 1892.' Elliotson's wish that 'we should lead the public' had evidently not been heeded.

Hypnotism was very much in the news in 1952. A number of popular books on it had recently appeared, including Dr van Pelt's, and Dr Mason's ichthyosis cure had caused quite a stir. This was also the year of the Hypnotism Act, which gave local authorities the power to regulate demonstrations of stage hypnosis. Having, on its own admission, done nothing about hypnotism for sixty years, the BMA now seemed anxious to make up for lost time, and to take the kind of initiative Elliotson had urged more than a century earlier.

In 1953, a BMA subcommittee headed by Professor T. Ferguson Rodger set out 'to consider the uses of hypnotism, its relation to medical practice in the present day, the advisability of giving encouragement to research into its nature and application, and the lines on which such research might be organised.' With the help of sixteen doctors, dentists and psychologists it did a thorough job, and its 1955 report is a model of clear and positive thinking combined with professional responsibility. Hypnotism, it said, was 'a proper subject for inquiry by the tried methods of medical research.' The BMA was 'satisfied after consideration of the available evidence that hypnotism is of value and may be the treatment of choice in some cases of so-called psychosomatic disorder and psychoneurosis.'

Hypnotism was also 'a challenge to medical science', and the BMA made several specific recommendations for further research, for which it was 'convinced of the need'. One was for 'the investigation of the relation of hypnotism and similar states to non-medical methods of treatment, including healing through religious agencies.' (The BMA gave its views on the latter in 1956, after a somewhat superficial study carried out at the request of the church, reaching the conclusion that 'we can find no evidence that there is any type of illness cured by "spiritual healing" alone which could not have been cured by medical treatment, which necessarily includes consideration of environmental factors.')

The BMA also urged that 'instruction in the clinical use of hypnotism should be given to all medical postgraduates training as specialists in psychological medicine', and that undergraduates should at least have access to information on it. In fact, the BMA later reported: it was all for it, there should be more research into it, and it should be taught far more widely than it was. In 1955, as in 1892, a new golden age seemed about to dawn.[18]

The need for more research was made clear in a remarkably frank *BMJ* editorial of 1958:

Five thousand years ago man knew a great deal about influencing the psyche for the benefit of the sick or stricken soma. To our Western culture, at least, this knowledge has been largely lost. Though the mechanical aspects of the technique for inducing hypnosis are easy to learn, successful induction largely depends on the interaction of factors in the personality of the patient which are but little understood, with factors within the hypnotist which are not understood at all.[19]

There was not exactly a stampede of researchers in response to the BMA appeal, yet such little original research as has been published since 1955 gives some idea of what might be accomplished if a few more BMA members heeded the call.

In 1960, for example, the first-ever controlled study of the effects of hypnosis on asthma appeared in print, coming up with negative results. Dr Mason and three colleagues thought that an experiment lasting only a month and involving a total of 25 patients should be repeated on a larger scale.

They took 53 patients and divided them into two groups. The control group (28 patients) was given conventional medicine for a whole year, while the 27 members of the study group were given regular hypnosis – but no medicine at all. The result: 'The control group showed on an average little change throughout the period of the trial ... Treatment by hypnosis was shown to be more effective symptomatically than treatment by an antispasmodic.'[20] This seems to suggest that when tested properly, at least one of those old-timers' claims stands up fairly well.

The BMA's appeal for more education in hypnosis was not very successful. More than twenty years after its 1955 recommendations, a survey revealed that out of fifty-one medical and dental schools sampled, only four were providing official training in it for undergraduates, and only three for postgraduates. 'Clearly,' said the *BMJ* editor, 'little action has been taken to carry out the subcommittee's recommendation: the teaching of hypnosis within the psychiatric services of the NHS [National Health Service] is very limited.'[21]

It certainly is, and I contacted the BMA to find out why.

'The BMA has made its position clear,' a spokesman told me. 'We can't tell deans of medical schools what to do. It's their decision whether to include hypnosis on their syllabuses or not.' He assured me that hypnosis was widely practised by individual doctors, with the BMA's full approval. However, of the 29,800 registered general practitioners in 1982, only about one thousand were members of the British Society of Medical and Dental Hypnotists. Since this society includes a number of dentists, I would estimate that no more than 3 per cent of Britain's doctors make any use at all of hypnosis.

One who does not wrote to the *BMJ* in 1979 to express his complete lack of enthusiasm for the subject. The supposition that hypnosis had been conclusively shown to be of scientific value was, he said, simply not the case. Controlled studies (he mentioned only one) had shown it to have little advantage over placebo techniques. He concluded that hypnosis seemed 'not to be of superior efficacy to simpler techniques'. He did not refer to any of the work of Mason and Black published in the same journal. Nor did he suggest a 'simpler technique' for curing ichthyosis.[22]

Writing in 1843, James Braid declared: 'I feel quite confident we have acquired in this process [hypnosis] a valuable addition to our curative means, but I repudiate the idea of holding it up as a universal remedy ... Nor do I even pretend to understand as yet the whole range of diseases in which it may be useful.'

We still have no idea of the potential uses of hypnosis. The research has not been done, and the great majority of doctors are never taught it in the first place. Even among the few who do practise it, there seems to be a tacit assumption that their art is strictly limited to the treatment of psychological disorders. This is an assumption based not on evidence, but on ignorance or outright rejection of existing evidence – reams and reams of it, and much of it from experienced doctors with clinics in Wimpole Street and equally fashionable addresses. The whole 200-year history of medical hypnosis has been one of promising starts, with individual doctors discovering for themselves that it can be as powerful as the scalpel or the syringe. It can literally kill or cure, as we shall see.

As recently as 1981, a London radiologist wrote in a medical paper that hypnotism was 'a valuable therapeutic tool that will ... eventually attain its rightful place in the range of therapies available to our patients'.[23] He might have been discussing something that had been discovered in the previous year, not in the eighteenth century. Eventually, indeed! Why has it not attained its rightful place already? And what is its rightful place? Such questions are not often asked.

One doctor who did ask them was Sydney van Pelt, who was both president of the British Society of Medical Hypnotists (as it then was) and a member of the BMA subcommittee's team of consultants. We can therefore assume he knew what he was talking about.

A woman came to see him suffering from migraine, which had made her life a misery since she was ten years old, with regular attacks every two weeks. She had undergone several operations and consulted numerous specialists. 'Finally, having been told that there was no medical cure, the patient decided to give up doctors. Hypnotism was sought as a last desperate resort.' It was immediately effective.

'The pity is,' van Pelt observed, 'that patients only seek hypnotic treatment when all else has failed. In cases such as these, hypnotism should be tried first, when there is no doubt that patients would be spared years of misery and unhappiness.' He was not only referring to migraine. He reported a total cure after only two sessions of a case of cardiospasm (inability to digest solid food) that had 'defied all medical treatment', and named several other conditions that he personally had either cured or substantially helped when all else had failed, including trigeminal neuralgia, thrombo-angiitis obliterans and phantom limb pain. In some cases, it would seem that the rightful place of hypnosis is as a first resort.

Dr van Pelt also had an answer to the question of why hypnosis is not more widely used, sharing the blame between stage hypnotists, Spiritualists, Christian Scientists, psychoanalysts, doctors and the general public. In fact, just about everybody. Stage hypnotists created a false and often frightening impression of what hypnosis can do, and his society had records of 'many patients who have suffered severe mental and bodily harm as the result of stage and amateur hypnosis'. He lambasted both the Spiritualists and the Christian Scientists for what he saw as their misuse of suggestion, and as for psychoanalysts, he commented that they, 'accustomed to spending several years ... in the leisurely investigation of a few wealthy patients, can hardly be expected to approve the introduction of a method which can achieve more in a few sessions than years of psychoanalysis.'

This is a controversial claim, as is almost any general statement about any aspect of hypnosis. I am merely quoting the opinion of a qualified professional. There can be no doubt that Freud's early rejection of hypnosis as part of his analytic technique had much to do with its neglect by his followers.

Dr van Pelt's overall conclusion was that 'Doctors unfortunately take their cue from the lay public in their attitude to hypnosis. One can hardly blame them, because, knowing that the lay public distrusts it, although quite wrongly and through ignorance of its real nature, they feel it is running the risk of professional suicide to use hypnotism or advise its use in their practice.'[24]

So it is all our fault. Elliotson's fears have come true. We, the public, are leading the doctors, instead of vice versa. But there is more to it that this.

First, we cannot expect doctors to practise hypnosis properly unless they have studied it properly, and as the statistics show, it is almost impossible for the majority of medical students, at least in Britain, to study it at all. Even keeping up with what little research is being done elsewhere is not easy. Of the three American journals devoted to medical and clinical hypnosis, not one is available in any library listed in the British Library catalogue. (University College, across the street from Elliotson's old hospital, used to take one of them, but stopped doing so in 1976.) As a direct consequence of the lack of facilities for studying it, hypnotism has acquired a very confusing image, as I found when I carried out an informal survey of my own.

Several doctors, psychiatrists and psychologists I questioned had no knowledge or experience of hypnotism at all. Among those who had at least some, the most frequent explanations offered for its under-use were:

'It's not practical, because you can't hypnotise everybody.'

This is true, although I suspect that the totally unhypnotisable percentage of the population is much smaller than generally assumed (5 to 10 per cent). Early in this century, Dr Otto Wetterstrand of Sweden reported that he had failed to hypnotise only 3 per cent of 3,148 subjects. Milne Bramwell reported a case in which he failed sixty-seven times with the same patient, but kept trying. It was a case of sixty-eighth time lucky, and the patient was cured (of eczema) in two weeks.

'It's not effective unless you can induce a deep trance state.' This has not been proved to the satisfaction of all hypnotists. It may be true for some and not for others. Even if true, it means that 5 per cent of the population (the accepted percentage of deep-trance subjects) could benefit from hypnosis. Stephen Black, who supports this theory very vigorously, has recommended early mass screening.

'It takes too long.'

This is a lame excuse. It can apply to any form of medicine. Some people take pills all their lives, and undergo regular operations. How about Freud's suggestion that people should undergo analysis for an hour a day, every day, for up to six years?

'Conventional methods are more reliable.'

This is an assumption based on ignorance of published evidence. In some cases, it is definitely not true. Conventional methods certainly make life easier for the doctor in an age of mass-production invasive medicine, but they do not always improve the patient's quality of life. Sometimes, indeed, pills and surgery terminate life altogether. In 1983, a drug called Opren was 'linked' to the deaths of sixty-seven people. There are areas in which conventional medicine is quite adequate and hypnosis is unnecessary. The reverse may also be true. Few have ever bothered to find out.

'The mechanisms are not understood.'

So what? As Braid wrote in 1843: 'Who can tell how or why quinine and arsenic cure intermittent fever? They are, nevertheless, well known to do so, and are prescribed accordingly.' In any case, the mechanisms are beginning to be understood.

'The chemical lobby would never stand for it,' a university lecturer in psychology, with some experience of chemical lobbies, told me.

'A major reason why doctors use standard methods is fear of litigation. Ask any American.' This was the opinion of a senior research scientist.

Stephen Black, despite his outstandingly imaginative and successful research into hypnosis, has some reservations about its use which may be purely personal. It may be safe for the patient, he says, but 'it is certainly the most dangerous therapy known from the point of view of the doctor'. This is because of the dangers of 'erotic rapport' arising from physical contact between hypnotist and patient. He does not explain why such dangers should be greater for a hypnotist than for a psychoanalyst, or any other kind of therapist.[25]

None of the above excuses seems to me to justify or explain the persistent under-use of hypnosis. Is this due to no more than good old-fashioned fear based on ignorance? Despite the efforts of Braid and his successors to free hypnotism from its occult image, something of this image has remained. The idea that one person can influence another by a simple combination of mind-power and ritualistic mumbo-jumbo that can be learned in half an hour (according to Dr Black) must be hard for some doctors to accept, even though they know it to be true. It seems to make nonsense of those long and arduous years of training during which medical students have to amass and store an enormous amount of precise information. It is more like magic than science.

Dr Black admits that after giving lectures on hypnotism to psychiatrists he has often been asked questions 'which clearly indicate an expectancy of magic', while Dr Mason believes that 'hypnosis is still embraced by many practitioners because they believe it is magic, and magic has great unconscious appeal especially when, as with hypnosis, it is given a cloak of science'. Others, he adds, reject it for the same reason, and reveal the extent of their fear of the unknown by the aggressiveness with which they reject it.[26,27]

This is a common reaction to confrontations with the paranormal, and since hypnosis cannot yet be fully explained it is still by definition paranormal. It remains in the prescientific stage, although at least one important aspect of it – suggestion – is widely used in general medicine.

Some applications of suggestion are obvious. They include the doctor's appearance, cheerful personality, smart car, bedside manner, and brass plate in one of the right streets. The placebo pill is a solid lump of suggestion and nothing else. Other applications are less obvious; being told that a disease has a name, for example, makes many patients feel better at once. Mason admits that it also makes the doctor feel better. The suggestion in the mind of both doctor and patient is that a disease named is a disease half cured.[28]

One practitioner, psychologist Dr Joseph Reyher of Michigan State University, made some very forthright remarks about the uses of magic, charisma and suggestion in medical practice at a scientific conference on hypnosis held in 1977. The way to get results, he said, was for the hypnotist 'to adopt a paternalistic or maternalistic demeanour and to reinforce his/her image as an authoritative, helpful professional by displaying impressive credentials in a setting reinforcing those connotative meanings'. Whereupon, 'presto, "miraculous" remissions occur'.

They do not occur every time, of course, and Dr Reyher then made a recommendation to which I will return later. 'Knowing he/she has lost his/her magic, perhaps the physician should encourage selected chronic patients to seek a "cure" in some charismatic alternative to the medical profession while maintaining a watchful, unobtrusive eye on the course of events.' It is interesting to hear the magical and charismatic aspects of healing mentioned in this context.[29]

Although doctors use suggestion because they know it is necessary and often effective, they have not pursued its application to a logical conclusion. They know that there is a mental or psychic factor at work in almost every disease of the body, and they should not have been surprised by Black's statement that 'certainly more than half the physical complaints treated under the National Health Service in Britain can be diagnosed as originating in the mind'.[30]

They also know very well that a patient's mental attitude can influence the course of anything, from a wart or a common cold to terminal cancer, for better or for worse. Yet the psychic factor is constantly pushed into the background. 'Psychosomatic' medicine has become a speciality in its own right, implying that other forms of medicine have nothing to do with the patient's mind. This is absurd, since no part of the body can operate independently of one or other of the nervous systems through which the mind is kept informed. All medicine is psychosomatic.

Yet the idea of actually studying some of the workings of the human mind (other than those on a trivial, easily measurable, and mechanical 'behaviourist' level) arouses emotions ranging from violent hostility to sheer panic. As any member of the Society for Psychical Research knows only too well, the serious study of man's psyche (mind) and its potential powers is more likely to be greeted with ridicule than with respect, however academically distinguished the researcher may be in 'real' life. It is fashionable to talk vaguely about the powers of the mind at cocktail parties, and perhaps to take them seriously for a couple of hours on Hallowe'en. But to study them is taboo.

Even the most successful hypnotists have been unwilling to explore the full potential of their art. The suggesters themselves have come under the destructive influence of mass negative suggestion. Hypnosis, they are told, can be helpful in psychological disorders and in some minor physical ones, but no more. When a Dr Mason suddenly shows that it can have dramatic and immediate effects on a major 'incurable' condition, there is a brief period of general surprise, and cries of 'Goodness me. Fancy that!' Attitudes then revert to their former state. A recent textbook written by and for medical hypnotists devotes a whole chapter to the treatment of skin diseases, and makes no mention of Mason at all. He might as well not have bothered.

The acceptance of limitations is in itself a form of negative credulity. Many discoveries will be made before long that are considered impossible today except by those who are about to make them. The histories of aviation and space flight are full of pronouncements by experts on the impossibility of this or that, the classic case being the British Astronomer Royal's statement that space travel was 'utter bilge' – the year before Sputnik 1 went into orbit.

'Too great a burden of knowledge', Arthur C. Clarke has said, 'can clog the wheels of imagination.' Lord Rutherford, for instance, refused to believe that nuclear energy could be harnessed, although he was a pioneer of nuclear physics. The first atomic bomb went off eight years after his death. Even Einstein was convinced in 1939 that it would never be possible to get a nuclear bomb off the ground. That was just six years before the bombing of Hiroshima and Nagasaki.

'Anything that is theoretically possible', Clarke says, 'will be achieved in practice, no matter what the technical difficulties, if it is desired greatly enough.' He names the main obstacles in the path of scientific progress as failure of imagination and failure of nerve, or the inability to realise that something is possible and the lack of determination to go ahead and do it.[31] When the first video recorder was made, by an American company, a Japanese firm promptly set out to produce one at *one hundredth* of the cost. They did just that and cornered world markets, because their desire was great enough.

There can be no field of science in which clogged imagination and failure of nerve have prevailed for so long as hypnotism. There is no easy explanation as to why this should be so, although fear clearly has an effect on both patient and hypnotist. For despite frequent claims to the contrary, it is possible to make people do things under hypnosis that they probably would not do in their normal state. This is a fact that must be faced, though it should not be allowed to outweigh the immense potential good that can be done by a hypnotist.

In 1947, Dr John G. Watkins, a Chicago clinical psychologist, published a paper entitled 'Anti-social compulsions induced under hypnotic trance'. One of the compulsions concerned was attempted murder. The subject, an army private with a good record, was persuaded to attack a man in the room under the impression that he was a dangerous enemy. He was in fact a US Army psychiatrist, a Lieutenant-Colonel.

'The subject opened his eyes. He then slanted them and began to creep cautiously forward. Suddenly, in a flying tackle he dove at the Lieutenant-Colonel, knocking him against the wall, and with both of his hands – he was a powerful, husky lad – began strangling the man.' He had to be restrained by three onlookers. The officer described the private's grip on his throat as 'strong and dangerous'. In a repetition of this experiment, the subject produced a knife, and showed every intention of using it.

In an even more sinister demonstration of the power of the motivated mind, Dr Paul C. Young of Louisiana State University persuaded seven out of eight hypnotised subjects to throw nitric acid at his assistant, a heroic fellow named Harcourt Stebbins. They were shown a coin disintegrating in real nitric acid, which was then surreptitiously switched for a similar-looking dish of harmless blue-coloured water, containing barium oxide to make it 'boil'. But on one of the trials, something went wrong. The subject got hold of the real acid and flung it in Stebbins' face. 'On account of the promptness of remedial measures, no scars were left on his face,' Young reported, 'although his heavy uniform ... deteriorated in large areas where the acid had struck.'[32]

'There can be no doubt', Auguste Forel wrote, 'that one can produce illness and possibly death indirectly (perhaps even directly) in a criminal manner by suggestion.'[33] As one unfortunate doctor discovered, one can also kill people by mistake. The patient was a ten-year-old boy suffering from asthma and multiple allergies, and the hypnotist was making him visualise a peaceful mountain scene, hoping the imagined fresh air would do him good. He mentioned flowers, birds, distant cowbells ...

The boy went into a violent asthma attack, turning blue in the face and frothing at the mouth. Cowbells meant cows. Cows had hair. And he was highly allergic to any kind of animal hair. The terrified hypnotist thought fast. He conjured up a helicopter arriving to pick up the boy and lift him high into the pure air above.

'That little 'plane didn't get here any too soon, did it?' said the boy afterwards. The doctor confessed it had been 'an unbelievably frightening experience' for him. It had been his very first hypnosis session, and he gave up the use of it then and there. He had found out, as he put it, that 'fantasy is as strong as reality'.[34]

This is undoubtedly true. If we believe something, the effect on us is the same whether it is really true or not. As Paracelsus put it in the sixteenth century: 'It is all one whether you believe in something real or something false. It will have the same effect on you. It is always the faith that works the miracle, and whether the faith is aroused by something real or something false, its miraculous power is the same.'[35]

Faith has been cynically defined as a belief in something you know to be untrue. This is only a slight exaggeration; William Sargant defines it as 'a profound and non-rational conviction of the truth of propositions to which the unaided intellect can at best accord only a temperate allegiance'. We need another word for this feeling, but until we have one Sargant's 'profound and non-rational conviction' will serve as a description of it; and it is a very good description of what seems to be one of the crucial factors of successful hypnosis.[36]

In all the cases I have mentioned so far, the one common feature is a total and uncritical acceptance by the subject of the hypnotist's suggestion. This in turn was given with conviction, and whether the conviction was rational or non-rational did not matter. Dr Ewin has a plausible rationale to back up his method of stopping blisters, but Dr Mason's conviction when he attacked that huge area of black stuff on John's arm was essentially non-rational. It was based firmly on a belief he soon found to be incorrect. It was no less effective, until shaken by a rational explanation.

We can, then, sketch out a flow-chart to illustrate a successful transfer of a suggestion under hypnosis. There are three stages:

A  The hypnotist has an idea in which he believes profoundly. Whether his belief is rational or non-rational is not important.

B  He conveys this idea to a subject in a 'hypnotic' state, in which part of the subject's consciousness has been forcibly set aside or bypassed. I will describe what that involves in more detail in the following chapter.

C  The subject accepts the conveyed suggestion totally and uncritically, and acts upon it instantly. If there is no resistance to it, the suggestion is carried out in full.

At least one of 'those factors within the hypnotist which are not understood at all' can now be identified as his belief system, and it seems that as the belief systems of mesmerists and hypnotists have altered over the centuries, so have the phenomena they were able to evoke. They get the results they expect to get. If Mesmer and his patients believed that animal magnetism poured from the eyes or fingers of healers, and that this mysterious substance cured diseases, it is quite likely that diseases were indeed cured, by belief reinforced by unspoken suggestion as much as, or rather than, animal magnetism.

'The phenomena cannot advance higher than the concepts of the operator. What he does not know and does not believe in, he cannot induce. The great error in hypnotic experiment is the limitation of the subject's powers by suggestion,' wrote James Coates, a lay hypnotist, in 1910.[37] In the same year, Wimpole Street consultant Dr Bernard Hollander wrote that in the hypnotic state 'there are no limits to the power of suggestion'.[38]

Forty years later Dr van Pelt, also of Wimpole Street, went even further: 'Hypnotism, by invoking a natural law, can make use of the wonderful power which is within all of us and increase the strength of the mind, just as it can increase the strength of the body. This increased strength of mind combined with the imagination which has been directed into proper channels, results in an irresistible power of dominant thought which brooks no opposition.'[39]

This stops only just short of declaring hypnosis to be the panacea to end all panaceas, and I cannot imagine a responsible doctor making such a statement unless he had evidence from his own practice to support it. It would be unethical to declare anything to be a panacea, even if it was, unless it was freely available to all. And hypnosis, at least in Britain today, is not freely available to anybody at all except a tiny minority who happen to be registered with a doctor who practises it. (There is, I understand, only one hospital in the United Kingdom that offers hypnotherapy on the National Health Service. Its director has asked me not to name it, or him. He has, he told me, a four-month waiting list.)

Hypnosis remains inadequately taught, too little used, and researched hardly at all. The doctors themselves have defined the problem, but have not even begun to solve it. More than half the patients needing treatment at public expense are suffering from complaints that originate in the mind, says Dr Black, who adds that under hypnosis direct contact is made with the subconscious mind which in turn, in Dr Maher-Loughnan's words, is what controls every function of the body. And in the opinion of Dr Mason, who should know, potentially any cure can be achieved provided the body has an embryonic model of the desired result in its programme.

Mesmer's claim that 'nature offers a universal means of curing and preserving mankind' remains neither proved nor disproved. Investigation has been postponed indefinitely. What has been proved is that under some circumstances a motivated mind can work what appear to be miracles once a critical level of faith is reached.

# 3

# Scylla and Charybdis

We often say we are 'in two minds' about something, especially when we are trying to make an important decision. The process of 'making up' our minds seems to involve reconciling warring factions within us, as if we had not one mind but two. One seems to be rational, sensible and practical, basing its decisions on facts, logic and common sense; the other manifests itself in hunches, intuitions and impulses that often seem to defy both logic and common sense. As many people know, such irrational feelings often lead to the making of what turns out to be the right decision.

We certainly have two brains: a left and a right hemisphere. They are joined together like the two halves of a walnut by a band of matter called the corpus callosum or callous body, containing about 200 million neurons by means of which one brain exchanges information with the other. Each hemisphere directs most of the activities of the opposite side of the body, so that the left brain controls the movements of the right leg and the right brain tells the left leg what to do. If our brains did not cooperate very closely, we would find it extremely difficult to walk.

(There are numerous other ways of subdividing the brain: front/back (frontal and temporal lobes), up/down (cortex and cerebellum) and old/new (limbic system and neocortex). They are not discussed in this chapter, which is concerned with a philosophical model of mind and not with anatomical models of brain.)

The two brains may be alike as far as their motor functions are concerned, but they are very different in other respects. I am now moving into an area even more controversial than that of hypnosis, so as before I will base my arguments on the opinions of recognised experts, although even they have not yet reached agreement as to the precise functions of each hemisphere.

Says Dr Michael Gazzaniga: 'Each hemisphere is endowed with certain capacities that are either lacking or poorly represented in the other half-brain.' For example, speech, analytical thought and logical reasoning originate in the left brains of most people, while abstract thought, imagery, emotions and instincts tend to come from the right side of our heads. The picture is complicated by the fact that each brain serves as a back-up system to the other, and can even take over most of its duties if the occasion arises early in life, as when a baby has to have half a brain removed. Yet on the whole it can be said that our two brain-halves are specialist organs that have their own ways of doing things, and do not always cooperate as closely as they could.[1]

'In the healthy brain,' says neuroscientist Dr Jane Oppenheimer, 'one of the cerebra is almost always superior in power to the other, and capable of exercising control over the volitions of its fellow, and of preventing them from passing into acts, or from being manifest in others.'[2]

Psychologist Roland Puccetti upset some of his colleagues when he told a conference in 1977: 'There are two of us here in the same cranium.' Yet Professor Roger Sperry, who won a Nobel Prize for his split-brain research, writes of 'two separate conscious entities or minds running in parallel in the same cranium, each with its own sensations, perceptions, cognitive processes, learning experiences, memories and so on'.[3]

He was referring to brains that had been forcibly separated by severing the corpus callosum to suppress otherwise incurable epileptic attacks; but if our two brains operate differently when they are separated, then they probably do the same, up to a point, when they are not separated, although they will naturally receive feedback from each other and so appear to be more equal than they may be.

Dr Joseph Bogen, one of the surgeons who provided the patients for Sperry and Gazzaniga's original research, reckons that each half of the brain is 'the basis for *a* mind'.[4] So it is quite reasonable to put forward a model of consciousness in terms of left-mind and right-mind modes, and I shall use these terms to describe the two complementary but often conflicting parts of a normal personality. I must emphasise that I am dealing here with *normal* minds, not those that have been damaged by schizophrenia, or those that have separated into 'multiple personalities'.

Since nature has given us two brains, each with a mind-component, we should presumably make full use of both. Often we do not, and it is the right half that has become the neglected partner. Some scientists still refer to the left brain as the 'dominant' one, since we use it for speech and writing (except for the 10 per cent of the population that is left-handed). This implies that it is superior in importance, an idea no more acceptable nowadays than an assumed superiority of race, sex or class.

To give an idea of what I mean by left-minded and right-minded types, here are a few words associated with each:

| Left: | | Right: | |
|---|---|---|---|
| | Objective | | Subjective |
| | Logical | | Intuitive |
| | Analytical | | Holistic |
| | Verbal | | Visual |
| | Calculating | | Dreaming |
| | Practical | | Creative |
| | Rational | | Irrational |
| | Steady | | Impulsive |

Most readers, looking at these two columns, will probably find that many of the words in each apply to them, and so they should. We all know people who seem to be definitely more left- than right-minded, or vice versa. The left-minded stereotype is often shown in films and plays as the bank clerk who catches the same train to work every day, does everything from banking to pruning his roses strictly according to the rules, and leads an orderly, useful, but unexciting life. The right-mind extremist acts on wild impulses and gambles on his instincts, experiencing both dramatic successes and disastrous failures, leading a life that is anything but quiet.

Psychologist Dr Julian Jaynes of Princeton University has a provocative theory that the mind of ancient man was bi-cameral, a mixture of left- and right-minded qualities, though wholly lacking in conscious awareness of the self. In pre-literate times, our right-mind components were fully in charge, feeding us with information presumed to be of divine origin and received by a process of what is now known as hallucination. Joan of Arc had many predecessors when it came to hearing voices and acting on their orders; Agamemnon, for example, went into battle at Troy on orders from Zeus, which he accepted without question. Whether Jaynes is right or not, it is a matter of record that man was a fine artist long before he could write (his first attempts at writing were in any case primarily pictorial), and his right-mind qualities must have had survival value.

Even today, hunting for food and avoiding predators calls for as much intuition as logical reasoning.[5]

Once upon a time, then, the right mind was in charge. With the spread of literacy, printing and rational thought, the left became dominant to the point where intuitions and instincts came to be regarded as occult superstitions not to be confessed to in public. Our education system became almost wholly left-mind oriented. Although the word 'educate' comes from the Latin *educare* – to bring or lead *out* – education came to mean putting *in*, cramming the head with facts and neglecting the cultivation of what is already in it and waiting to be brought out.

'Like many successful revolutions, the left-brain revolution has come so far that what is needed is a counterrevolution,' says Thomas Blakeslee, an inventor and computer expert. As he points out, the development of the computer, itself a triumph of man's left-mind abilities at their best, is gradually taking over many of the functions of the brain that invented it. 'With routine and linear thinking left to computers,' he says, 'we will have no more need for "human computers" with atrophied right brains.' Our left brains, hopefully, will have less input and therefore more channels open to receive what our right brains are trying to convey to them.[6]

The French surgeon Paul Broca usually gets the credit for being the first to map out areas of the human brain, in the mid nineteenth century; but duality of both brain and mind was known, or at least intuitively grasped, long before then. In 1748, Emanuel Swedenborg noted that 'the left eye or the right part of the brain represents all that relates to the understanding of truth', while the right eye and left brain did the same for the 'appreciation of goodness'. Although he seems to have got his hemispheres the wrong way round, he wrote ten years later: 'The mind consists of two parts, one called the understanding and the other the will', which is a fair description of right- and left-brain attributes respectively.[7,8]

In 1844, Arthur L. Wigan published a book on insanity subtitled 'The Duality of Mind', in which he referred to the brain as 'two distinct and separate organs', each with its 'separate and distinct processes of thinking'. The two processes could be carried out simultaneously, he said, although one brain would tend to be 'superior in power' – the very phrase used by Dr Oppenheimer in the description I have already quoted.

In 1885, Frederic Myers, one of the founders of the Society for Psychical Research, put forward a theory linking the right brain to what he called the secondary self, which he defined (thirty years before Freud's first formal statement of his model of the unconscious) as follows:

'Coincidently with our normal or primary self there is within us a potential secondary self, or second focus of cerebration and mentation, which is not a mere metaphysical abstraction, but manifests itself occasionally by certain supernormal physiological or psychical activities.' (He hastened to add that by supernormal he meant 'beyond what usually happens'.) In his lengthy study of automatic writing, which he was one of the first to identify as 'the operation of unconscious cerebral action' rather than the work of spirits, he wrote that 'in graphic automatism the action of the right hemisphere is predominant, because the secondary self can appropriate its energies more readily than those of the left hemisphere, which is more immediately at the service of the waking mind'.[9]

Myers himself did not apply his two-brain model to hypnosis, but in a book first published in 1889, Dr C. Lloyd Tuckey (also an SPR member) included this interesting comment in a discussion of the methods of Liébeault, whom he had visited:

The reasonable and deliberative side of the patient's brain is suppressed, while the emotional or instinctive side is developed, and in proportion as the latter is predominant the greater generally is the success of the treatment.[10]

This is a clear description of left- and right-brain attributes as currently understood, and it is surprising that nearly a century was to pass before what was beginning to seem rather obvious was actually stated: that hypnosis is a means of suppressing or bypassing the left mind and communicating directly with the right. Thus the hypnotist is talking to the subject's unconscious.

In 1893, an American newspaperman named Thomson Jay Hudson put forward his model of a dual mind in a popular book. He saw the mind in terms of 'objective' and 'subjective' components; the former (which is what I am calling the left mind) perceiving the objective world by means of the five senses, and the latter (the right) operating quite independently of them by what Hudson could only describe as 'intuition'. It was the subjective mind, he said, 'which makes itself manifest in a hypnotic subject when he is in a state of somnambulism', or what we would now call deep trance. It could only perform to the limits of its ability, however, when the objective sense were 'in abeyance'.[11]

Leslie LeCron, a recognised authority on hypnosis, has pointed out that 'long before Freud, Hudson described perceptively the activities of the unconscious mind in a most modern way, arriving at conclusions later reached by Freud'. (And, I might add, earlier by Myers.)

The clues have been lying around for a long time, but as far as I have been able to discover it was not until 1982 that the conclusion to which they lead was spelled out in detail, in a talk given on 1 November at the Royal Society of Medicine by Dr David Pedersen, president of the British Society of Medical and Dental Hypnosis.

'When we hypnotise a patient,' he said, 'what we are doing is altering their mode of consciousness to the right hemisphere by inhibition of the left.'[12]

Dr Pedersen supported his proposal with a good deal of evidence, both experimental and observational, including the split-brain studies of Sperry and Gazzaniga, the high hypnotisability of children and art students compared to that of old people, science students and schizophrenics, and the discovery that dreams can be either suppressed or induced by interfering with the right hemisphere. (Some people with damaged right brains stop dreaming altogether, and the surgeon Wilder Penfield showed in his classic 1959 experiments that people can be made to dream while wide awake by having parts of their right brains electrically stimulated.)[13,14]

What seems to have settled the matter was the simple method of making electroencephalogram (EEG) recordings of the hypnotised brain. This had been done since the 1940s, and for a long time it was wrongly thought that the electrical activity of the hypnotised brain is the same as that of one in the normal waking state. Only in the early 1970s did it occur to anybody to see if there were any differences in the EEG traces of left and right brains of hypnotised subjects.

There were. Dr Crisetta MacLeod-Morgan, then at Flinders University of South Australia, found that the ratio of alpha brain-wave activity in the two hemispheres of forty-four hypnotised subjects was very similar to the ratio found in the brains of unhypnotised people who had been given right-brain tasks (such as visualisation exercises) to perform.[15]

'Hypnosis', she concluded, 'is a right-hemispheric task.' She also made the important point that highly hypnotisable people can perform it whether they are being formally hypnotised or not. There are good reasons to support T. X. Barber's view that we should drop the word hypnosis altogether. It is after all a state some people can enter any time they feel like it in their normal everyday lives. Stephen Black has already told us that the hypnotist makes direct contact with the subject's unconscious mind. Now we are told that the hypnotist is taking over the functions of the subject's left brain and communicating directly with the right. Can we thus conclude that the right brain is where the unconscious mind is? No, we cannot. The right brain and mind are just as conscious as the left. Neurologists may argue that, for all their complexities, our brains operate as single units; nevertheless, our minds can often appear un-coordinated — leading to extremist 'left'- or 'right-minded' behaviour. I shall therefore use these labels until more accurate ones appear. The right mind, then, is the 'antechamber' to the unconscious. [16] It is an antechamber with a two-way door that can be very hard to open. Often it gets completely stuck. Sometimes it swings open of its own accord, only to be rudely slammed by a blast of left-mind reaction. Under hypnosis it opens effortlessly, a suggestion is left there, to be carried away by invisible employees of a secret factory and obeyed to the letter, provided all the holes are punched in the right places on the suggestion-card.

The unconscious is only unconscious because we do not know consciously what it is doing. This does not mean that it is inactive. Far from it. It works a twenty-four-hour shift, never falling asleep on the job. While the left mind sleeps, the unconscious is busy clearing up the mental rubbish of the day, sometimes recycling it in the form of dreams, which are read on the right mind's visual display unit and often fail to get through to the left mind. Sometimes the unconscious pieces together bits of information it finds lying around and presents them as solved problems to the waking left mind, either as hypnopompic (waking) images or as 'inspirations' that arrive during breakfast. Throughout the night, the unconscious also keeps the body running, attending to numerous specific jobs at precise times, and remaining on guard in case the baby cries or a burglar scratches at the kitchen window. The unconscious is the ideal labour force. It never downs tools, goes slow, or disobeys orders.

But to carry out any supernormal task — one 'beyond what usually happens' — it must be given exact instructions. When we are in the hypnotic state of partial and temporary sleep (that is, left-mind sleep) we obey orders without question if they are given in the right way, whether they involve changing the skin, producing a blister (or not producing one), or trying to murder a superior officer. We can, it seems, be made to do anything that is theoretically possible under hypnosis, and as we shall see, one or two things that theoretically are not possible.

When I talk about left/right minds and behaviour, all I want to imply here is that in some people some of the time those capacities known to be associated with one brain or the other come into prominence at the expense of those associated with the other. Ideally, we should make full use of both of our minds, but in practice, at least in Western society, we usually do not. Left-mind attitudes have come to dominate. We have become mentally unbalanced to the point where our right minds are in danger of atrophy.

Nowhere is this more apparent than in the field of healing, one in which hypnosis has already been conclusively shown to be of immense potential value. How did we become so unbalanced? If we look at this question with the help of the two-mind model, a possible answer presents itself. It is that too little attention has been paid in the past to the state of mind not of the subject, but of the hypnotist.

If he is replacing his subject's left mind, he is performing a mental transplant, and the mind, like the body, has an annoying way of rejecting anything unfamiliar, whether this is somebody else's heart or somebody else's idea. Then again, paradoxically, it can be made to welcome an unfamiliar idea, just as a body can be deceived into accepting an organ transplant the molecular shape or form of which has been suitably altered.

The hypnotist's problem, clearly, is to present the suggested idea in the right way, or in one of two possible right ways, and it is these that I will now try to describe.

A distinguished American hypnotist, the late Professor Ronald E. Shor, compared the pitfalls of his profession to those navigational hazards immortalised by Homer: Scylla and Charybdis.

Scylla was a menacing rock that guarded the narrow Straits of Messina, and Charybdis was a nearby whirlpool. The dilemma facing the ancient mariner was that, as a later writer put it, '*incidis in Scyllam cupiens vitare Charibdim*' – if you keep well clear of the whirlpool you risk crashing into the rock. Likewise, if you go out of your way to avoid Scylla, you vanish down the plug-hole of Charybdis. Unless you steer a well-balanced middle course, you cannot win.

The hypnotist, Shor says, faces a similar dilemma. If he is a good scientist, in the generally accepted sense, he will be careful, well-disciplined, methodical and objective, or what I would call highly left-minded. Unfortunately these are not the qualities that make a successful hypnotist, who needs to be adventurous, risk-taking, and above all subjective. Shor defines the Scylla and Charybdis of

hypnotism as 'insufficient caution' and 'insufficient conviction'.
'The more the scientist-hypnotist tries to avoid one of the two
dangers,' he says, 'the more likely it becomes that he will succumb to
the other.'

He likens the hypnotist to a chemical catalyst, which can be
positive or negative. A positive (chemical) catalyst is a substance that
increases the rate of a chemical reaction while remaining unaltered
itself, whereas a negative catalyst decreases it. Obviously, the hypnotist must be a positive catalyst. The hypnotic process only gets under
way when, in Shor's words, 'the positive psychological catalysts of
assured confidence, expectant enthusiasm, and persuasive authority
are present in notable concentrations'. If they are not, or if they are
'offset by the negative psychological catalysts of scepticism, dis-
couragement, and the impression of possible failure, then only
diluted and incompleted versions of the hypnotic phenomena can
generally be produced'.[17]

We can easily pick out the positive catalysers, from Mesmer,
Puységur, Esdaile, Elliotson and Liébeault to Mason and Black, and
those who managed to steer a middle course, such as Braid and
Bramwell. The names of the negative catalysers have not survived.
They sank without trace, after defending to the last their sceptical
and cautious behaviour with impeccable left-mind logic. But they
did not get any results.

Some of the positive catalysers also came to grief. Shor mentions
Elliotson as one whose 'evangelistic zeal' in the face of his hostile
critics spiralled upwards and outwards until it had little contact with
reality, finally to collapse leaving only a residue of 'absurdity and
charlatanism'. (An unfair assessment of Elliotson, in my opinion.)

It is easy to make fun of the right-mind extremist who socialises
with extraterrestrials, communicates daily with the spirits, and has
somehow gained access to a body of knowledge denied to the rest of
us. The left-mind extremist is just as ridiculous, and a good deal less
entertaining as well. But let us forget about extremists of both
factions and look at the positive features of each category. To save
space I will call them Scyllans and Charybdocrats.

The Scyllan, with his right mind usually in command, has unlimited imagination, idealism and determination to break new ground.
He is not bothered about whether something is possible or not, he
just goes ahead and does it. Sometimes he fails, as when trying to
build a perpetual-motion machine but, when he succeeds, he leaves
his mark on the world in a way no Charybdocrat can equal. Arthur C.

Clarke has observed the major breakthroughs in science often come from people who do not know that what they are trying to do is supposed to be impossible.

Einstein, like all geniuses, made full use of his right mind. He thought in images, and would do his calculations by closing his eyes and letting the figures 'dance'. 'The words of the language, as they are written or spoken, do not seem to play any role in my mechanism of thought', as he put it.[18] The mathematician Gauss is supposed to have said once : 'I have the result, now let me see how I arrived at it.' A successful inventor I know has told me that he tends to work backwards, starting with an image of his finished product and then finding out how it can be built. Like Gauss and Einstein, he knows how to make his right mind work for him, and when it is time to bring in the left to make the dreams come true.

The Charybdocrat's place in the scheme of things involves more than debunking frauds, explaining why things cannot be done, and pouring cold water on anything that smacks of Scyllanism. His positive side is his methodical approach to complex problems, his patience, and his self-effacing modesty. He is a good team member and a loyal party worker, and his qualities are often needed by his Scyllan counterpart. The architectural fantasies of visionaries like Le Corbusier or Frank Lloyd Wright, for example, might not have become reality without good left-minded structural engineers finding ways to keep them upright. And not all scientific break-throughs are wholly Scyllan in origin; the discovery of the DNA molecular structure did not come in a blinding flash of light to Crick and Watson. It came after years of meticulous observation, experiment, and cries of 'back to the drawing board' by them and their colleagues Wilkins and the late Rosalind Franklin. No true Scyllan would have been able to stay the course.[19]

It is a pity that Scyllans and Charybdocrats waste so much energy attacking each other, forgetting that each have in their own heads what they condemn in the enemy, and could probably benefit by making use of it. It is also a pity that neither faction seems to realise that life would be better for all if we did our best to make full use of both minds, and to know when the qualities of each are called for and when they are not. For there are times when one mind can hinder the work of the other rather than help it, and to illustrate this I will leave the mysteries of the mind for a moment and turn to something much easier to understand: tennis.

Every time we move a muscle, we demonstrate the power of mind over matter. When we go for a walk, we do not have to think about the problem of putting one foot in front of the other. We just do it. The right messages get through to the right muscles without any conscious effort, and most of us have not the faintest idea which muscle or brain cell is where and how they communicate. The subjective, secondary or unconscious self can get on very well without any interference provided it knows what it is supposed to be doing.

This is the idea behind what US tennis teacher Timothy Gallwey calls 'the inner game', and it is worth looking at here because it applies to many activities other than tennis. Gallwey hit on the idea after noticing that his students kept talking out loud while on court, especially when they were not playing very well. One day it occurred to him to try and find out who exactly was talking to whom and why.

'I'm just talking to myself,' he was told crossly. But that was no explanation. 'Obviously,' Gallwey wrote, 'the "I" and the "myself" are separate entities, or there would be no conversation.' He called them Self 1 and Self 2, and noticed that Self 1 would give the orders (out loud) whereupon Self 2 would play a stroke which Self 1 would promptly criticise. Bad players seemed to be fighting themselves rather than their opponents.

On the other hand, when somebody was playing well, onlookers would say things like 'He's unconscious! He doesn't know what he's doing.' The secret of peak performance seemed to be to let the body do what it had been taught to do without consciously interfering with it. Once Self 1 had done its work during the long hours of practice, learning the rules and techniques, Self 2 should be left to get on with the game. The hot streak of a winner would continue until Self 1 started thinking about it and making a conscious effort to keep it going. 'As soon as he attempts to exercise control,' Gallwey noted, 'he loses it.'[20]

Gallwey teaches by showing rather than telling bodies what to do. With Bob Kriegel, he has applied the same approach to skiing, and Thomas Blakeslee reported 'exceptionally good results', especially with children, who respond to nonverbal education methods much more readily than adults. Blakeslee noted that they only worked with people who could break habits of verbally-oriented teaching and learning. 'You can't change a lifetime of thought patterns in a single lesson,' he wrote, but he reckoned the method 'clearly demonstrates the human potential that is wasted by our present overly verbal education system'.[21]

Gallwey sees his two selves in terms of mind and body, but Blakeslee emphatically equates them with left and right brains, or what I prefer to call left and right minds. 'Regardless of the terminology,' David F. Brown wrote in 1977, 'the process remains one of unlearning the programmed habits and concepts that interfere with our natural ability to learn by trusting the body's innate intelligence.'[22]

It is interesting to note in passing that left-handers seem to have an advantage in one-handed sports such as tennis or fencing, a fact now being taken seriously by doctors at France's National Institute of Sport and Physical Education (INSEP). They note that champions Jimmy Connors and John McEnroe are left-handed, as were all the semi-finalists in the 1982 French Championship and the six finalists in the men's foil at the 1980 Olympic Games. The left hand is guided by the right brain, and this is also the hemisphere that specialises in perception of form and spatial relationships. In other words, it sees the target more accurately than the left brain does. Left-handers thus have the benefit of a few crucial hundredths of a second in their reaction times compared with their right-handed opponents. So if you are left-handed, take up one-armed sports.[23]

Another example of the potential of nonverbal right-mind education comes from Moscow, where swimming is 'taught' to new-born babies, who can hardly be expected to understand verbal instructions of any kind. But their little bodies, which have been sloshing around in the womb for several weeks, know exactly what to do when they find themselves in another warm pool. They swim, even under water, long before they can walk, and they obviously love it. Some have even been born under water, by a procedure developed by an enterprising Soviet named Igor Charkovsky. Sadly, the mini-pool ran into trouble in 1983 when a baby apparently drowned, though a Soviet doctor has told me that no autopsy was made public, and it is not clear if the baby would not have died anyway from what the textbooks unhelpfully called Sudden Infant Death Syndrome.[24]

The Moscow experiment shows how a human body, even a brand new one, can perform at least one function that some people never manage to learn at all, when simply allowed to do it unaided. (It could be argued that adults who cannot swim have already known how to, but have forgotten.) Blakeslee reports that most children can become really 'hot' skiers in just one day, although babies are not born knowing how to ski.

I hope it is becoming clear what all this inner swimming, skiing and tennis might have to do with inner healing. If a body can function more efficiently when it is under the control of the right mind, we would expect a type of suggestion aimed specifically at the right mind to be more effective than one formulated in rational and precise terms. In fact, visual or abstract ideas should get better results than any verbally stated ones. There is some evidence to support this, but it does not mean that verbal suggestion is no use at all. It certainly can be. In fact, there are two paradoxically different ways of getting a suggestion-programme through to the right mind, and they seem to produce véry similar results.

An American psychologist, Dr Peter B. Field, calls the two methods 'humanistic' and 'mechanistic'. Mechanistic suggestion is like moulding a piece of plastic in a machine. You press a button, the machine goes klunk, and out pops a soap dish or whatever. In this kind of suggestion method, the suggestion is stamped into the mind automatically and instantaneously, provided the mind accepts it. For the mind, unlike a sheet of plastic, will not accept the mould unless it wants to, or unless there is no reason why it should not accept it.

Humanistic suggestion is quite different. It is done by what Dr Field calls 'indirection, hinting or intimating'. 'Instead of asking a person directly to do something,' he explains, 'the [humanist] hypnotist asks him to let it happen involuntarily, or to imagine that it is happening and to find that it then does happen.' In this kind of 'agreement between two wills', Dr Field sees the hypnotist as 'not only a stage director, but also a painter who communicates through vivid images; a creative writer who holds his readers spellbound; a musician who communicates through intonation, rhythm and timbre; and a poet, who induces feeling through creative and evocative use of words.'[25]

These two methods can both work. It is not a question of one being right and the other wrong, but of knowing when to use which. A sergeant-major does not persuade his squad to turn left by humanistic imagery. He yells 'LEFT TURN!', and left it turns, or else. This is mechanistic suggestion, reinforced in this case with a strong element of threat, and it is obeyed by conditioned reflex. Direct suggestion under hypnosis can be effective in much the same way, as in stage demonstrations where the hypnotist drills the mind much as the sergeant-major drills the squad.

He does not have to yell, as Father Faria used to do. Indeed, as Black points out, 'a weak stimulus which is *unexpected* is likely to evoke a larger response than a stronger one to which the subject had become accustomed'. This, he explains, is because an unexpected stimulus is more improbable than an expected one, and so contains more information.[26] When taken by surprise, it seems, the mind tends to act first and think afterwards, if at all. Faced with an expected stimulus, containing little or no new information, its response is weaker or even nil. It may be, as Black suggests, that the response might even be related inversely to the intensity of the stimuli by which they were evoked. In other words, the sergeant-major approach might solve a simple and well-defined problem, such as getting rid of a wart or making a limb go rigid, but more complex problems call for the other approach.

For healing purposes, it seems that the image is mightier than the word. Suggestion is at its most effective when it induces an emotion or visual image in the patient's mind. If a hypnotist were to give a patient precise instructions, using all the correct medical terms, the patient would have no idea what he was talking about. Canon J. D. Pearce-Higgins, a leading Church of England authority on exorcism, once remarked to me that the traditional ceremony of exorcism would probably only work on an evil spirit with a degree in theology! Likewise, precisely-worded hypnotic suggestion would only work on subjects with a detailed knowledge of anatomy. This may explain why Black's experiments, with nurses and medical students as subjects, were so successful.

Doctors, understandably, have tended to favour the authoritarian mechanistic technique. They have been trained to give exact prescriptions and orders, and it must go against the grain to be told that hypnotic suggestion sometimes has to be vague and abstract. Yet some of the great hypnotists of the past were undoubtedly humanistic rather than mechanistic. Liébeault, for example, according to an eye-witness (Lloyd Tuckey) rarely gave precise verbal suggestions. He would usually just put his hand on his patient, suggest warmth, and say that the pain would go away and not come back. This sounds more like faith healing than orthodox medicine, yet Liébeault was one of the most admired and imitated medical hypnotists of all time. Hippolyte Bernheim, a professor of medicine, set out to debunk him and ended up collaborating with him; Freud was profoundly impressed by him and learned his hypnotism from him; Lloyd Tuckey dedicated his book to him 'in admiration of his genius'. Surely he must have done more than pat people on the head and murmur comforting words?

From all accounts, it was not so much what he did as the kind of man he was. Liébeault had that quality known as charisma. This is not easy to define, or to teach to medical students, but as it is a quality that seems to be very useful when it comes to influencing the minds of others, we should try to find out what it is and how to get it.

The dictionaries are not much help. My 1,536-page Concise Oxford Dictionary leaves it out altogether. The American Heritage gives two definitions: 'a divinely inspired gift of power, such as the ability to perform miracles', and 'a rare quality of power attributed to those persons who have demonstrated an exceptional ability for leadership and for securing the devotion of large numbers of people'. The word comes from the Greek for divine gift, but there was nothing divine about the undoubted gifts of Hitler or Charles Manson, each of whom secured the devotion of relatively large numbers of people.

Authors Alan W. Scheflin and Edward M. Opton Jr have, I think, identified the essential feature of charisma, good or evil, in their thoroughly-researched study of mind manipulation and control. 'More than just possessing an attractive magnetism which draws people toward him or her, the charismatic person commands respect by representing contact with some higher order of existence', they say. 'Charismatic leaders have an intensity, an authority, a conversiveness with spirituality that most people cannot match in their own lives. The desire to reach that level of living, or at least to be in contact with someone who does, is a readily observable fact of life.' The charismatic person, with 'one foot in the present and the other in the eternal', satisfies an apparently universal urge to escape from the reality we know into the greater world we feel must exist. (Or, if you like, that we have found it necessary to invent.)[27]

More than that, the successful charismatic convinces people that he can deliver what his followers really want. When he does, as for example Hitler did for a time, he becomes even more charismatic. The same must be·said of other aberrant and abhorrent people like Manson and the extraordinary Jim Jones, who led eight hundred of his followers to mass suicide in Guyana. When a charismatic movement is founded on a false or evil reality, it becomes one of those spiral structures mentioned by Ronald Shor that collapses on itself. When it responds to more noble urges, it becomes indestructible, especially in the form of a religion.

The hypnotist is doing on a small scale what the great charismatic leaders have done on the large scale. He is offering the expectancy of a sudden alteration in the quality of life, even if this only involves getting rid of a headache, and as the evidence shows he very often delivers it. When he fails, it could well be that as James Coates suggested it is because his own imagination has let him down, not that of the patient. The successful hypnotist must have one mind (the left) in the present and the other (the right) in the eternal, and like the charismatic he must master the difficult art of keeping them in balance while using both at full power.

Most charismatics offer their followers the promise of an alternative future. On the other hand, charismatic healing (which is what hypnosis can amount to) may be doing exactly the opposite: offering a return to the past, by fulfilling the patient's desire for a return to a lost state of innocence and freedom from illness. Stephen Black speculates that the hypnotic induction process may in effect send subjects back to the womb, by the Pavlovian process of conditioned reflex.

The two essential features of this process are constriction and rhythmic stimulation. By staring at his subject, pointing his hands at him, or holding an object in front of his eyes, the hypnotist is constricting the subject's field of awareness and inducing a state of what Braid called monoideism – the presence of a single dominant idea. In this state, as the early mesmerists found, subjects were apt to become rigid, like a cat picked up by the scruff of its neck, without any verbal suggestion. The rigidity was not total; arms and legs could be bent forcibly into any position, where they would remain. This is known medically as *flexibilitas cerea* (wax-like flexibility), and the fact that it can be induced in animals as well as humans shows that there must be some kind of inborn reflex mechanism at work.

Babies, before birth, live in a very constricted environment, and Black suggests that 'owing to such a confined environment, the first conditioned reflex of all experience might then be set up'. Any kind of constriction after birth then acts as a conditional stimulus, and produces the response of immobility combined with wax-like flexibility. Animals, he points out, tend to take up a foetal position when hypnotised.[28]

As for rhythmic stimuli, the pounding of the mother's heart right in the baby's ear is the first stimulus of any kind of which it can become consciously aware. The sudden loss of this stimulus at the moment of birth may well explain why so many babies seem to come into the outside world in a towering rage. The sudden loss of any familiar stimulus is a terrible shock.

In 1977, London medical researcher Dr Michele Clements dis-covered something that seems so obvious one wonders why nobody had thought of it before: babies like being born to the sound of rhythmic music. During a delivery in the City of London Maternity Hospital, where she was working, a baby became completely stuck and the obstetrician could not move it. Dr Clements then put on a Vivaldi record, whereupon the baby literally danced its way out of the womb.[29] I am sure it is no coincidence that many baroque allegro movements are played at 72 crotchets to the minute, the normal heart-beat rate, and it is not surprising that a rhythmic beat will act as a stimulus to which a new-born baby will react favourably. Busy mothers might try playing some Vivaldi next time their baby yells instead of rocking it to and fro and singing lullabies. Or they could make a tape recording of their own heart-beat, using a contact microphone, and play that back.

When a rhythmic stimulus, such as the voice of a hypnotist, is combined with the stimulus of constriction, we are recreating the environment in which we evolved. The voice may not sound much like a beating heart, but it is resonant, monotonous and rhythmic, making much use of repetition and counting. Verbal hypnotic induction is a kind of scientific lullaby; it soothes the subject into a partial sleep, or even total sleep if that is what is desired. As for the stimuli of touch and staring, these are among the first stimuli of any kind to which a newborn baby becomes conditioned. On the whole, there seems to be a good deal of evidence to support my view of medical hypnosis as charismatic healing based on the exploitation of conditioned reflexes and responses. The latter are stimulated by purely mechanistic means, whereas the successful application of charisma calls for the humanistic approach.

This is a nice simple theory, but if it is the right one it has to explain all the evidence. How about those remarkable cases of Mason and others of ichthyosis, which I take to be examples of the outer limits of hypnotic healing as established so far? What exactly happened inside the mind and body of that young boy after Dr Mason had told him to come back the following week with a brand new arm?

This is a difficult question to answer, because it was not a matter of restoring body tissue to its normal state, as with a headache or a wart. The patient's body tissue had never been in a normal state to start with. His skin was not restored, it was *created*. It was as if a film of his whole life, from cell division to young adulthood, had been wound back, edited and wound forward again. This was regression, not to the womb but to the blueprint, where the genetic programme was altered to remove the mistakes that prevented normal skin from growing. This sounds far-fetched. To grow a new arm of skin in a week also sounds far-fetched, yet it happened. Any explanation for it, which nobody has yet attempted to provide, must inevitably sound far-fetched in terms of present knowledge.

To sum up: we are in two minds about everything, all the time. There are two separate components of behaviour in us, associated with some of the functions of the left and right hemispheres of our brains. I called them the left mind and the right mind, and to what extent they correspond to left and right brain functions is not important. What is important is to accept that there are two of us here in the same cranium. One is logical, the other intuitive. Presumably, they are supposed to be compatible, but in practice they often are not. Logic suppresses intuition in some people, the reverse being the case in others. In Western society, we tend to practise a kind of cerebral apartheid, with the right mind being treated very much as a second-class partner.

The right mind is the antechamber to the unconscious, which is distributed throughout the body and runs most of its functions all round the clock. The right mind has access to the control centre of the body, the left mind has not. The left mind can communicate only with the right mind, which it tends to censor or suppress entirely instead of cooperating with it. Under hypnosis, the subject's left mind is silenced altogether, and the communicating with the right mind is done by the hypnotist, who uses a delicate balance of his own minds to coax the subject into receiving his suggestions.

Once a right mind has been told what to do, it will do it unless prevented by the left mind. It will only perform at its best, however – whether playing tennis or reorganising a sick body – if it is properly programmed and then left alone. It is capable of doing anything that is technically possible and desired greatly enough.

One method of reprogramming the mind for good or bad is the charismatic encounter, which can have an instantaneous effect. Accepted reality can be thrown out and replaced on the spot with an alternative reality, which immediately becomes as real as the one it replaced, and provided it is supported by total faith, rational or not, it can last indefinitely. The more charisma the hypnotist can transmit, the more successful he is likely to be.

Another method of mind-reprogramming involves a purely mechanistic technique, in which staring and touching have the effect of removing patients from the present and sending them into another dimension. This, I believe, is what happens when no verbal suggestion is used.

Each of these methods has enormous potential that has barely been tapped, although each has been in medical use for more than two hundred years. Now that we have some idea of what mesmerism and hypnosis really are, will they perhaps be used more often?

The discovery of a pill or a machine that could cure or alleviate as many diseases as hypnosis is known to be able to do would earn a fortune for its inventor. While we are waiting for such a discovery, why not make full use of a technique we already have?

In a somewhat left-minded book published in 1977, psychologist Dr H. B. Gibson remarked that 'no one in their senses' would suggest treating cancer with hypnosis. He referred to only one specific type of this disease, but he gave the impression that anybody who tried to treat any type of it in this way must be out of his mind.[30]

However, if, as I have suggested – basing the suggestion on the published opinions of experienced professionals – the mind can control any function of the body, the ultimate test would be to see if it can control the course of a disease that is often fatal. If warts can be made to go away by hypnosis, why not tumours? The one is not so unlike the other; both are unwanted growths that serve no useful purpose.

I do not want to raise false hopes. It cannot yet be claimed that hypnosis cures cancer. It can be claimed that under certain conditions hypnosis has cured some cases of cancer. Can we identify those conditions and re-create them to order? Thanks to some recent research, much of which is published here for the first time in a form accessible to the general reader, this now seems possible.

# 4

# Miss Barber is Cured

'The case which I am about to relate is one of the most splendid triumphs of mesmerism, and is the most splendid hitherto accomplished under my hands.' This is how John Elliotson introduced his 25-page report, published in 1848, on a *Cure of a true cancer of the Female Breast with Mesmerism*.

The patient came to see him on 6 March 1843, complaining of an insistent pain that had been troubling her for fifteen months. Examining her, Elliotson found an 'intensely hard tumour in the centre of the right breast, circumscribed, moveable and apparently about five or six inches in circumference'. He reckoned it was malignant, although nowadays moveable tumours are thought more likely to be benign. Anyway, he regarded the disease as 'such as the art of medicine has never been known to cure'.

At first, even the confident and enterprising Elliotson had no intention of trying to cure his patient. He agreed with two other doctors that the right breast would have to come off. The best he could do, he thought, would be to mesmerise the woman to induce general anaesthesia, so that at least she could be operated on without pain. (Chloroform and ether were not then available in Britain.)

Elliotson had a good deal of experience in the suppression of pain. He had also cured the patient's aunt of 'violent fits' with mesmerism, and it seems that the patient herself had come to him under the impression that her pain, whatever it was, could be removed in the same way.

'Unwilling to make her unhappy,' Elliotson wrote, 'I said no more, and allowed her to suppose that the mesmerism was intended to cure her disease.' The woman duly told her other two doctors that she was going to try this form of treatment. One said that if mesmerism cured her, he would believe anything, while the other confessed 'he knew nothing about it and therefore should say nothing against it'.

'This display of common sense is deserving of all imitation by medical men,' Elliotson noted.

As far as we know, he used no verbal suggestion at all. His treatment consisted only of 'slow passes and a fixed look in the eyes'. Sessions lasted half an hour, and would be repeated indefinitely, it seems, until the patient either recovered or died. It should be remembered that in 1843 a cancer patient had little choice between available therapies. Mesmerism was the only alternative to the agonising prospect of an operation without an anaesthetic. It was the second, and last, resort.

After her first session, the patient reported spending 'a much better night than usual', and as the daily treatment went on, Elliotson noted with satisfaction that she spontaneously developed insensitivity to pain and muscular rigidity of the wax-like type I mentioned in the last chapter. These were signs that she was responding to her daily doses of staring and hand-waving.

After six months of mesmerism, however, the tumour seemed to have got bigger. Yet neither doctor nor patient seems to have been unduly discouraged. The faith of the patient in this case seems to have been as strong as that of the doctor, if not stronger. The treatment went on and on, and to cut a very long story short, it seems that at some point about two or three years after her first session, the woman's tumour turned around and began to go into slow and gradual remission. By the summer of 1846, she was able to report that the pains had entirely ceased, and two years later she, Elliotson and the two other doctors who had seen her previously agreed that the breast tumour had gone away. Dr. W. C. Engledue testified in writing: 'I have just seen her again, and I find the disease entirely removed.' Dr John Ashburner pronounced: 'Miss Barber is cured – a fact, about which there is no mistake.'

'Mesmerism', Elliotson concluded, 'tends to augment the power of the body to shake off disease.'[1]

Before we go any further into the controversial and emotive subject of cancer and possible ways of curing it, one point must be made quite clear. As Dr Kenneth S. Bowers of the University of Waterloo (Canada) put it in 1977:

'It must be admitted that scientifically proving the case for the effectiveness of hypnosis as a treatment for cancer would be a logistic nightmare ...' It would, he said, involve selecting subjects and classifying them according to what type of cancer they had and to what extent they were hypnotisable. Then there would have to be a control group of patients who were not hypnotised at all, and those who were would have to be followed up for at least five years.[2]

The ethical dilemma facing the doctor is an appalling one. If he really thinks hypnosis can cure cancer, and wants to prove it, he must take a large number of patients and make sure they receive no other form of treatment, such as surgery, chemotherapy or radiation, each of which is already known to be able to cure cancer – sometimes, at least. Then he must take another group of patients with the same type of cancer, of which there are innumerable varieties ranging from the harmless to the lethal, and deliberately deny them the form of therapy he is trying to prove to be effective. No research programme of this kind would ever get past an ethics committee.

According to the left-minded way of looking at things, you cannot cure cancer by hypnosis, because there is no evidence that you can, and if you set about to gather the evidence you are breaking the medical code of ethics. End of story.

But not end of this chapter. There is a way out of the dilemma, and it was found by the redoubtable Miss Barber. It was her choice to have her breast tumour mesmerised, not Elliotson's. Ironically, it was Elliotson himself who protested that 'we should lead the public, not the public us', yet it was one of his own patients who led him on that occasion, and recovered. Even Elliotson's old enemy, *The Lancet*, in a very outspoken editorial to be quoted in more detail later, wrote in 1983 that 'where a believer is being treated in a context of his religious faith, it would not merely be churlish but also bad clinical practice to deny the support of that belief'.[3] I see no harm in expanding this admirably sensible statement to include the context of faith in the patient's own mind. There are times when patients should take the initiative, and in recent times, as we shall see, an increasing number of them have been doing this.

Dr Bowers said quite correctly in 1977 that there was no scientific evidence that cancer could be cured by hypnosis, though he mentioned one case in which remission had 'at least temporarily coincided with the use of hypnosis'. He may have been referring to a case published in the same year which, although unfortunately reported at second-hand, offers a tantalising glimpse of what might be possible.

The patient was a terminal one, meaning that there was nothing more that medicine could do for him. He had cancer of the bladder,

and secondary growths all over his body. After his hospital colleagues had given up, a man named as Dr H. decided to try hypnosis, to
which there can hardly be any ethical objections once all else has
been tried without success. He found that the patient was one of the
5 per cent or so of the population who can be put into deep trance, a
state in which they retain no conscious memories of what goes on
during the session, so that the left mind has no chance to interfere
with suggestions given. Not surprisingly, this is the state in which it is
generally agreed that verbal suggestions are most effective.

Dr H. used a simple fantasy-visualisation technique, asking the
patient if he could find the control centre for the body's blood supply.
The patient said yes, he could. It was a sort of boiler room full of
valves and pipes. The hypnotist suggested locating the pipe that
carried blood to the tumour down in the bladder, and turning off the
supply. The patient obeyed, and to cut another fairly long story short
(it is not clear how many hypnosis sessions were held) he got so much
better that he was able to leave the terminal ward, something not
many people ever do on their own feet, and go home. His tumour
shrank from the size of a grapefruit to that of a golf-ball. Then one day
during a routine examination, another doctor accidentally ruptured
the wall of the tumour, and in a few hours the patient was dead.[4]

Dr Elmer Green of the Menninger Foundation, who reports this
case, is one of the pioneers of research in biofeedback, the process
of becoming aware of body operations normally performed
unconsciously and of being able to control them. He uses the phrase
'passive volition' to describe that special state of mind you have to be
in if you want to alter your heartbeat, temperature or whatever. He
sees the mind as a duality, but not in left–right terms. 'The cortex
plants the idea in the subcortex and then allows nature to take its
course without interference. That is passive volition,' he says,
likening it to the actions of a farmer who plants some seeds, visualises
what kind of crop he wants, and then just leaves it to nature to get on
with it. This is a perfect example of left–right mind cooperation
between man and nature; man doing the left-mind work, writing the
programme, then inserting it in the soil.[5]

The same principle applies whether man is collaborating with
plants or with the other half of his mind (whether this is seen in
left–right or up–down terms is not important here). 'Mind over body,
inside the skin, is a special case of mind over nature,' Green says.
Part of what goes on inside our bodies is nature at work. The same
growth process goes on, whether it is a plant in the ground or an idea

in the mind. An idea is a seed, and once it is planted it needs no attention at all. It grows much better if left alone.[6]

Many people are surprised to find that they can alter the behaviour of their bodies just by deciding to do so. There are now several biofeedback machines on the market with the aid of which one can actually see the effects of thought on blood pressure, galvanic skin response, or brainwave pattern. Geoffrey Blundell's ingenious Mind Mirror indicates on a display unit the rhythmic performance of each half of the brain; with electrodes fastened to the scalp, the subject sits and watches flashing lights indicate how much beta, alpha, theta and delta brainwave activity is being generated.

During a session with Britain's leading biofeedback researchers, C. Maxwell Cade and Isobel Cade, I found that while I was in my normal daytime state of consciousness nearly all the lights were on up in the beta band, but when I sat passively, not thinking of anything, they all went out and there was a visible surge of alpha activity. With a little practice, I found I could easily switch from one state to the other. It was great fun, and I felt very pleased with myself until I found that most of the others in the class were much better than I at brain-control. Later, in a London laboratory, I was able to generate half an hour of steady alpha even without visual feedback, and I have yards of chart paper to prove it.

By connecting both a healer and a patient to Mind Mirrors, Maxwell Cade has been able to identify and describe a specific 'healing pattern'. It is a well-balanced one, with both hemispheres showing a big bulge in the lower alpha band and roughly the same amount of activity in all the other bands. Working with some of Britain's best healers, including Edgar Chase, Rose Gladden, Bruce MacManaway and Addie Raeburn, he has found that when the healing pattern falters, the healing effect weakens.

Cade has also discovered that a healer can impose his own brainwave pattern on a patient even when the two are in separate rooms. This seems to open up a new area of research, and even if it means no more than that a healer's working brainwave pattern happens to coincide with a patient's 'expectancy-state' pattern, this fact is interesting enough in itself. It seems to be a very clear illustration of Mesmer's 'agreement between two wills'.

This effect has been demonstrated, on closed-circuit television, to an audience of four hundred. On this occasion, the healer (Rose Gladden) and the patient (a doctor's wife) were in the same room.

'After about fifteen minutes,' Cade reports, 'both healer and patient appeared to be completely attuned. It was such a clear-cut and undeniable demonstration, in terms understandable and convincing to all, that the audience was stunned.'[7]

Equally clear-cut evidence for the ability of the mind to alter the working of the body was obtained in February 1981, when a team of American and Indian scientists led by Dr Herbert Benson of Harvard Medical School carted $100,000-worth of equipment up a 2,800 metre mountain in India to see if those travellers' tales about yogis being able to alter their body temperature at will were true.

They were. All three subjects tested showed they could raise the temperatures of their fingers and toes by up to 8.3 degrees Centigrade, while other parts of the body either stayed the same or dropped slightly along with the room temperature. This experiment was published in *Nature*.[8]

Another well-tested yogi is Swami Rama, who alarmed a roomful of scientists in Elmer Green's laboratory by stopping his heartbeat altogether, and performed a number of other unusual feats including the production of a cyst (a small lump of fatty substance) beneath his skin and making a needle revolve on a pivot at a distance. He did the latter, one of the few convincing cases of psychokinesis in a laboratory, in response to a challenge from a sceptical colleague of Green's. 'When I am challenged, all of my powers come up and I can do everything,' the Swami commented.[9]

Now, if people are able to stop their hearts, warm up their fingers and toes, alter their brain rhythms and grow lumps on demand, the possible limits of what the mind can achieve seem to recede over the horizon and out of sight. If we add the recent biofeedback evidence to the older body of evidence from hypnosis and mesmerism, it seems fairly clear that when we are motivated in the right way, or in one of several different right ways, very considerable powers 'come up' and can do anything that is theoretically possible. The well-documented evidence from the biofeedback researchers, which has found its way even into conservative journals like *Nature*, makes some of the claims of the hypnotists and mesmerists far more plausible.

The evidence has improved, but the conclusions drawn from them are still the same, though expressed more convincingly. Elliotson regarded mesmerism as something that 'tends to augment the power of the body to shake off disease'. Alyce Green, wife and co-worker of Elmer Green, says essentially the same thing a century and a half later: 'It isn't biofeedback that is the "panacea", it is the power within the human being to self-regulate, self-heal, re-balance. Biofeedback does nothing to the person; it is a tool for releasing that potential.'[10]

We now need evidence that this kind of approach can be effective on a large scale against major disease, and there now follows an account of how someone very much in his senses used it, achieved positive results, and published them in a professional journal. It is, as far as I have been able to discover, the first project of its kind ever published.

In 1975, Dr Bernauer W. Newton embarked upon a programme involving the use of hypnotherapy on cancer patients at his Newton Center for Clinical Hypnosis in Los Angeles. There was plenty of published evidence by then, some of it dating back fifty years, to indicate that a cancer patient's personality and emotions had something to do with the disease that was still causing nearly one fifth of all deaths in the USA, despite considerable advances in conventional methods of treatment. Some of the best of the more recent evidence came from psychologists, notably Dr Lawrence LeShan, who began to write on the subject in the 1950s, but some of it came from the oncologists (cancer specialists) themselves. Dr O. Carl Simonton, one of the pioneers of the new approach, began his career as a radiation therapist, while back in 1962 Dr D. W. Smithers, one of the world's leading cancer specialists, made his views on the subject to which he had devoted his life very plain:

'Like other names used in science, cancer is just a shortened way of saying something that cannot be simply defined ... [It] is no more a disease of cells than a traffic jam is a disease of cars. A lifetime of study of the internal combustion engine would not help anyone to understand our traffic problems. Cancer is a disease of organisation, not a disease of cells.' Whole functioning organisms needed studying, he added, as well as cells. We must develop a 'social science of the human body'.[11]

So, while oncologists take care of the trees, as it were, it seems there is a useful role for the clinical psychologist in looking after the forest floor, the ground from which the trees get their nourishment. It is the condition of the body, Dr Newton believes, that 'greatly determines whether a malignant cell is to be allowed to remain in the body long enough to produce a tumour'.

Newton (a psychologist) began his programme by telling his patients that they could play an active part in their own treatment.

They could change their feelings of passive helplessness into positive attitudes of initiative and participation. It was known that some tumours (though not all) developed as the result of a breakdown in the body's immune or self-repair system. It was also known that people could influence their immune systems, for good or bad, by the state of their minds. So the logical approach was to get the mind into a state in which it, in turn, could get to work on its own sick body.

This was sound mechanistic (left-mind) logic, and even in 1975 there was a fair amount of published research from the biofeedback laboratories to back it up. To put his theory into practice, Newton opted for the humanistic right-mind approach. He worked out a series of visualisations which, implanted under hypnosis, enabled patients to see 'powerful healing forces' teaming up with whatever conventional treatment they were receiving, dismantling their tumours and flushing them out of the body by the back door. He gave his patients tapes to enable them to get into the hypnotic state at home, and experience their visualisations in comfort. He also tackled 'specific symptom problems through direct intervention with hypnosis'. In addition, patients were given the full range of standard psychotherapies and psychological tests, to help them get better acquainted with themselves and their problems.

Newton provided no details of the kind of visualisations he gave his patients, and I think he was right not to do so. A scientific paper is supposed to provide enough information to enable anybody else to repeat the experiment, but visualisation exercises lose much of their effectiveness when written out. They are designed to be experienced by the right mind of a patient who needs them, and since some readers of this book may need them one day, I will not weaken their possible effects by describing a typical one here. They will be more effective if they take the right mind by surprise. Moreover, as will be explained later, it is not the visualisations themselves that are the most important part of this kind of therapy.

Newton's theory was quite straightforward, but he had many problems when putting it into practice. No two patients were alike, and nor were their diseases. Some seemed resigned to the fact that they were going to die, and would only come along for their weekly therapy session because their wives or husbands insisted. Some would think up any excuse for missing an appointment; one man claimed he had to stay at home because somebody was coming to buy his lawnmower. Apparently this meant more to him than staying alive.

As the programme continued, it became clear that something very encouraging was happening. Hypnotic suggestions of the visual kind were helping, if only at first on such relatively minor symptoms as pain, nausea, insomnia or loss of appetite, and this only had to happen once to set a 'snowball effect' in motion. Patients would suddenly realise that there was something they could do for themselves after all. A slight turn for the better would snowball into the discovery that it was worth fighting for life.

It seems that some of them won. By the time Newton published his results in 1982, he had given therapy to a total of 283 patients, whom he classified under three headings:

*The Unknowns*. These had dropped out after less than three sessions. There were 121 of them, or 43 per cent.
*The Inadequates*. These had been seen less than ten times, and in the opinion of their therapists had lost the will to live. They numbered 57, or 20 per cent.
*The Adequates*. These had attended at least ten hour-long sessions and they totalled 105, or 37 per cent.

By 1982, all but 10 of the inadequates, or 82 per cent of them, were dead. Of the adequates, 48 had died and 57 had not – 54 per cent were still alive, exactly three times as many in percentage terms as the surviving inadequates. And within this group of surviving adequates there was a subgroup of 24 who had either received no orthodox medical treatment at all, or had abandoned it six months or more before they first came to the Newton Center. So they could not be said to have benefited from standard treatment during their hypnotherapy programme. Of this group 15 (62 per cent) were still alive, and 9 had been pronounced by their doctors to be 'in full remission', in other words, apparently cured. All of this group, incidentally, had 'an active disease process' when they first came to the Center.

Newton considers his most important result to have been 'a significant improvement in the quality of life for all of the adequately and inadequately treated patients ... with only two exceptions', that is, for 160 out of 162 of them. He also notes that there was a considerable increase in the median survival time of his patients. For breast cancer, for instance, nationwide statistics showed that a patient diagnosed as having advanced metastatic disease could expect to live for 16 months. The median period for Newton's patients was

42.5 months. The figures for bowel cancer were 11 and 40 months, while for cancer of the lung, generally reckoned one of the most difficult to treat, the survival time was only 6 months nationwide and 24 months at the Newton Center. His patients were living longer as well as more happily.

More than 40 per cent were, of course, still alive when he wrote his report. Not surprisingly, that old favourite 'spontaneous remission' has been wheeled out to explain away his results, to which he replies: 'It seems to us that ours occur at much greater frequency than appear in the population at large.' Pointing out that the term is a confession of ignorance in itself, he adds: 'Perhaps what we are doing is just to stimulate those very processes that are operating without intervention in those cases that seem to be "spontaneous". If all we are doing is to increase the frequency with which they occur, it is certainly worth the effort.'[12]

They do not occur very frequently elsewhere. According to a report published in 1966, there were only 176 cases of spontaneous remission of cancer published between 1900 and 1965, an average of less than three a year.[13] For nine such cases to turn up all at once in the same place is, to say the least, suggestive. Dr Newton feels justified in concluding that his results 'strongly suggest' that what he calls hypnotherapeutic intervention, in which visualisation (a right-mind function) plays an important part, 'can result in lengthening the duration of life and in some cases arrest and reverse the disease process'.

As I mentioned earlier, it is not all done by visualisation alone, or by hypnosis alone. 'We have had many individuals do very well with no visualisation at all,' Newton says. 'We are becoming more and more convinced that it is the profoundly altered state of consciousness that is the single most important factor, and that this is effective because it produces an extremely deep state of calm. Deep hypnosis on a continuously repeated basis produces this. It is in this profound inner quiet that the normalising of the psychological balance in the body can take place, and healing can be maximised.'

Visualisations certainly help, he adds, probably by reinforcing patients' belief in their capacity to fight disease, but they are only fully effective when they are combined with altered consciousness, or a shift from left-mind to right-mind function. This is where hypnosis comes in. 'We believe', he says, 'that hypnosis as we use it assures the greatest degree of this alteration.'[14]

Elliotson, we may recall, believed that mesmerism 'tends to

augment the power of the body to shake off disease', and it seems likely that those daily silent sessions with him helped his patient, Miss Barber, to achieve a deep state of calm. It begins to seem possible that a really deep state of calm is something rather more powerful in itself than we have appreciated.

When a research paper is published in a professional journal, the author is not claiming to have proved anything, at least he should not be. All he is saying is 'Hey, fellows, this is what I did, and how I did it. See if you can do it again.' When several independent researchers have done what he did and got the same results, it is time to start talking about proof. We cannot yet throw our hats in the air and claim that hypnosis cures cancer. On the other hand, it can no longer be claimed that there is no evidence that it can, in some cases, or that there is no theory as to how it does. A start has been made.

A start has also been made, on a smaller scale, on the other side of the world. While Newton's programme was under way, a psychiatrist in Melbourne, Australia, named Dr Ainslie Meares published five individual cases of his own, the results of which led him to state; 'Some cancers regress after intensive meditation in absence of any orthodox treatment which could account for the regression.'[15] How he came to be able to make such a forthright statement is quite a long story.

Shortly after World War Two, Meares began to treat a number of cancer patients with hypnosis, to help them overcome pain and depression. He had no idea in those days that he could do anything to affect their tumours directly, being mainly concerned with the problem of pain. Long before it became fashionable to do so, he visited India and spent time talking to yogis, learning from them how to achieve states of extreme serenity and detachment in which pain was still felt, but with the 'hurt' taken out of it, as one of them put it to him. Meares taught himself pain-control with such success that he was able to have several teeth pulled out without an anaesthetic. The dentist took a lot of persuading, and seems to have suffered more than the patient.

'I was so relaxed and so unconcerned about it all', Meares recalls, 'that I was not aware that he'd called in the dentist from an adjacent room, and it was another man that was actually operating on me.' Afterwards, he said, he revived the original dentist and bought him a whisky.[16]

At about this time, in the early 1960s, Meares began to ask himself what it was that made patients get better. Why, he wondered, did some recover after only two or three visits when he had done very little for them, if anything at all? Was it no more than suggestion at work? There was of course a strong element of suggestion involved in the patient's decision to come and see him in the first place. So there must have been in the case of those who had been to see other doctors, but whose conditions had not improved, and what was really baffling was the fact that some of his most successful 'cures' were of the patients with whom he had spoken least, and on whom he had not used any hypnosis or direct suggestion at all. 'The patient simply gets well', he wrote in 1961 (in *The Lancet*), 'in the absence of any clear rational explanation in terms of current psychological teaching.' Unexpected remissions simply did not fit into any of the accepted categories of therapy or analysis, yet they kept occurring and instead of shrugging them off as just 'spontaneous', Meares was determined to find out why they happened, and to see if they could be made to happen more often.[17]

He knew that patients would often lose their nervous symptoms after standard medical or psychological treatment, or after such non-medical activities as prayer, yoga, meditation, a talk with the family doctor, or 'just a good holiday'. Could all these apparently unrelated healing agencies, he wondered, have some 'basic mechanism' in common?

He reckoned they could, and he developed a theory which tackles the question of 'spontaneous remission' head-on, attempts to explain it, and predicts ways of making it more likely to take place. The basic mechanism in question was what he called 'atavistic regression' and defined as 'the process by which the mind ceases to function at a logical critical level, and reverts to a biologically more primitive mode of functioning'.[18]

The faculties of logical thought and critical ability were relatively recent in human evolution, he noted, and before they emerged man's mind operated at 'a simpler, more primitive level of integration'. The problem with some patients nowadays was that they could not stop their critical faculties from working flat out all the time, or restore the balance between what I have been calling left- and right-mind modes of thought.

This was written (again in *The Lancet*) in 1962, the year in which Sperry and Gazzaniga began their split-brain studies, and seven years before Jaynes first publicly announced his bicameral mind theory, with which a concept of atavistic regression is fully compatible. Meares did not mention left, right or bicameral minds in those terms, but what he wrote in 1962 fits so well with subsequent research, of which I have mentioned only a small sample, that I feel justified in discussing his theory in left/right mind-mode terms.

Meares is not suggesting that we should all climb into sheepskins and go and live in caves, as the word atavistic might imply. (It comes from the Latin word for ancestor.) What he is suggesting is that many modern ailments are caused by excessive left-mind activity, and that they can be alleviated, sometimes totally cured, by what amounts to a good dose of right-mind *inactivity* to restore balance.

Having formulated his deceptively simple theory, he promptly set about putting it to work in what he called 'some rather crude experiments in a consulting-room setting'. His idea was to see if atavistic regression could be encouraged to take place without any form of therapy at all, even hypnosis, and with 'the least possible use of speech'. He wanted to still the minds of his patients, and he could not do that by talking logically to them, for then they would have to keep their minds active in order to take in what he was saying, thus defeating the main purpose of the whole exercise.

Meares set out to demonstrate relaxation himself instead of teaching it in words. He would arrive at work calm and relaxed after a meditation session on the sunny balcony of his high-rise apartment and a stroll through the park, and when his patients arrived, he would let his own calmness and relaxation be a suggestive communication in itself. He would listen sympathetically as patients described their symptoms, but saying as little as possible himself. Then he would examine them physically, not, as he admits with disarming honesty, to learn anything about the patient, but to give the patient a chance to learn something about him! Once patients had become used to being touched and prodded, which they expected anyway, the essential process of building up rapport was well under way. Wills were entering the state of agreement.

Patients would then just sit in comfortable chairs and fall into a state of reverie. Meares, who eventually developed his procedure so that he could see a dozen patients at once, would do his best not to make any logical communication with them. He would move around the room, occasionally making reassuring noises or saying 'a few unstructured things that haven't got any meaning' if a patient showed any sign of anxiety. After an hour, patients would leave after being encouraged to carry on their self-taught method of intensive meditation at home, for up to two or three hours a day in serious cases.[19]

Is all this beginning to sound familiar? Meares's approach is remarkably similar to that of some of the early mesmerists, although he does not make use of tubs of water, soft music, or deliberately-induced hysterical crises. One wonders if some of the pioneers, such as Elliotson and perhaps Mesmer himself, had instinctively discovered atavistic regression without knowing it.

Not surprisingly, Meares's methods have upset some of his more conventional colleagues. In 1981, a photograph of him appeared in an Australian newspaper with the headline 'Meares Ostracised by Oncologists'. It is easy to see why. Here was a man who, though medically qualified, was carrying on like some crazy faith healer, just telling his patients to sit around and do nothing. How has he got away with it? How is it that *The Lancet*, instead of giving him the treatment it gave Elliotson, has frequently offered him the hospitality of its columns?

There are two reasons. One is that Meares has a far more plausible basis for his theory than Mesmer had, and he justifies it in several papers in medical journals and a book on medical hypnotism, in addition to a number of popular books. The other is that at least some of his medical colleagues know from their own experience that his methods sometimes work when theirs do not. Here are two examples.

In 1961, a fellow doctor asked Meares to see a young woman who had been severely disturbed for several years and had tried to kill herself more than once. She had been through months of psychotherapy, narcoanalysis and electroconvulsive therapy (ECT), but was still 'acutely distressed and impulsively suicidal'. Meares set to work on her, and a month later her doctor telephoned him to say:

'I have just seen the patient I sent you. She is really marvellous. She has not been as well as this for three or four years. I believe you fixed her without ECT?'

'Yes,' Meares replied.

'One of the new tranquillisers?'

'No. I told her she need not take any drugs.'

The doctor asked if she had told Meares something that she had kept from the other psychiatrists. Meares replied that she had told him very little. Had he hypnotised her, then? No, he had been unable to hypnotise her in the state she was in. The doctor asked what Meares had talked to her about, only to be told that he had hardly talked to her at all. He gave up.

'This is crazy,' he said. 'I am going to stick to proper medicine. Anyhow, I am glad you fixed her.'[20]

Nine years later, Meares came to the rescue of another professional colleague, and this time the patient was the doctor himself. He had a papilloma – a kind of internal wart – on his vocal cord, and it was the sixth to appear in exactly the same place. Five times he had undergone surgery, successfully, but every time another papilloma had grown, and the doctor was seriously thinking of having his larynx removed altogether. This would leave him unable to speak. Luckily, he knew a little about hypnosis, and he asked Meares to try it on him, which he did. It was the first time Meares had attempted direct control over a cell growth by this method. It worked, the papilloma went away, and ten years later there was no sign of another.

One of Meares's most interesting cases involved a woman who came to see him with breast cancer in an advanced state, for which she had already received chemotherapy. After three months of atavistic regression, the tumour began to get smaller. Meares then had to leave town for three weeks, and when he got back to Melbourne he found that everything had gone wrong. The woman had found a 'better way' of meditation, involving an attempt to attack her symptoms directly, and had relapsed. Meares managed to get her back to meditating his way, whereupon there was a second sudden and otherwise inexplicable remission. Although the remission lasted for another eighteen months, this unfortunately was not the end of the story. When a friend told her about a man in a distant part of Australia who was claiming to have found a new miracle cure for cancer, the woman decided to go and see him. She gave up her home meditation, and two weeks later she was dead.[21]

Cases like this make the job of collecting statistical evidence very difficult. Was it a success or a failure? Or two successes and one fatal failure? Meares had some trouble in getting his first individual case report published. The editor of an American medical journal told him it would be 'unconscienceable' (a nice Freudian slip) to print it without evidence for tight statistical control, to which Meares replied that when you are venturing into a new field, such control is something you simply have not got. For a controlled statistical study, you have to have a control group, and it would be ethically unthinkable for Meares to set aside some of his patients to serve as controls and deprive them of the form of treatment he believed could help them. The job of a practising doctor is to get his patients better, not to use them as laboratory animals. In this field, we are going to have to do without 'tight statistical control' for some time. The statistics are beginning to pile up, thanks to the work of LeShan, Meares,

Newton and Simonton, but nothing has yet been proved. It can only be said that their approaches have all been found effective in some cases, and that although they are all slightly different they have one feature in common: the motivation of the patient's mind. This, perhaps, is the 'active principle' that requires further research.

One of Meares's most provocative observations is that patients who use his technique without any other form of treatment at all tend to do better than those who combine it with chemotherapy or radiation. The motivation of the former group, he suspects, may be stronger than that of patients who are 'backing it both ways' by trying a bit of everything. It seems that when the patient has *total* faith, a cure is more likely to follow, and a patient who is trying several forms of treatment can hardly be said to have total faith in any of them.

Chemotherapy and radiation both tend to depress the immune system, which is precisely what Meares's method seeks to strengthen. This is not to claim that the standard therapies are less or more effective than his, only that they work (when they do) in a different way. They are invasive, whereas his is defensive. Proving the superiority of one over the other is not going to be easy, as Meares is well aware.

'The difficulties in statistical evaluation seem to be insurmountable', he told me in 1984. 'When I first started, I intended to see only those cancer patients who for reasons of their own had decided that they would not have chemotherapy or radiation. However, I soon came to realise that this might be making unreasonable demands of the patient. So, as it turns out, most of the patients whom I see have in fact had some chemotherapy or radiation, which of course makes it impossible to determine the effect of the meditation.

'However,' he added, 'there is a small group who have had no chemotherapy or radiation whose cancers have in fact regressed in quite extraordinary fashion.'[22] As mentioned above, Dr Newton has reported an identical result; 62 per cent of his group of patients who received no conventional treatment at all were still alive after five years.

In 1981, Meares made an informal comment about statistics (at a lecture, not in a scientific paper). By then, he had seen seventy-three cancer patients more than twenty times each, and reckoned he could claim clear evidence for either remission or a slowing of tumour growth in about 20 per cent of them.

This did not mean that the other 80 per cent were total failures.

Meares, like Newton, found that when patients kept up his form of treatment on a daily basis there was an improvement in the quality of their lives in almost every case. They felt better and happier even if they were on the point of death – as some were when they came to see him in the first place. One woman, who was going downhill fast, told him that the past six months of atavistic regression had been the best of her life.

We cannot dismiss testimony of this kind from somebody who is dying. We can argue about statistics, but we cannot argue with people who claim that they are enjoying a better life, and have banished their fear of death. They should know. It is their life, not ours.

Ainslie Meares developed his theory of atavistic regression almost exactly two hundred years after Mesmer announced his theory of animal magnetism; and despite the obvious differences between the theories and methods of these two working doctors, they have one thing in common. Both tried to bring methods previously considered occult into the consulting room, and to provide a scientifically-based rationale for them.

Meares's theory takes us back to the dawn of the healing art. He has brought the techniques of the Egyptian and Greek sleep temples and the yogi masters to twentieth-century Australia, and he has made a serious attempt to explain them. He has put his patients' minds to work, and shown that healing is not something done to them, but something they can do to themselves, by what amounts to self-mesmerism.

The fact that he has done away with visualisation exercises and verbal suggestion does not imply that his method is the right one and everybody else's is wrong. It means that there is more than one right way of mobilising and motivating the mind. I have concentrated here on the ways developed by Newton and Meares because they are less widely known than those of O. Carl Simonton and Lawrence LeShan, both of whom have described their work very clearly in popular books.[23,24]

There is a more direct approach to the mobilising of the mind (or the immune response system) of the cancer patient. For some time, a few doctors have felt that straightforward hypnosis might be of use as a means of attacking cancer directly. Speaking at a meeting at the Royal Society of Medicine in 1981, a distinguished medical hypnotist (whom I will not name, as he was speaking off the record) made this comment in the context of Meares's work:

This is a subject that I personally have felt very strongly about for many years, for this reason: some of us – I'm not one of them, I'm ashamed to say – can influence benign growths, the removal of warts, a thing they've done from ancient times in witchcraft. But in the field of hypnotherapy, a lot of people are quite masterly in removing warts. Now if benign growths can be affected in this way, I always felt in my own heart of hearts that somewhere or other along the line something ought to be possible in the field of malignancy.

One doctor who has reason to feel the same is Dr Richard Newman, a general practitioner in a rural part of southern England, who had treated a total of seven terminal cancer patients with hypnosis by 1983. Statistically, his success rate is zero, since all seven died. As is so often the case, the statistics are very misleading, for there was a partial improvement in every case. With four of them, Dr Newman was able to improve the quality of life for the time they had left, which is no mean achievement in itself, especially when it is done by strengthening and calming the mind instead of pumping the body full of morphine. I quote his own words on the other cases without any additional comment of my own:

The fifth patient was a girl of 21 who had gone slowly downhill with lymphatic leukemia, without remission over two years. Fortnightly transfusions were required to keep her alive. After commencing hypnotherapy she required only one further transfusion. Her haemoglobin and full blood counts returned to normal, but her platelet count remained low, and I could not correct this. Unfortunately, she moved to . . . a year later, and even though her blood counts were normal, she was given an incompatible platelet transfusion, which killed her.

The sixth patient had a massive breast cancer and a spinal secondary. Both tumours regressed with treatment, the breast tumour having reduced to less than a quarter of its original size when she became comatose, and died. It was diagnosed that she had a cerebral secondary, which was previously missed.

The seventh patient, a lady of 83, was emaciated, jaundiced, and dying of carcinomatosis (multiple epithelial malignant tumours). The consultant physician was called to advise on management, and felt at the time it was unlikely she would survive more than a few days. Therefore, we decided she should be nursed at home. Being tired by repeated night visits to give morphine injections, I attempted to control the pain with hypnotic suggestion. I was too inexperienced at the time to contemplate treatment.

The suggestions were combined with an ego-boosting routine in which for some reason I told her that I would take her for a walk on the beach in three months' time. The hypnosis greatly relieved the pain with no more than one session. In a week, the jaundice was fading, and the tumour masses regressing.

Three months later, she was fit enough for that walk. She died suddenly two years later of heart failure after a myocardial infarction.

Dr Newman concludes; 'It seems that the mind can be taught to deal with any problem that it understands, but it is difficult to formulate suggestions to cover problems which patient or doctor are unaware of.'[25]

How many other doctors have treated cancer with hypnosis, I have no means of knowing. I learned of the cases above, which are published here for the first time, purely by chance. At least one other doctor, however, has published similar cases.

In November 1969 a physician from Fair Lawn in New Jersey, Dr Howard B. Miller, read a paper to the American Society of Clinical Hypnosis Convention in San Francisco on 'Emotions and Malignancy', published the following year, in which he stated that 'hypnosis and psychotherapy can be used as a direct therapeutic agent in the treatment of organic diseases and not merely relegated to the minor position of a psychic tranquilizer'. He made it clear that he was referring to *all* types of organic disease, including cancer, and called for recognition of the fact that 'there is a wider area of conscious manipulation and communication between (mind and body) than was previously recognised'.

An interesting detail, noted on two of his own cases, is that tumours began to regress while patients were being given hypnosis for something else. Dr Miller was giving suggestions of general relaxation, increased confidence, freedom from fear, and an improvement in normal tissue and cell repair or replacement. During the course of treatment, one woman's malignant breast tumour shrank to a quarter of its original size, the other's benign growth disappeared altogether.

Encouraged by this unexpected development, Dr Miller then took on two cervical cancer cases and gave them the same type of suggestion, whereupon 'both cases resolved significantly', both patients remaining stable for a year.[26]

'I truly believe that thought is a force entity of itself,' Dr Miller told me, 'a force that *uses* our brain and body.' He defended this proposition in detail in his 1969 paper mentioned above, in which he pointed out that electric currents can be made to occur in the body by the very act of thinking. 'Thought alone can therefore, in and of itself, be the stimulus to induce an electric current to flow down any nerve to the affected tissue – demonstrating that thought is a source of energy.' The involuntary nervous system, he thinks, 'is not necessarily involuntary at all. The cases observed tend to show that it is more under our conscious control than previously believed'. As for such negative thought processes as anxiety and fear, which he regards as physical as well as mental states, the emphasis has always been on finding the right chemical to alter them. But the simplest and most effective way to alter any thought process is hypnosis.[27]

If the thoughts of a hypnotist can directly influence those of the subject, then an entirely new model of hypnosis begins to emerge, one that will force on us a very drastic revision of mind–body concepts.

I will end this chapter on a practical note concerned with the here and now, and especially with cancer patients who may feel impelled to dash off to Melbourne or Los Angeles in search of miracles, which I strongly advise them not to do. What they should seek is not the individual miracle worker but the general principle behind so-called miracle cures, to which much of the rest of this book is devoted.

As an introductory guide to the principle, none is more practical than that of an experienced self-healer, Rear Admiral E. H. Shattock, a former commander of HMS *Glory* and naval ADC to the Queen. Using a technique he has worked out on his own, he has managed to cure himself of osteoarthritis of the hip joint and benign enlargement of the prostate gland. Dr Alec Forbes notes in his foreword to Admiral Shattock's invigorating heal-it-yourself manual that these are both conditions 'for which the only relief orthodox medicine can offer is surgical operations'.

Naval officers are trained never to give orders unless they know how they can be carried out, and although Admiral Shattock had twenty years' experience of yoga, which he studied in Burma, and was fully convinced of the power of the mind, he spent long hours studying anatomy before issuing his orders to his 'autonomic mind', his term for the division of the subconscious that handles physical as opposed to psychological tasks. He wanted to know precisely what the body did before telling it what he specifically wanted it to do for his hip and prostate gland.

His technique involves a regular programme of very precise visualisations, in which specific blood vessels are ordered to send extra blood where needed, and specific cells told to remove waste matter and reconstruct damaged tissues. He has shown that it is possible to run the body much as a captain runs a ship, which is an 'organised organism', the efficient running of which depends on everybody from the captain to the junior bottle-washer and the ship's cat knowing exactly what to do and when and where to do it. A ship's crew is a kind of autonomous mind, with the captain as its brain giving the orders after visualising the task to be carried out and knowing it to be possible.

This approach is of course in complete contrast to that of Meares, and confused patients may well be wondering which one is right for them. The answer is, I am sure, whichever one they think is right for them, for the mind has a remarkable ability to behave according to whatever model we use to explain its workings. I suspect that right-minded patients will respond more readily to the Meares approach, while the left-minded will find it easier to identify with that of Shattock, although both techniques are largely derived from features of yoga that have now been scientifically proved to be genuine, including the ability to alter bodily functions as described earlier in this chapter.

Shattock's technique is also based on sound medical reasoning, such as that of US Air Force medical scientist Dr Lawrence E. Lamb, who argues that the concept of joints 'wearing out' is incompatible with that of the body's ability to replace its tissues. It should be possible, he says, to learn to control the regeneration and replacement mechanisms, thus 'making the wear and tear concept obsolete'.

Stimulated by powerful positive suggestions of this kind, Admiral Shattock found out how to control the appropriate mechanisms, and his success with his hip joint and prostate gland encouraged him to tackle other problems including root-canal infection, frozen shoulder, back pain and polyps (small wartlike growths) in the nose.

None of these can be called a life-threatening disease, but there is no logical reason why the methods used to overcome them should not be applied to more serious disorders.[28]

The study of the relations between mind, brain and body's natural defence system is now a recognised field in its own right, with the splendid name of 'psychoneuroimmunology'. After reviewing about fifty studies of psychological aspects of cancer, Drs J. Achterberg and G. F. Lawlis concluded in 1984 that there was quite enough evidence to justify a new approach to its treatment. 'To withhold psychological intervention until "all the facts are in" is unethical,' they wrote. 'The facts may never be "all in".'[29]

Such facts as have come in indicate plainly that the human will can affect more than body temperature or brainwave patterns. It can even alter the functioning of the blood, by increasing both the number and the activity of the germ-fighting white blood cells. This, says American medical hypnotist Dr Howard L. Hall (whose own research in this area has been independently and successfully repeated), has 'tremendous implications for a variety of medical disorders'. In 1983, he published a paper entitled 'Hypnosis and the immune system. A review with implications for cancer and the psychology of healing'.[30]

It is indeed possible to 'augment the power of the body to shake off disease' as Elliotson claimed in 1848. What is not yet possible is to establish either the limits of that power or the degree to which the motivated mind can augment it.

# 5

# The Tower of Pisa

When the President of the British Medical Association (BMA) rose to speak at the dinner held to mark its 150th anniversary, in December 1982, it might have been expected that he was about to soothe the digestions of his medical listeners with some words of praise for past achievements, delivered with the charm and good humour for which he is famous. But this is not quite what happened. The President – HRH the Prince of Wales, heir to the British throne – chose this occasion to give the medical profession a fair-sized piece of his own independent mind, in what amounted to an impassioned defence of non-medical healing and an attack on the current state of medical affairs that went further than one might suppose etiquette to allow on such occasions. In short, the doctors were given a right royal dressing-down.

Prince Charles began by mentioning the 'deeply ingrained suspicion and outright hostility which can exist towards anything unorthodox or unconventional' as among 'the less attractive traits of various professional bodies and institutions'. It was inevitable, he admitted, that strong feelings should be aroused in those who felt that their wisdom was being challenged. 'Human nature is such that we are frequently prevented from seeing that what is taken for today's unorthodoxy is probably going to be tomorrow's convention.' It also seemed inevitable that the unorthodox individual had to wait a long time before mankind was ready for his message, one that he might find difficulty in explaining, but one that came 'from a far deeper source than conscious thought'.

The Prince then launched into a lengthy commemoration of one such unorthodox individual: the sixteenth-century Swiss doctor, alchemist and philosopher Paracelsus. He was no charlatan, but a kind of 'one-man BMA' who castigated the quacks of his day and urged his fellow doctors to develop closer ties with nature by uniting the philosophical, psychological and chemical skills with their own 'specific virtue' – the intuition needed to help patients mobilise their own will to overcome disease. 'Science has become estranged from nature,' said Prince Charles, 'and that is the moment when we should remember Paracelsus.'

There were many doctors, he went on, who still believed in Paracelsus's principles. But modern medicine was largely based on a mechanistic approach to healing. It had lost sight of the patient as a 'whole human being'. The time had come to 'reincorporate the notion of healing into modern medical practice'. He then gave the clearest possible statement of what the alternative, complementary or 'fringe' medicine revolution is all about.

For centuries, he said, folk-healers had been guided by a traditional wisdom that saw illness as 'disorder of the whole person, involving not only the patient's body, but his mind, his self-image, his dependence on the physical and social environment, as well as his relation to the cosmos'. Medicine today had become 'fascinated by the objective, statistical, computerised approach to the healing of the sick'.

'I would suggest that the whole imposing edifice of medicine, for all its breathtaking successes, is, like the celebrated Tower of Pisa, slightly off balance.'

What was this imbalance costing the nation? 'It is frightening how dependent upon drugs we are all becoming, and how easy it is for doctors to prescribe them as the universal panacea for our ills.' The drug bill for the National Health Service, he noted, came to £2,000 million a year. But human health depended on behaviour, food and environment as much as pills and surgery, and the name of Paracelsus 'should be synonymous with the common health, which I have been asked to toast this evening'. Prince Charles ended with a statement that clearly came from his own heart:

'With all the conviction of a man who follows his inner voice, he made a desperate supplication that "would we humans knew our hearts in truth, nothing on earth would be impossible for us".'[1]

In June 1983, the Prince gave the BMA another strong dose of his personal brand of medicine, at its conference in Dundee. On this occasion, he drew attention to 'those ancient unconscious forces which will help to shape the psychological attitudes of modern man', and to the 'long-neglected methods of medicine which, in the right hands, can bring considerable relief, if not hope, to an increasing number of people'.

We were, it seemed, seeing a revival of the royal touch. But unlike his predecessors, Prince Charles was not laying his hands on individual sufferers, but trying to heal the whole nation at once by persuading the medical profession to alter course.

A few weeks later he was making the headlines again and giving the Tower of Pisa another powerful shove towards its correct alignment. The occasion was his opening of the new £300,000 premises of the Bristol Cancer Help Centre,[2] where the 'long-neglected methods' he had mentioned in Dundee were already being applied. The original centre had attracted a good deal of interest with its radical departure from standard approaches to cancer treatment and its adoption of such therapies as meditation, biofeedback, visualisation, hand-healing, large doses of vitamins and enzymes and a strict vegetarian diet. How it came into being is quite a story.

Several years previously Canon Christopher Pilkington, Rector of the City of Bristol, and his wife Pat had decided they should revive the Christian tradition of healing the sick. They began in a very modest way, with a small group of helpers, praying and laying on hands in the chapel, but since their fine mediaeval church was a major tourist attraction, the healers found it hard to concentrate while a steady stream of visitors tramped around discussing the beauties of the architecture. They had to find somewhere else.

At this time the Canon inherited enough money to buy a house in a quiet suburb, convert it into a healing centre, and set up a charitable fund to run it. Then disaster struck. One of the Pilkingtons' most active helpers, a vivacious young woman named Penny Brohn, suffered a treble tragedy; both her parents died suddenly, and a few months later she found she had breast cancer.

'To us, cancer meant death,' Pat Pilkington recalled later. But Mrs Brohn, an acupuncturist by profession, already knew something about the methods I have mentioned in the previous chapter, and she decided to use them. There was nowhere in Britain that offered any kind of alternative cancer therapy of the kind she wanted, so at great expense she went off to a well-known private clinic in Germany, undeterred by the unfavourable publicity it had attracted some years previously when a young British athlete, Lilian Board, had died there.

Pat Pilkington went out to visit her friend after nine weeks, finding her in very good shape physically if not financially. The two women asked each other why it was necessary to go abroad and spend an enormous amount of money to get what was really a very simple form of therapy. Why was there no clinic in Britain like this? Without bothering to answer that question, they decided to start one, and Mrs Brohn insisted that it would have to be run under medical supervision. For all her involvement in complementary medicine, when it came to treating cancer she wanted a doctor in charge, but it would have to be a doctor who was familiar with the new approaches and willing to put them into practice.

Pat Pilkington went home to Bristol determined to find one, and not having the faintest idea where to start looking. She drove herself home from Heathrow Airport, to find a large pile of letters waiting for her. Without taking her coat off, she opened one of them and found it was from a clergyman friend asking if, by any chance, she could help a Plymouth hospital consultant, Dr Alec Forbes, who was looking for a small centre where he could try out his complementary methods of healing ...

When the pupil is ready, it is said, the teacher will appear.

'I literally screamed at the ceiling,' Mrs Pilkington recalled. 'I was in the grip of something very strange at that moment.'[3]

Things then moved very quickly. Dr Forbes left his safe job and his large house in Plymouth for a small flat and a very uncertain future in Bristol, and on 9 October 1980 the new Centre opened its doors. It was, as Penny Brohn had planned, under the supervision of a doctor, and by 1983 Dr Forbes and his team of unpaid helpers had seen about a thousand patients (free of charge) and were able to conclude in an official statement:

'Of those who really do follow the method in all its aspects, all feel better and have a better quality of life than before. It is too early to say more.' The statistics would have to wait, but in the meantime it was clear that the 'school for living', as Dr Forbes and his colleagues call their centre, was getting results identical to those reported by Meares and Newton. Its graduates would face the prospect not of inevitable and possible imminent death, but of newly enjoyable life, however short.

Prince Charles had 'no hesitation', he said, in accepting the invitation to open the Centre's new premises, which had been built with a large loan from a sympathetic local bank. He praised Dr Forbes and his team for 'marshalling the psychological and spiritual forces of the patient', and emphasised that just because treatment 'at physical, emotional and spiritual levels cannot be proved in a clinical laboratory to have a value to a patient does not mean it is completely

worthless or harmful'. Many had already benefited from the 'alternative approach', he said, and he thought it only right that they should
be given the chance to opt for it, in cases where they felt that standard
treatment had not done enough for them.

He spoke to a 53-year-old man who had opted for the Bristol
approach on being told, after several operations, that nothing more
could be done for him. 'You look extremely well,' said the Prince.

'I feel terrific,' the man replied. 'I would not be here today but for
the treatment I've received.' His 'inoperable' tumours were rapidly
disappearing.

The Prince seemed pleased when one of the healer-counsellors
reminded him of an ancient tradition, saying: 'Sir, as an anointed
prince, you are a healer.' And in his speech (of which Pat Pilkington,
a professional BBC radio journalist, commented 'We couldn't have
written it as well as he did') he returned to one of the themes of his
BMA address, referring to 'that invisible aspect of this universe
which, although unproved in terms of orthodox science as man had
devised it, nevertheless cries out for us to keep our minds as open as
possible, and not to dismiss it as mere hocus-pocus'.

Dr Elizabeth Whipp, a radiotherapist at Bristol's Royal Infirmary,
promptly did just that. 'I don't want to dash people's hopes,' she was
reported as saying (which is precisely what she seemed to be trying to
do), 'but I do feel strongly about the Prince of Wales making a royal
tour of something that is full of bogus notions. Many people might
believe it works, and maybe delay diagnosis and conventional
treatment which could be curative.' She overlooked the fact that
conventional treatment is not always curative, which is why many
people had gone to the Bristol Centre in the first place. Dr Forbes
and his colleagues have, incidentally, always made it very clear that
they are complementing existing therapies, not seeking to replace
them.[4]

Some reactions were even more extreme, as members of a BBC
television team found while researching for a series of documentaries on the Centre. One patient's doctor not only refused to talk to
the producer, but would not let his patient have his own records,
which led to time-wasting duplication of tests. Another patient had
been struck off his general practitioner's list after forty-five years, for
asking help, he said, in keeping up the Bristol methods at home.

'Don't I have any rights in this matter?' he had asked.

'No,' said his doctor, who had referred him for all kinds of costly
therapy in the past, 'you don't.'[5]

This kind of attitude is not likely to help people take charge of their own recovery from disease, and it is one that other cancer patients have come across. One of the most articulate is writer and broadcaster Brenda Kidman, author of a book about her experiences with both conventional and alternative therapies. Of the former, she said in a 1983 interview:

'They were treating me as a patient, as a body in a bed, and not telling me the nature of my illness, what the future might be, *anything* that I could do to help myself. I just had to be the recipient of whatever they handed out.' The National Health Service had, in her experience, become a 'disease service', by decreasing patients' responsibility for their own health and thereby actually increasing disease. For a patient to tell a doctor 'I put myself entirely in your hands' was, she felt, unfair to both doctor and patient.

In 1977, Mrs Kidman was in pretty bad shape. She had recently been divorced, she had a young son to bring up, and her mother had died after a long illness. To add to her problems, and perhaps partly because of them, she developed breast cancer. She underwent conventional treatment with only partial success, but six years later after committing herself to the whole complementary works from relaxation, meditation and visualisation to raw carrots, she was an entirely new person.

'These therapies are not selective,' she said. 'When they put you right, they put your whole system right. From being a very sceptical and agnostic character, I am now a firm believer that I am in the hands of my Creator. It's a nice feeling.' When I met her in 1981, she struck me even then as somebody whose whole system – physical, psychological and philosophical – was in perfect running order. And she was putting in a harder day's work than most people of her age that I know.

Penny Brohn's little daughter Justine gave her views on the new approach to cancer treatment in one of the BBC television documentaries on the Bristol Centre. She recalled what it had been like to be told by her school friends that her mother was going to die because she had cancer. 'But now I know it's just an illness,' she said, 'and if you try you can get better.'

Brenda Kidman tried and got better, and knows many who have done the same. 'I've seen people crawl over the doorstep at Bristol,' she said, 'and in three or four weeks they're just renewed.'[6]

This kind of renovation of cancer patients has in fact been going on in Britain since the early 1970s, when Dr Ann Woolley-Hart of St

Bartholomew's Hospital, London, and Gilbert Anderson of the National Federation of Spiritual Healers organised a small group in order to put Carl Simonton's theories into practice. Two of the patients, both with diagnosed advanced cancer, went into remission almost at once, and one of them was alive and well more than ten years later.[7]

The most vigorous campaigner in Britain for new attitudes to health and sickness is Marcus McCausland, a retired Lieutenant-Colonel who gave up a career in industry to found and run the Health for the New Age Trust. From this, in the early 1980s, there emerged the Association for New Approaches to Cancer (ANAC).[8] McCausland's personal approach to cancer is that of a military commander planning a major offensive – hit the enemy with everything you have got. This includes, in his words:

'Love, meditation, relationships, healing, group dynamics, touch, altered states of consciousness, positive thinking, suggestion, the placebo effect, laughter, music, harmony, imagination, visualisation, guided relaxation, self-healing, hope and expectation.'[9]

ANAC's initial skirmishes with the enemy took place in McCausland's own home in London, with seven lay healers and seven medically diagnosed patients meeting every Friday morning for ten weeks. He chose the number seven deliberately for its magical associations, explaining 'We don't exclude the wisdom of ancient rites. They can all contribute to the healing process, which works on so many different levels.' But nor does he exclude the wisdom of modern doctors such as Meares, Simonton and Forbes. In fact, he was one of the first to promote their ideas in Britain.

The seven patients, or 'participants', as he refers to call them, sat in a circle for fifteen minutes of silent meditation. Then each in turn moved into the centre to receive silent hand-healing from each of the seven healers. Next, there were relaxation exercises, group discussion, more individual healing, and finally a good wholefood lunch. There was no charge, and as at Bristol, participants were encouraged to carry on their self-healing at home.

Results were immediate. 'Seeing a cancer patient walk out of here with a smile on her face is a result,' an ANAC member told me. And although the statistics will have to wait, for reasons already explained, participants have already made it quite clear that they have experienced personal results. Some examples:

'Nothing had prepared me for the feeling which engulfed me as soon as I entered the healing circle ...'

'Coming to these meetings still makes me feel rejuvenated, and a "part" of something ...'

'My faith in healing is getting so much stronger, that I am convinced it is going to get me better – as opposed to the hospital, where my morale gets very, very low. But here I am uplifted ...'

'Some enthusiasm has entered my life again ...'

'During the healing, a great wave of peace came over me ...'

'I have not found anywhere the practitioner I want. I've decided to take over myself – to heal myself spiritually, mentally and physically. When I'm cured, I'll become a healer.'

One participant, a professional woman in her forties, reported: 'Last night I went out and laughed a lot. The lump was still there when I went to bed, but I haven't been able to find it this morning.'

Her words recall the case of US writer Norman Cousins, who cured himself of a serious disease (ankylosing spondylitis) by hiring comic films and laughing himself back to health, and concluded: 'I have learned never to underestimate the capacity of the human mind and body to regenerate – even when the prospects seem most wretched.'[10]

Some doctors, not surprisingly, are none too happy about this brave new world in which patients sit in circles, roar with laughter, chew raw carrots and throw away their medicine. Dr Jimmie Holland of the Sloan-Kettering Institute for Cancer Research has been quoted as describing the work of Carl Simonton as 'a cruel hoax'.[11]

The most reasonable critics of the new-approach movement claim that its methods are based on the assumption that cancer is the result of stress, wrong living and other emotional and psychological factors. How come that plants develop tumours, they ask. Are they feeling guilty about their relationships with other plants? Is it not well known that some tumours can develop in animals and people without any apparent psychological influence?

This would be fair criticism if the new-age crowd were claiming to be able to cure all cancers without exception with nothing more than the methods listed above by McCausland. But I have never come across such a claim from anybody mentioned in this book. What I suspect is happening is that a certain percentage of cancers *can* be attributed to psychological causes, that the victims themselves are often aware of this, and if they attack the psychological cause successfully, the symptom goes away. That is my own speculation. I also believe, for reasons already given, that if somebody has sufficient faith in something, true or false, it will become true for them. This also applies to the left-minded type who has total faith in conventional medicine.

As for the psychological life of plants, I would just note that following the discovery in 1983 that trees are able to communicate information to each other by chemical 'airborne cues' such as pheromones, it seems that the sensitivity of all living things may be far greater than we imagined.[12]

Another reasonable criticism of new approaches to anything is that there is a curious tendency for any kind of new treatment to work for a time, and then to be found ineffective after controlled studies. There is something in this, and I will return to it later.

Apart from such criticisms based on plausible assumptions, participants in new-approach healing programmes also have to face some that are not. In 1981, an article appeared in a medical magazine under the title 'Why Health for the New Age is harmful', a statement that might well be considered libellous. The author, Karl Sabbagh, gives his reasons as follows:

'It could well be said that such organisations [as Health for the New Age] should be left to get on with their well-meaning efforts – after all, what harm can they do? Well, I believe that misplaced and unjustified hope, involving treatments that are often expensive, *is* harmful, particularly when it keeps patients away from orthodox treatments that might be effective.'[13]

Mr Sabbagh's article appeared on a page headed 'Mere Words', which is presumably the title of a regular feature. It describes the contents of the page below it better than I can.

In 1983, a British cancer specialist was asked why he had not looked into the new-approach methods I have been describing. 'We can't investigate everything,' he said. 'In any case, there is no scientific proof that they work.'[14]

Turning to the serious debate on new-approach methods, we find the establishment point of view clearly expressed in a *British Medical Journal* editorial of 1980, entitled 'The flight from science'. This, the editor said, was a trend that had been evident throughout the preceding decade. 'What is wrong', he wrote, 'is the refusal by the critics and the fringe practitioners to accept the standards of proof that medical scientists have developed in the past hundred years; not for nothing has the concept of the randomised, double-blind controlled trial been described as one of Britain's most important contributions to medicine since the war.' He added: 'New ideas have to be set up as hypotheses, tested by experiment, and revised in the light of the results.'[15]

However, new ideas cannot be dismissed until they have been tested and found to have results, positive or negative. To claim that they are 'bogus notions', a 'cruel hoax', harmful or unsupported by scientific proof implies that they have been investigated and shown to be bogus. This is not the case with the methods I have been describing. They have not been investigated at all. To reject them out of hand is an instance of clogged imagination at work, or of what the Greeks called misoneism – hatred of new ideas.

The new approaches to cancer are being tested by experiment – on cancer patients. (How else can they be tested?) They are also based on a plausible hypothesis: that the power of the motivated mind is without established limits. As for results, I have already pointed out that one cannot begin to contemplate talking about a permanent cure until a large number of patients have lived at least five years after being diagnosed as terminal, or at least inoperable. As I have also pointed out, we cannot ignore the evidence that the new approaches have already had a profound, positive and lasting effect on the lives of many who have tried them. If a patient says he is feeling better after atavistic regression, raw carrots or whatever, then he probably is. If his friends and neighbours agree, as Bernauer Newton took the trouble to check in his long-term study, then he definitely is. Even if he then dies, after finding the last days of life among the best, he has demonstrated a very positive result.

There are two other points to be made on the question of statistics, controlled studies, and so on. One is that even when statistical proof exists, there is no guarantee that it will be accepted by the misoneist, or extreme left-minded diehard. The classic case of this was the statement by French scientist Edmond Rostand that if his compatriot Dr Michel Gauquelin (a professionally qualified statistician, by the way) had proved astrology by statistics, as to some extent he has, then he no longer believed in statistics. Similar remarks have been made about the statistical work in parapsychology by J. B. Rhine and Louisa Rhine at Duke University.

Furthermore, even the most correct scientific procedure can be totally misleading. The first fully controlled large-scale experimental study of hypnosis, for instance, was not carried out until 1933 (forty years after the British Medical Association had declared itself in favour of it). And the result? According to Leslie LeCron, it 'cleared up some aspects of hypnosis, failed to shed light on others, and made the situation even more confused as to still others'.[16] All it proved was the truth of Ronald Shor's Scylla/Charybdis analogy: 'the posture of impartial neutrality simply does not evoke in subjects the enthusiastic expectance and deep emotional commitments that mobilise and sustain the hypnotic process'. The same applies to the self-healing process, of cancer or anything else.

In October 1983, *The Lancet* published an editorial headed 'Alternative Medicine is no Alternative', which I mentioned briefly in the last chapter. It gave a good idea of the impact made by the new-approach movement on the medical profession in that year, much of the impact being due to Prince Charles's publicly-declared interest and to a survey to be mentioned shortly.

The editor reminded doctors that alternative medicine should not be regarded as alternative at all, but as part of conventional medicine, bearing in mind that the phrase had come to include everything from the 'frankly fraudulent and foolishly harmless to the probably useful'. To decide which was which was merely a matter of experiment, and he quoted recent examples of controlled studies of homoeopathy that had given negative or inconclusive results. But the doctor should remember that he 'must sometimes act even when there is no scientific evidence that his actions will be beneficial', relying on his own judgment and knowledge. 'When so much medical practice is not supported by rigorous scientific testing,' the editor wrote, 'what right have clinicians to criticise the practitioners of alternative therapy?'

He then turned to 'the most difficult matter of all', the question of suggestion and the placebo effect. Was it right, he asked, to deny a patient access to a treatment he believed in, even if the doctor did not?

'There should be no ambiguity in the medical response to such a proposition,' he went on. 'If the theories on which alternative medical practices are based are invalid, orthodox medicine would be a feeble institution indeed if it condoned such practices rather than replacing them with a more soundly based approach.' This approach did not need a new name, such as 'holistic'. It is 'simply the practice of treating patients as they should be treated by an adequately trained physician'. And he concluded:

'If patients are resorting in increasing numbers to practices based on the obsolescent relics of the prehistory of modern medicine this requires urgent attention. In that case, the subject of the next BMA investigating committee should be contemporary orthodox medical practice.'[17]

This outspoken and constructively critical editorial raises a number of important questions, but seems to avoid the central one altogether. This is the question I have been asking throughout this book: how do we motivate the mind of the patient? Experimental studies of homoeopathy, herbal medicine, acupuncture and so on are very necessary in order to sort out the useful from the harmless and the fraudulent. Any experimental study of a therapy in which the active participation of the patient's mind is involved is bound to run into the dilemma stated by Ronald Shor in the context of hypnosis: if carried out with the scientific impartiality needed for an acceptable statistical survey, it is simply not going to get positive results. The experimenter's attitude is inevitably going to affect the outcome.

All is not lost, however. As the editor pointed out, faith healing should be 'as susceptible to scientific testing as any other practice', whatever the religious beliefs involved. So it is, but unfortunately people who finance scientific experiments have not been susceptible to the idea of testing it properly. So it has never been done, although there have been quite a number of individual researchers who have carried out successful experiments with individual healers such as Olga Worrall, Oskar Estebany, Dean Kraft and Matthew Manning, in laboratory experiments with cells, bacteria and enzymes.[18] As for large-scale studies of human patients, healers such as the late Harry Edwards have repeatedly offered their full cooperation, but there have been no takers with the exception of Dr Louis Rose, who appears to have worked on the assumption that any result claimed by Edwards must have had an alternative explanation.[19]

What really needs investigation, as I have said, is not hand-healing, homoeopathy, extracts of apricot pips or anything else that is applied to the patient, but the mind itself of the patient. If this is what often makes the difference between sickness and health, or life and death, surely it is worth examining as an entity in its own right, rather than as some kind of abstract epiphenomenon?

In 1983, the British Medical Association announced that it was going to carry out an inquiry into alternative medicine, reportedly on the orders of its president. Institutes for alternative or complementary medicine seemed to be popping up all over the place. The subject was debated at length on the correspondence page of *The Times*.

On 30 July, the *British Medical Journal* published the results of a survey of young doctors' views on alternative medicine, the first of its kind ever carried out in Britain. Dr David Taylor Reilly sent questionnaires to 100 trainee general practitioners, receiving replies from 86 of them – a very high return rate for any kind of poll. His findings revealed 'a striking degree of interest in alternative methods of treatment among younger doctors'.

Of the 86 respondents, 70 said they would like to train in one or more of the alternative techniques. Hypnosis, still considered 'alternative', was a clear winner as first choice. Of the young doctors 31 had already referred patients for alternative therapy, 12 admitting they had sent them to non-medical practitioners. This, as the *BMJ* editor pointed out, would have landed them in front of a board of inquiry not so long ago. The most surprising discovery was that 18 of the doctors were already using one of the alternative therapies, while more than a quarter of them had either tried one for themselves or were actually practising one.

Was this another sign of a 'flight from science'? Dr Taylor Reilly thought not. 'The whole person deserves a whole doctor who can assess his whole problem and who can refer him to a specialist, orthodox or alternative, if required,' he wrote. He reminded his fellow doctors that there were almost as many practitioners of alternative medicine in Britain as there were general practitioners – 27,800 and 29,800 respectively.

Medicine – whether we call it allopathic, alternative, complementary or holistic – is still something that is poured into patients or done to them rather than by them. The new approaches to cancer treatment I have mentioned depart radically from conventions, both conventional and alternative, in that their main aim is to mobilise the self-healing abilities of the patient. The vitamins, carrot juice and hand-healing are no more than supportive substances and therapies. They are not the cure.

The obvious link between standard medicine and self-cure is the well-known placebo (Latin for 'I will please') effect, the potential of which has not been fully explored even by the new-approach community. The use of it is standard practice in the testing of new drugs, one lot of patients being given the new miracle multinational pill, and the control group being given a pill that looks like it but is actually made of chalk or sugar. The new superpill tends to get better results, but the 'worthless' placebo pill almost invariably gets some positive results as well, which in theory it should not.

In the nineteenth century, a Dutch doctor named Durand carried out an amusing double-placebo experiment. He gave a ward full of patients a drink of sugar and water, telling them it was a powerful new medicine. Half an hour later he rushed into the ward and exclaimed 'Sorry, I've made a terrible mistake. What I just gave you was a strong emetic!' Half the patients promptly threw up.[20]

A less amusing case of placebo at work in both directions involved a controversial substance made from horse blood named Krebiozen. A terminal cancer patient heard that the drug was to be tested in the hospital where he was lying bedridden and not expected to live for more than a few weeks. He begged for a shot of the stuff, got one, and ten days later there was no trace of the tumours that had been as big as oranges. He was discharged.

Two months later he was back in hospital, his faith shattered by unfavourable press reports of the drug, and his cancer reactivated. An enterprising doctor then gave him an injection of pure water, telling him it was a new type of double-strength Krebiozen, where-upon the patient recovered even more rapidly than before and was again discharged. Two months later he learned that the American Medical Association had declared Krebiozen to be worthless. Within two days of returning for the second time to the hospital, he was dead.[21]

'Most new treatments work wonders for a few years until they are found to be valueless,' a somewhat cynical old doctor once told me. (They were all due to 'suggestion', something he evidently did not feel to be very important.) Orthodox doctors have frequently pro-moted their personal panaceas, as in Shaw's satirical and not entirely fictional play *The Doctor's Dilemma*, which he wrote in 1906. For one, it was cutting out the 'nuciform sac' (even when the patient was found to have no such organ). For another it was 'Stimulate the phagocytes. Drugs are a delusion.' Shaw even included a sympa-thetic description of a doctor who might have made a good hypnotist or faith healer:

'He radiates an enormous self-satisfaction, cheering, reassuring, healing by the mere incompatibility of disease or anxiety with his welcome presence. Even broken bones, it is said, have been known to unite at the sound of his voice.' He is however considered by his jealous colleagues to be 'a colossal humbug'.

The most colossal of recent humbugs, in the opinion of many, is the so-called psychic surgery of Brazil and the Philippines, in which abdomens are supposedly ripped open by the bare hands of amateur 'surgeons' with or without the help of spirit guides. I will not go into the question here of whether all psychic surgery is humbug, or whether the same methods are used in the two countries. In an earlier book I described my own experiences in Brazil, and have nothing to add to or subtract from what I wrote in 1975, except to draw attention to the similarity between rusty-knife eye operations performed by Arigó and the slightly more normal (but only very slightly, in my opinion) transorbital lobotomies performed with a gold-plated ice pick by US psychiatrist Dr Walter Freeman.[22,23]

However, I am glad to include the views of somebody who has studied psychic surgery more carefully than most, including myself, and has come to a conclusion that is likely to upset sceptic and true believer alike. This is the first time it has been published in book form.

Loren Parks is a successful manufacturer of medical electronics equipment from Beaverton, Oregon. He has academic qualifications in psychology, and studied hypnotism with Leslie LeCron and David Cheek. He was interested in all forms of healing, and made two trips to the Philippines, saw a number of well-known 'surgeons' at work and witnessed several apparent cures. He became a true believer, and remained one until a friend named Dick Wright (now deceased) returned from an extended visit to the islands with the startling news that he had discovered the secret of the bare-handed healers. He had gained their confidence and learned how to do psychic surgery himself, and the secret was that it was all based on sleight of hand. They concealed tiny razor-blades in their fingernails. They used a white powder that turned blood-red when moistened. What they removed from the supposedly opened abdomens of their patients were bits of chicken, grass, string and even plastic. It was all a fraud.

Parks was dismayed at first, but his experience in psychology and hypnotism led him to realise that while the techniques might be false, they could still produce genuine cures, which was what mattered. He made two more trips to the Philippines, now knowing what to look for, and returned all the more convinced that 'trickery is the most effective form of healing'. He explains:

There is no stronger suggestion I know of than believing that someone with divine powers can enter the body with bare hands, remove diseased tissue, and close up the incision without leaving a scar and with no infection. I've been through it, as a believer, got a cure and witnessed many cures. It really works, yet it is as phony as a three-dollar bill. *It is the fastest, most effective form of healing that I know.*[24]

He has been following the progress of two patients with diagnosed multiple sclerosis who went to the Philippines in 1972, had 'phony' operations, and immediately went into remission. One later became a marathon runner, covering thirty-six miles at a stretch, and both now lead normal lives. Parks intends to publish an account of their cases in a medical journal, and until he does I will make no further comment.

He agrees that it does not work every time, and that the patient must be 'set up' in order to reach the necessary level of expectation. Important factors in the setting-up process are the general reputation of the healer and the state of faith in which the patient comes to see him. This is strongly reinforced by watching the healer at work on other patients – the Philippine surgeons normally perform their operations in front of an audience. Then, when it is the patient's turn, provided the critical level of faith and expectation has been reached, it is just a question of 'pushing the right button', as Parks put it to me.

I remember an enigmatic remark made to me by the Brazilian healer Edivaldo, when I interviewed him in 1972, a couple of years before his death in a road accident. His patients, he had told me, were already being operated on as they waited in line. The part where they lay on the bed in front of him was only the end of the process, a ritual designed to convince them that they were being treated.

'How would the client feel if he got onto the bed and was told his operation was over?' Edivaldo asked me. Yet he ascribed the operation itself to his spirit guides and not to the patient's self-pushing of the right button, and I felt he really believed this. He invariably worked in what seemed to be an altered state of consciousness or dissociation, in which he produced several examples in my presence of clairvoyant diagnosis. The psychic surgery of Brazil and the Philippines is clearly far more complex than either the sceptics or the believers have realised.

The control centre of our autonomic minds, where the right button is located, can be reached in either of two paradoxically different ways: by shock tactics or by a subtle combination of patience, repetition and timing. There is a third way – outright deception. This was used by Shaw's Dr Schutzmacher, whose panacea was a dose of Parrish's Chemical Food and who painted the words CURE GUARANTEED on his surgery window. His methods never let him down, and he took early and prosperous retirement.

Like Schutzmacher, the psychic surgeons present their patients with the single suggestion, usually unspoken, that a cure is going to take place right now. The well-known Brazilian journalist Carlos Neto has given me an eye-witness account of how Arigó produced an instant cure of some stomach ailment by giving a woman patient a hefty sock in the guts.

What the psychic surgeon does is set up a crisis. We tend to think of this word only in connection with economic disaster, but its original meaning is 'turning-point', from the Greek *krinein*, to separate. In medical language, it means a sudden change of course in a disease, and such a change can be for better or worse. It need not involve hysterical screaming and yelling, as in Mesmer's salon or at Charcot's theatrical demonstrations of hypnosis at the Salpêtrière Hospital in Paris. It can be silent and unnoticed. It is closely related to what happens during the charismatic encounter.

We have come to think of healing as a slow process that takes its 'natural' course. A small cut on a finger can take days to heal. But there are numerous accounts, from the Bible to the *British Medical Journal*, of virtually instantaneous cures of conditions more serious than cut fingers. Dr Mason's ichthyosis case is a good example. His patient did not turn white in ten seconds, and in fact never recovered completely, for reasons I have already suggested, but he did make a dramatic, visible and fully documented improvement in his organic, congenital and supposedly incurable disease *within a few days of first being hypnotised*. Something happened very quickly indeed. To be cured, even partially, in less than a week of something you have had for sixteen years can be considered relatively instantaneous.

Something changed course after a single session with a hypnotist who, on his own admission, did not know exactly what he was trying to do. It was not spontaneous remission, previous wrong diagnosis, or sudden response to previous conventional treatment, the excuses wheeled out by Louis Rose to explain away Harry Edwards's equally impressive cases. It was an immediate cure of an incurable disease, and the only possible direct cause of this cure must have been a sudden change, or crisis, in the very object that hypnosis is supposed to influence: the patient's mind.

It was noted at the time that this remarkable case alone called for 'a revision of current concepts on the relations between mind and body'. Yet except for Stephen Black, no such revision was even attempted by anybody. There were in any case no useful concepts of mind–body relations thirty years ago. There were any number of philosophical models and theories dating all the way back to Plato and Aristotle, but none of them was of the slightest help in explaining what went on under the skin of that anonymous ichthyosis patient. That is one reason why this book was written. I may not have solved the problem, but I have at least identified it. If we can find out what happened inside that boy's body, many other problems will have solved themselves.

Whatever did happen, it was a form of crisis provoked by a single suggestion under hypnosis. It was a curious example of charismatic healing at work, with the control centre in the boy's mind accepting a suddenly suggested alternative future and making it come true. We know that people can change their behaviour and beliefs both radically and very quickly. It happened to St Paul on the road to Damascus. It happened to one of Charles Manson's 'converts' in a parking lot outside a supermarket. We also know that people can change the organisation of their bodies just as radically and quickly. There must be something in common in the mechanisms involved in each case, and it seems that we have a control centre which, when a programme is inserted in the right way, carries out new orders to the letter, without question and without delay.

The simplest way to bring about such changes in mind or body is by the use of suggestion under hypnosis, although there are many other ways, including silent mesmerism, atavistic regression, or the more gradual form of self-reprogramming now being used by the new-approach cancer therapists. One day, perhaps, we will all know instinctively how to reprogramme ourselves without artificial aids of any kind, but at present we do not, and hypnosis remains the most practical and helpful reprogramming technique, as well as the easiest and cheapest.

Hypnosis is often referred to as an altered state of consciousness, which it is, although the phrase explains nothing. What exactly is supposed to alter? The answer now seems to be that what alters is the balance between the two components of our minds, left and right. Hypnosis is therefore a state of *separated* consciousness.

When we have a puncture, we must wrench the tyre off the wheel, pull out the inner tube, find the hole and stick a patch on it. When we have a mental puncture, which brings part of the body to a halt, we have to separate the inner mind from the outer one in order to be able to get at it.

There is a very simple method of communicating directly with the right mind (or inner mind) which, although introduced early in this century by hypnotist Milton Erickson, seems to have gone out of fashion. It makes use of what are called ideomotor signals, which are involuntary movements usually of the head or fingers that reveal to a trained observer what a person is really thinking. Some of these signals are well known, such as shifting the gaze when telling a lie, or clasping the thumb with curled fingers when having 'something to hide'. Professional interrogators make good use of such spontaneous lie-detector tests, and I have had them demonstrated on myself by Loren Parks, whom I mentioned earlier.

He told me that one of my fingers was to be the 'yes' signaller while a tiny movement of another finger would mean 'no'. Then he asked me to take my conscious mind off to the beach or mountains while he had a chat with my subconscious. I was not to say anything, or even pay attention to his questions. My fingers would do the talking, and it seems they did, for in a very short time he had extracted a good deal of personal information from me without my having said a word. The whole session, which took place in a railway station waiting-room, lasted about ten minutes. In some cases, he told me, he could diagnose and treat certain diseases in a matter of seconds. This brief demonstration did more in a few minutes to convince me of the potential of hypnosis than the reading of dozens of books.

In these five chapters I have tried to show that the mind is not a philosophical abstraction, but a working part of the body, and when treated as such it can obtain results that border on the miraculous. I have also shown that the workings of the mind become easier to understand if we look at it as a team of two minds forming a single entity. Yet although some ways of getting the mind to work are ridiculously simple, the mind itself is anything but simple. We may have two brains and two minds, but we still have a lot to learn about how they work together. There are people who are 'ambicerebral' as well as ambidextrous; they can write with either hand and apparently think with both minds equally well. Others, however, are very 'lateralised', tending to use one mind rather than the other most of the time.

What has been put forward here is a model of mind and not of brain. It owes much to the thesis originally published in 1957 in which psychologist Peter McKellar described what he called 'R-thinking' and 'A-thinking' in terms very similar to those used later by Sperry and his colleagues to describe some of the specialities of the left and right brain hemispheres respectively. R-thinking, in McKellar's words, includes 'realistic appraisal in terms of the evidence, critical evaluation, and logical inference of the valid kind', while A-thinking is 'autistic' in the original sense of the word:

'fantasy-dominated, self-generated, and uncorrected by reference to external reality'.[25]

This must be taken into account when trying to heal by suggestion or mind-programming. We should be measured for healing as we are for a new suit. A highly left-minded person will tend to respond to a rational and logical form of conventional therapy, while a right-minded patient should be treated in a more imaginative and intuitive way. If, in the future, we all had our degrees of brain lateralisation and hypnotisability tattooed under our armpits, it would be possible to bring immediate help to many casualty-ward patients.

Hypnosis is not a panacea. The mind, however, has panacea-like qualities, and if these are aroused they can save the medical services much time, effort and money. (Drugs and surgery are not panaceas either, I might add, though they are often prescribed as if they were.) If the medical profession, like the Tower of Pisa, is 'slightly off balance', this is no more than a reflection of the overall state of the western society mind, which is weighted heavily to the left and will not function properly until the balance is restored.

One way this can be done is by looking at some of the suppressed abilities of the right mind, and seeing how they can be developed and put to work for us.

# Part II

# MIND

# Introduction

So far, in my search for the limits of the mind's abilities, I have dealt only with its power over its own body, with or without the help of a hypnotist. I have concentrated on healing, because of its obvious practical importance, and we have seen that mind power can be discussed from a base of hard visible evidence reported by professionals, chiefly doctors and clinical psychologists, and published in scientific journals.

Now, if we read the history of mesmerism and hypnotism with a balanced mind, we cannot help noticing that right from the start there have been reports of what have come to be known as the 'higher phenomena'. These include telepathy, clairvoyance, and community of sensation, whereby a hypnotised subject shares the hypnotist's subjective impressions of taste, pain, or emotions such as fear or pleasure.

Some of these reports were published in as much detail as cases of medical cures, sometimes by the same people, such as Puységur. If we accept the medical phenomena of hypnotism, why should we reject the others? Both have been repeated under modern conditions; the higher phenomena admittedly less often than the medical ones, which may be simply because few hypnotists ever try to repeat them, although as we shall see, now and then they do. Some of the better reports of the higher phenomena can tell us a lot more about the workings of the mind than the medical cases, where even today the state of the patient's mind is seldom mentioned in any detail.

One reason why the higher phenomena have been rejected is that although they were first reported more than fifty years before the birth of the Spiritualist movement, they came to be identified by sceptic and believer alike as part of this movement. This led to instant and permanent polarisation: either you accepted the philosophy and the phenomena, or you rejected them both. This polarisation is still with us today, and one of my aims in Part Two is to try to disentangle the one from the other, and to concentrate on the phenomena rather than the philosophy.

In June 1983, I addressed an international scientific conference in Czechoslovakia on 'Psychotronics and the subjective mind', which I will mention in more detail later. My main point was that while we can reject the Spiritualist philosophy if we like, we have no right to reject any well-reported *facts*. I made it clear that I was neither defending nor attacking Spiritualism, and the same applies to the following chapters, which deal with life before death and not after it.

In the November 1983 issue of the French scientific magazine *La Recherche*, a University of Paris historian named Pierre Thuillier made precisely the same point, far more eruditely than I. He quoted a remark made in 1863 by the astronomer Camille Flammarion: 'Who can say that Spiritism is not an entirely new path opened in the domain of psychology that will lead to the study of the faculties of the soul, through which we will perhaps finally get to *know ourselves*?' (The differences between Spiritualism and the movement founded by Allan Kardec and called Spiritism are not important in this context.)

Before I plunge into areas generally considered paranormal, which means only that they await an explanation, I should make my own position clear. I have been interested in such things as telepathy (mind-to-mind information transfer at a distance), clairvoyance (awareness of objects or objective events by other than normal means) and psychokinesis (physical movement caused by the mind) for some time, and have had plenty of experience of them, as described in three books.[1] Recently, I have stopped trying to persuade other people that they exist, and concentrated on finding ways of experiencing them myself and on looking for practical uses for them. I found this much easier than I thought, and I will give precise instructions in due course for anybody who wants to do the same.

Throughout my own investigations, which began in 1972, I have noticed that however intriguing paranormal phenomena may be, the effects they tend to have on people are even more mysterious. In no other field does the Scylla–Charybdis factor operate so powerfully, with bizarre speculations by right-mind extremists matched in absurdity only by even more bizarre 'explanations' by left-mind extremist critics. Overlooked in all the sound and fury are the facts.

One reason why this is so is that the facts do not fit into any generally accepted scheme of things in physics, biology or psychology. Psychical research, it could be said until recently, is a waste of time because it is no use. This is no longer true. The phenomena lumped together for convenience under the labels 'extra-sensory perception' (ESP) or simply 'psi' not only relate to each other, but have a direct bearing on hypnosis. They can therefore be put to use within the existing framework of conventional medicine, as I believe they already have been for some time.

If thoughts can be transmitted from one person to another, which they unquestionably can be under the right conditions, and if such thoughts can lead to action on the part of the receiver, which I also consider to have been proved beyond any reasonable doubt, then a new model of healing presents itself. (It will not seem new to those who believe in the efficacy of the oldest known form of applied psi, namely, prayer.)

Much argument still rages over whether psi phenomena exist or not. The intensity with which some sceptics attack the whole field suggests to me that they have a lurking fear that they do exist, but that they do not fit into the left-minded scheme of things and must therefore be suppressed at all costs. Why else would the editor of *Nature* devote a whole editorial to a book in which a well-reasoned argument is put forward by a scientist with impeccable qualifications for the existence of a psi factor in biology, and head it 'A Book for Burning'? Not so long ago, no doubt he would have recommended burning the author himself.

Psi phenomena do exist, but they are mainly subjective. That is, they happen to some people and not to others. As we shall see, whether they happen or not depends on the state of mind of those concerned. If you want them to happen and believe that they can, then they will. If you would rather they did not happen, they probably will not.

You can be intellectually convinced that they do happen by reading some of the vast amount of evidence for them, but to be emotionally convinced of anything, you have to experience it yourself. For example, my left mind is satisfied that man has stepped on the moon. I was working for the American Embassy in Brazil in 1969, and part of my job was to publicise Neil Armstrong's giant step, which most of the world saw on television.

However, a New Orleans newspaper suggested that all these dramatic shots of astronauts bouncing around on the lunar dust were really filmed in Universal City, Hollywood. Technically, this would have presented no problem. I remember a very convincing moon walk in one of the old James Bond films that looked just like the real thing, if not rather better. But try convincing Armstrong and his successors that they never went to the moon. They are satisfied both intellectually and emotionally that they did.

Their conviction is not shared by all. Astronaut Edgar Mitchell has reported meeting people who still refuse to believe it, and people who experience psi phenomena often find themselves facing the same reaction. The left-minded extremist does not follow the example of Elliotson's colleague who knew nothing about mesmerism 'and therefore should say nothing against it'. He rejects psi a priori, for there is no place for it in his universe.

Those who make full use of their right minds, on the other hand, will know that it is not a question of whether psi exists or not, but a question of allowing it to take place. This, as I now know, is remarkably easy.

# 6

# Glad Day

It was a hot February night in 1972. I was about to fall asleep in my house in Rio de Janeiro, Brazil, when to my surprise I seemed to be having a dream, although I was sure I was still awake. It was as though a colour slide had suddenly been projected on an invisible screen in the darkness in front of my closed eyes. The colours were strong and clear, and the focus was perfect. I was seeing what seemed to be the interior of a very ordinary-looking store, with not much on display and a few people wandering around. It was nothing like any Brazilian store that I knew, and I was sure I had never seen it before.

I found this sudden if unexciting vision rather intriguing, and tried to examine it in more detail. Yet as soon as I concentrated on it, the picture disappeared as suddenly as it had arrived, and before I could figure out what had been going on, I was asleep.

A few nights later, I had another pre-sleep vision. This time it was of a large red machine, like an old fire engine. Again, it was sharply focused and brightly coloured, and this time it did vaguely resemble something I had seen before. An antique fire engine had been on show in a square in the centre of Rio several years previously, and I had in fact taken a colour photo of it. Again, when I tried to look more closely at my vision, it vanished.

I began to look forward to what soon became an almost nightly slide-show, although I should say that they were more like brief moving-film clips, because there was sometimes definite movement, but not much. The scenes were interesting enough in themselves, and were also useful; they meant I was about to go to sleep, which can be a problem during the hot and sticky Rio summer with midnight temperatures up in the nineties. The best way to ovecome the heat and humidity was, I knew, to lie perfectly still as if self-hypnotised into being unable to move even a muscle, and to breathe very slowly. My brief midnight movies were a sign that sleep was on the way.

Two years or so later, I came across an article in an old number of the *Proceedings of the Society for Psychical Research* and found to my surprise that my nocturnal visions had a name, and that other people besides myself had seen them. They were called hypnagogic images. I also learned that mini-dreams just after waking up were known as hypnopompic images. That seemed to be just about all that anybody knew about them.[1]

I soon found I could have a hypnagogic image almost every time I wanted one, and here is what I do, in case any reader would like to try it. I close my eyes and think 'blue' until my field of vision goes uniformly blue. Then I go into a state of what Zen teachers call relaxed concentration, which is the same as what the biofeedback scientists call passive volition. This involves doing absolutely nothing except lie and wait for something to happen and – most importantly – *assume* that something is going to happen. You must make no conscious effort, but you must have no doubts at all. Just switch off your left mind and wait. You might find it helpful to visualise yourself going round a large empty room turning off lights and pulling out plugs until the left mind room is all dark and silent.

Next I imagine I am the only spectator at a vast open-air drive-in cinema somewhere up a mountain, waiting for the programme to begin, and not knowing (or caring) what the film is to be. Then I usually notice small stars appearing here and there. I choose one and concentrate on it in a vague and disinterested way. Sometimes it disappears, in which case I simply wait for the next one. Eventually, one of the stars explodes into a fully-formed hypnagogic image. These images tend to wobble around a bit, but can be kept still with practice.

Unfortunately, you are not likely to see any street signs telling you where you are. I have occasionally seen written signs and placards, but have been unable to make sense of the letters. This experience of being unable to read is exactly like Sperry's descriptions of those of his split-brain subjects, or Susan Hampshire's account of what it feels like to be dyslexic, unable to take in letters and words in their proper sequence.[2,3] In my experience, the images never last more than a few seconds, and I do not try to prolong them because their appearance means that I am about to go to sleep, which is the main object of the exercise.

What are hypnagogic images? It seems to be assumed by the few psychologists who have taken any notice of them that they are 'residues' of the last thought we have in our heads before we drop off. One eminent parapsychologist has told me this with great authority and conviction. In my case he is quite wrong. With the sole exception of that Brazilian fire engine, never in all of the thousand-plus images I must have seen over more than ten years have I once recognised a scene or a person, or anything remotely connected to my last waking thoughts or my bedtime book. My images are distinguished by their absolute ordinariness. The most common ones are of street scenes, landscapes, or heads of ordinary-looking people on pillows, apparently asleep. Psychologist Peter McKellar has described them very well as 'resembling lantern slides which have been mixed up and shown in the wrong order'. And, I would add, to the wrong audience.[4]

Elmer Green, a psychologist who has seen hypnagogic images himself, relates them to those states of reverie in which important information can be obtained, such as the image of the snake biting its tail that gave the chemist Kekulé the solution to the ring structure of the benzene molecule. Dr Green reports having had a preview of the building where he was to spend most of his research career, several years before he first went there, but nothing like this has happened to me. If my images are precognitive, I am in for a very dull life.[5]

Some years after I began getting my images, I read an article about something called a Ganzfeld. This is German for 'whole field' or, in this context, 'uniform field'. It is used by psychologists to describe a state of information deprivation (but not sensory deprivation, which is something quite different and very dangerous), and it is very easy to get yourself into it. Here is how:

Cut a ping-pong ball in half. Lie down underneath a weak-coloured light, and put the half-balls over each eye, packing them with cotton wool for comfort. (Or wear goggles with a sheet of thin paper over them, which I find more comfortable.) All you need is to be able to lie on your back, eyes open, and see nothing but uniform light.

Then you put on a pair of headphones and plug them into your radio. Ideally, you should have a tape of multi-frequency 'white noise', but tuning to about 120 MHz on the FM band, where there should not be any broadcasting going on, is the next best thing. Turn up the volume until it is loud without being uncomfortable. All you can now hear is uniform noise, and all you can see is uniform light. You are in a Ganzfeld. There is no signal or information in the noise or the light, so your left mind has nothing to do. This is of course similar to the state you are in while waiting for your hypnagogic image. The difference is that you are not about to fall asleep. You are about to become telepathic.

Early in the 1970s, three researchers hit on the idea, more or less simultaneously, of using the Ganzfeld as a means of deliberately inducing telepathy. They were Charles Honorton in New York, Dr William Braud in Texas, and Dr Adrian Parker in Edinburgh. Honorton, who was the first to get positive results into print, was already involved in sleep and dream research at the Maimonides Laboratory. Going over the early records of spontaneous telepathic experiences, he noticed that people who received such messages always seemed to be in a highly relaxed state – asleep, convalescing after illness, or just sitting around doing nothing.

So, he thought, why not recreate this relaxed state in the lab and see if it helped induce telepathy? He already had good evidence that images can be transmitted into the minds of dreamers, but the work was time-consuming. In fact, it took all night, and scientists have to sleep themselves. A half-hour period of artificial 'sleep' during normal working hours was much more convenient, and as Honorton and some of his colleagues soon found, it got similar results.[6]

Before long, they found that they had, at last, what the critics were forever complaining that they did not have: a repeatable experiment under fully controlled laboratory conditions that produced statistically significant results. Honorton's results coincided almost to the day with the hundredth anniversary of Professor William Barrett's original and unsuccessful attempt to interest the British scientific community in 'thought transference' after some experiments of his own had convinced him that thought could be transferred.

The Ganzfeld work arrived in England on the initiative of Dr Carl Sargent, the first psychologist to get a PhD with a parapsychological thesis at Cambridge University. He went to see Honorton in 1978 and tried the Ganzfeld experience for himself.

'It had a very powerful effect on me,' he told me later. 'I found it really did produce an altered state of consciousness, and I even had an incipient out-of-body experience.' I should mention that Sargent is no dreamy-eyed mystic, but an exuberant extrovert who is as knowledgeable on cricket, chess and rock music as he is on the workings of the mind.

Back in his Cambridge laboratory, he set to work, and by April 1981 he had put 145 different people through the Ganzfeld routine on a total of 411 occasions. The 146th subject to be tested was me.

I lay on a mattress on the floor of a room in the Psychology Laboratory building behind Downing College. Heidi Bartlet, one of Sargent's undergraduate assistants, helped fix me up with ping-pong ball halves and headphones, and adjusted the lamp so that its weak red light shone into my covered eyes. Sargent turned up the volume of the white noise until all I could hear was a steady hiss and crackle. Then I could just hear him say 'Right, the experiment has begun' as he clicked his stopwatch and left the room, locking the door behind him.

Meanwhile, Heidi Bartlet had retired to the room next door to keep an eye on me through a one-way mirror and record whatever I said on tape, noting the exact time of each statement. Sargent went to another room down the corridor, selected an envelope at random from a shelf of about sixty identical envelopes, opened it and took out the four pictures. He generated another random number between one and four to find out which was to be today's target picture. He then sat down, with the target picture in front of him, and for 35 minutes tried to send its contents to me, making notes as he did so of his own impressions of the picture.

According to chance, subjects should guess the correct picture once out of every four sessions, so that over a long period the number of correct choices should be around 25 per cent. This is not what has happened. Sargent and at least ten other independent researchers, most of them in the US, have found that people consistently choose the right picture far more often that they ought to by mere guess-work. The results of Sargent's 411 trials were as follows:

First choice correct: 37.9 per cent. Second choice correct (I will explain what that means in a moment): 25.2; third: 20.4; and fourth: 16.5 per cent. Not only have far more people 'guessed' correctly than incorrectly, but even among those who did not, more placed the target picture second than third, and more placed it third than fourth. In any other field in which statistics are involved, this would be accepted as being as close you can get to proving that something other than chance is at work. As we shall see, the statistics give no idea of the quality of some of the evidence.

Left alone in my Ganzfeld, I settled down, switched off my left mind, and decided to get into the 'springboard to sleep' stage I have already described. This was not easy at half past two on a sunny afternoon, but I was determined to test my own theory: that the hypnagogic state was the one you had to be in if you wanted to pick up telepathic messages. It took me about seven minutes of what I would call passive determination, but it worked, and here is exactly what I said on the tape:

'Ah, yes. There we go. Very clear. Dark animal standing on a rock, and a blue background. Mountain. Blue. Very clear, that.' It was indeed very clear, a typical hypnagogic image – the first I had ever had in the middle of the day. After disappearing as usual, it came back again, but it was slightly different this time. The animal had gone, and the rock had come closer. It was so clear that I could see cracks and holes in its surface. This also faded away, and nothing much came into my mind for another seven minutes, when there was a fainter but still recognisable image. My comment was:

'Like a pyramid seen from the air. Rocks, same as before. Like the top of Mount Everest, or something. It's a very bleak landscape. Big blob in the middle – perhaps it's the hole in the Earth?' I began to feel cold and depressed, and at 21 minutes Heidi Bartlet noted me as saying:

'I'm still getting this desolate moon landscape.' Until the end of the session, that remained my strongest impression.

When my time was up, Heidi Bartlet came in and helped me take off the ping-pong ball halves. Then we sat at a table, and she produced a duplicate set of the four pictures from which Sargent had chosen his target. She had written down almost everything I had said over the 35-minute session, which was also safely recorded on tape, and she asked me to match each statement I had made to each of the four pictures and give it a score. If there was no resemblance at all, I should score it as zero, and if the resemblance was very strong I could score it up to 99.

What happened next was very confusing. I looked at the four pictures, and saw at once that I seemed to have picked up bits of three of them, though nothing at all from the fourth. One had a blue background. Two contained animals and rocks. One did have a pyramid-shaped mountain in the background, *and* a round white lake that looked very much like a hole in the ground. Another, a Heath Robinson cartoon showed a boat that was the same shape and colour as my rock, and the way the artist had drawn the waves reminded me of my moon-landscape impression. When we added up my scores, it was the boat picture that came first by a small margin.

Heidi Bartlet then went to fetch Sargent, who produced his copy of the target. It was not the Heath Robinson, to my disappointment, but my second choice. This was a landscape painting by the Italian artist Giuseppe Palazzi, the one with the mountain and the lake, and an animal being led past an oval rock in the foreground. I immediately wondered how on earth I had managed to get it wrong, and reckoned that I had been fooled by the shape of the Heath Robinson boat as well as by its size. It filled most of the picture, whereas Palazzi's rock was much smaller in proportion to his painting, which contained several other details of which I had picked up no impressions at all. I was still kicking myself when Sargent showed me the page of notes he had written while trying to send me the target image. One phrase leaped off the page at once:

'Rather like the surface of the moon.'

'But that's almost exactly what I said!' I exclaimed. 'Look, here's what Heidi wrote: "I'm still getting this desolate moon landscape".' Moreover, I had said this at almost exactly the same time as Sargent had written down his phrase. That struck me as quite a coincidence, and when Sargent showed me some of the records of his previous sessions, I found it was far from unique. For example:

When the target picture had been of a brightly coloured butterfly, the subject had said: 'I can see sort of leopard spots. The shape of a butterfly.'

With a photo of a motorcycle race as target, the subject's comment had been: 'I can hear a car . . . a cyclist gone past on a racing cycle . . . an old lady, and next to her a man with a 1920-style haircut.' Two of the people in the photo matched this description exactly.

Another subject, a Fleet Street journalist, had been set my Heath Robinson cartoon as a target. He made repeated references to water and a boat throughout his session, mentioning little else. 'Still the feeling of water and a boat,' he said at one point.

One subject actually named a painting correctly. Another said: 'I keep thinking of firemen and a fire station.' The target was a photo of a group of men in training at Cambridge Fire Station. The subject even mentioned that one fireman had his face turned towards the camera, a detail Sargent had not consciously noticed.

Some experiments had produced intriguing evidence for precognition. A sceptical Dutchman had dreamed the night before his Ganzfeld session that the target would be a surrealist painting by Magritte. It turned out to be one by Dali, the only surrealist painting in Sargent's entire collection. British journalist Roy Stemman reported seeing images of Spanish dancers and a Mayan temple, which had nothing at all to do with his target picture. When he got home, he switched on his television set and immediately saw a group of Spanish-style dancers in a film about Mexico, land of the Mayas.[7]

The Ganzfeld experience seems to stimulate lucky guesses, at the very least, and Sargent has shown that it can do more than that. For one series of experiments, he decided to see if previously successful subjects could score better than previously unsuccessful ones. They certainly could; the group of 'failures' made 27.3 per cent correct first choices, almost exactly what chance would predict, whereas the star performers achieved an astonishing hit rate of 83.3 per cent. This result could be expected to turn up by chance alone just once in sixteen thousand similar tests. Telepathy, it seems, can be learned like any other skill.

Ah, say the sceptics, but improbable events do happen. The chances that you will win on the football pools is about one in twenty million. Yet somebody wins the jackpot several times every season. True, but that is known to be likely in advance. In the case of the Ganzfeld experiments, it is not known in advance that there will be any result at all, and the chances of a specific statement about boats, firemen, butterflies, etc., are one in infinity, there being an infinite number of possible target subjects. As for the chances of making two ostensibly telepathic pick-ups on the same day by mere coincidence, this amounts to one in infinity squared, if there is such a number. Yet that is what I did.

I had got it wrong on my first attempt, although I counted the moon, mountain, lake, animal and rock impressions to be partial hits, at least, and it was some consolation to learn later that Sargent had asked an independent judge to go through my statements and score them against the same four pictures. He had rated the correct picture a clear winner.

I wanted to try again right away, but it was getting late and Sargent had an evening appointment. Then I had an idea.

'Look,' I said, 'why don't we try this at long distance? I'll go home to London and go to bed at the same time as you here in Cambridge. I'll get into a proper hypnagogic state, and you just take any picture you like and try to send it over. It won't be a full-scale experiment, obviously, just an informal one-off for my benefit.'

Sargent agreed, and we fixed 11.45 p.m. as a convenient time for both of us. He would just lie in bed and concentrate on a picture for fifteen minutes, not the usual thirty-five, while I would write down whatever impressions I got, if any, and mail them the next morning to Trevor Harley, one of Sargent's most experienced Ganzfeld research colleagues. He would do the scoring for me, checking my statements against each of four pictures without knowing which one Sargent had selected.

As luck would have it, I caught the slow train to London instead of the express. By the time I got home and had eaten something, it was almost time for the long-distance experiment. I was not feeling like going to sleep. But I dutifully climbed into bed, notebook by my side, and shut my eyes at exactly a quarter to midnight.

For fifteen minutes, I saw absolutely nothing. Total failure. Oh well, I thought, as I switched on my bedside lamp and began to read, you can't win them all ...

A quarter of an hour later, I felt slightly more sleepy, and wondered if it might still be worth trying. There was poor old Carl working hard fifty miles away, trying to send me a message. The least I could do was try to pick it up, and if distance was no barrier, why should time be? I decided I was going to get a hypnagogic image if I had to stay awake all night.

I switched off my lamp and gave my brain strict instructions to get on with it. Then I went into the most totally passive state I could manage, and just lay and waited. For another twenty minutes there was nothing, no blue space, no stars, no thoughts of any kind. Then, with the usual suddenness, there it was.

It was a very quick image, but as clear as usual. For the first time I could remember, it was not in colour, but in a bluish-black and white. This only made its outlines even clearer, and it could not possibly have been mistaken for anything other than the figure of a man standing on a pedestal, with a bright halo of light behind it. For some reason, I decided it was a statue of Chairman Mao Tse-tung, the Chinese leader at the time.

I reached for the light switch, grabbed my notebook, and wrote: 'Figure on pedestal. Mao. Light.' I drew a sketch of what I had seen, noted the time – 12.35 – and then went off to sleep (with no more images) satisfied that at least I had tried.

This is what I wrote the following morning to Trevor Harley:

'I got nothing at all until 12.35, when there was a clear but brief flash of a figure on a pedestal with a bright light behind it, and I had the impression it was Mao Tse-tung. That was all.'

A few days later, I learned that Harley had matched my single statement against each of the four pictures from which the target had been chosen. The scores, reduced to percentages, were 18, 38, 39 and 75. He had no difficulty in deciding which picture most closely fitted my description, and Sargent confirmed that it had indeed been the one he had tried to send to me. The picture was a postcard reproduction of a painting by William Blake called Glad Day, which I am quite certain I had never seen at the time. (I have always had something of an aversion to Blake's art.) It shows the figure of a man standing on a rock with a bright halo of light behind him, *and nothing else*.

There were differences, to be sure. Blake's figure is an angel, unmistakably male, naked and with arms outstretched. (I think it is hideous.) My image had been clothed, with arms folded, and was on a rectangular pedestal, not a jagged rock. Yet the fact remained – and there was written evidence to prove it – that I had correctly named the only three elements of the picture: the figure, the pedestal and the halo. My mention of Mao was an interpretation of what I had seen, not a description. It seemed my right mind had done its work with an accuracy close to one hundred per cent, and my left mind had interfered with a logical but wrong deduction.

This was precisely what had happened in the Cambridge session. I had picked up the right-mind impressions correctly, and made a wrong logical deduction while doing my scoring. If my left mind had not interfered, I would have chosen the correct picture as the winner on points, as Harley had done (his ratings were 65, 53, 42 and 34). I concluded, from my two experiments, that the hypnagogic state was one in which telepathy (or chance coincidence) was likely to happen, and also that I should learn to trust my right mind.

Four months later, in August 1981, I gave a lecture at the Hayes Conference Centre in Swanwick, Derbyshire, on 'Ganzfeld Image Transmission' to an audience of eighty-five people, most of them elderly and many of them Spiritualists. They were attending a week-long symposium organised by Win Wood's and Charles Bullen's Institute of Psychic and Spiritual Technology. I thought this would be a good occasion for a spontaneous experiment. I would not only talk about psychic technology, I would show the audience how to use it there and then.

I knew I could count on a sympathetic audience, thanks to the magical combination of the rural beauty of the site and Win's and Charles's skill in creating an instantly harmonious group from individuals from all over the country. I was also lucky that before my talk Matthew Manning had given an impressive demonstration of his healing methods, and by the time it was my turn to speak the audience was in an ideal state of interest and expectancy.

I began with a short history of Ganzfeld research, and then announced that we were going to do an experiment right then. I would be the sender and the whole audience would be receivers. Obviously, it would be a much simplified version of Sargent's method, I explained, and my main purpose was just to show people how telepathy could be expected to happen, and how they could try it themselves at home.

I tuned the FM radio to 120 MHz and turned the volume up until the room was filled with 'white' hisses and crackles. I had to do without ping-pong balls, and asked people either to stare out of the big window at the grey overcast sky or to shut their eyes. They could even take a nap if they felt like it, but must remember any images they picked up before dropping off.

I had brought four postcards with me, numbered one to four, and selected my target by asking the nearest person to read the last digit on a pound note. This was 7, so I took card 3 (4 + 3), which was a view of Chatsworth, a well-known English stately home. It showed the façade, a bridge, a river and some thick woodland.

Retiring behind an improvised screen on the stage, I sat down and stared at Chatsworth, mentally repeating the words 'castle, bridge, river, trees' and visualising them filling the room. When time was up, I switched off the radio, waited for one or two of the older folk to wake up, and then asked people to call out any particular strong impressions received. Among the first words I heard were 'trees, river, bridge'. This was quite startling, but I made an effort to show no reaction.

Then I passed all four cards round the audience, asking people to respond to their overall impressions and not to try too hard to guess correctly. If they had no impressions at all, I said, it was quite all right just to guess. When everybody had seen the cards, I held up each one in turn, gave a detailed description of it and asked for a show of hands.

The first card was of the interior of a Canadian restaurant; the only scene of the four with which I had personal connections. I had picked it up after eating there earlier that month. The second was a sixteenth-century Flemish painting of a walled city by a river. The third was Chatsworth, and the fourth showed some French pine trees and nothing else. Results of first choices, in percentage terms, were:

| Canadian restaurant | 10·6 |
| Flemish painting | 24·7 |
| Chatsworth | 35·3 |
| French trees | 16·5 |
| No choice | 12·9 |

'Well done,' I said. 'You've got it right.' I explained that this had not been anything like a controlled experiment, just an informal demonstration of how telepathy can be made likely to happen. Any scientist will already have spotted several procedural flaws in my method, the most serious being the calling out of impressions. These could have had a suggestive effect on undecided members of the audience. The reason I asked for them was to get immediate impressions, before people had had time to think too hard.

Afterwards, I noticed something rather curious. I had chosen the cards more or less at random from my own collection, and had deliberately not studied them very carefully. Now, I saw that three of them had something in common. There were trees in all of them, trees and a river in two, and trees and a castle in two. (Chatsworth is not really a castle, but it is a very large house.)

It could be argued either way that this made my results more or less significant. Personally, I would have thought that since three of the pictures had something in common, guesses should have been divided evenly between them, if no more than guesswork was involved. Yet the correct card received only five votes less than the other two containing trees together.

My experiment did however lead to one scientifically acceptable result. A member of the audience told me she had no hesitation in picking the right picture, and had already experienced telepathy on a number of occasions. She said she would be glad to take part in a proper experiment, so I immediately made arrangements for her to go to Cambridge to be tested by Carl Sargent. She went a few days later, and once again picked the correct target.

For me, the experiment was well worth while. It confirmed my belief that telepathy could be made to happen spontaneously, provided the conditions were right and three simple rules were obeyed:

1 All parties involved must want and expect to be successful.
2 The receiver's left mind must be shut down completely.
3 There must be no normal information input.

I cannot promise that everybody who tries an experiment like those I have described will get it right first time. There is still a great deal we do not know about telepathy, and I am concentrating here on what we do know. All I am claiming is that the Ganzfeld method is an easy way for beginners to find out if they are any good at it. Covering the eyes with ping-pong ball halves and listening to white noise is not essential. It is quite possible to practise telepathic transmission in your own home without any accessories at all, and instructions on how to do it had been in print for nearly fifty years when the first Ganzfeld experiments were done. They are still the best available, and are worth looking at in some detail.

In 1930, the American novelist and social reformer Upton Sinclair published a detailed account of a long series of experiments in what we might call domestic telepathy, in a book called *Mental Radio*. He himself was usually the sender, and his wife Mary Craig Sinclair was the receiver.

She had given regular demonstrations of telepathy as a child, as many children do before their left minds are fully developed, at around the age of eight, and had always been a keen student of the human mind. She wanted to know 'what the mind really is, and how it works, and what can be done with it'. Yet, her husband insisted, 'never was a woman more "practical", more centered on the here and now, the things which can be seen and touched'.

He gives several examples of her ability to find lost objects, even over the telephone, and to announce what was just about to happen. On the day that her friend the writer Jack London committed suicide, she had a sudden feeling of worry about him, and she always seemed to be able to find out what her husband was doing by the technique now known as remote viewing. This is an ability other wives might envy.

Mary's most remarkable talent, and thanks to her husband the best documented, was for reproducing drawings at a distance. Upton would draw something on a piece of paper while Mary, in another room, would relax, concentrate, and draw what came over her 'mental radio' or write a description of the image. They repeated this experiment several hundred times, with some impressive results, as when Upton drew a comic cow with its tongue hanging out and Mary wrote 'Muley cow with tongue hanging out', or when he drew a sailing boat and she simply wrote 'Sail boat'.

'I tell you – and because it is so important, I put it in capital letters:

TELEPATHY HAPPENS,' Sinclair concluded, insisting that like anything else it could be 'cultivated and used deliberately'. One of the many witnesses to some of the Sinclairs' home experiments was Albert Einstein, who wrote a preface to *Mental Radio* in which he said the book deserved 'the most earnest consideration, not only of the laity, but also of psychologists'. Fortunately, it received such consideration from one of the most eminent psychologists in the US, Professor William McDougall, former head of his department at Oxford University who took over the same post at Harvard. He also had a first-hand demonstration of Mary's abilities, and told Sinclair that they had an influence on his decision to set up a parapsychology laboratory at Duke University in Durham, North Carolina, with his assistants, Drs J. B. and Louisa E. Rhine.

Mary Sinclair thus made a considerable impact on the academic world. Her most valuable contribution to psychical research was her detailed account of how she worked. As McDougall pointed out, this was fully in keeping with what was already known: that 'a peculiar passive mental state or attitude seems to be a highly favourable, if not essential, condition of telepathic communication'.

Even after fifty years, her instructions for achieving this condition have yet to be expressed more clearly. They fill sixteen pages of her husband's book, and I will summarise them briefly while urging all do-it-yourself telepathy enthusiasts to consult the original.

She begins by stressing the importance of relaxed concentration, or as she puts it – not thinking, but inhibiting thought. (As I would put it – shutting up the left mind.) 'Perhaps', she says, 'we each have several mental entities, or minds, and one of these can sleep (be blankly unconscious) while another supervises the situation.'

She goes on to give an excellent description of the hypnagogic state, which she seems to have understood very well long before it came to the attention of psychologists. She also worked out a technique for entering it during the day, and prolonging it at will. This involved becoming aware of the state and just passively deciding to prolong it. This may sound vague, but it really is all you have to do.

Thus balanced on the springboard to sleep but determined not to fall off it, she would take a piece of paper, hold it over her solar plexus, and give her unconscious mind a mental order to tell her what was on it. The order had to be given 'clearly and positively', but with 'as little mental exertion as possible'.

'Repeat, as if talking directly to another self: "I want to see what is on *this* card." Then relax into blankness again and hold blankness a few moments, then try gently, without straining, to see whatever forms may appear on the void into which you look with closed eyes. Do not try to conjure up something to see; just wait expectantly and let something come.'

It is strange how we all seem to discover things for ourselves. These instructions describe the method I worked out for myself forty years later much better than I can, and when she wrote them hardly anybody in the West had even heard of Zen meditation, or such phrases as 'relaxed concentration' or 'trustful expectancy'. I doubt whether she had read James Braid's account of 'monoideism' – the fixation of the mind on a single thought – and she can have known nothing about biofeedback or brain hemisphere functions in 1930.

She knew plenty about her own mind, however, and she knew how to get it to work for her. If tape recorders had been available in her time, I am sure she would have got better results than she did, for she kept having to break her hypnagogic state in order to write down the fragments of images as they appeared. If she did not do this, she would invariably forget them. This is why Ganzfeld researchers use tape recorders; it is much easier for the subjects to murmur dreamily into a microphone than to sit up and write words on paper.

One of Mary Sinclair's most useful instructions is on how to tell the difference between false impressions and the real stuff. She discovered the technique by giving herself a dummy run, that is, going through the motions of doing an experiment but without having any target at all. Holding a blank sheet of paper to her body, she would still get images, which would build up by a process of association of memories, real or imagined. She observed very carefully how this happened.

'I learned, in a more or less vague way, how these things behaved, and how I *felt* about them. This enabled me to notice, when later I got a true vision, that there was a difference between the way this true vision came and the way the "idle" visions came.' Her full description of such hypnagogic images has yet to be equalled for accuracy of observation and intelligent comment.[8]

Having trained herself by practising in this way, Mary was able again and again to pick up an image of what Upton was drawing in another room. She did not succeed every time, and she was one of the first to notice what became known as the decline effect, whereby results of telepathy experiments tend to be positive to begin with but then to become less and less successful, though sometimes picking

up again towards the end of a long run. If you sit in a laboratory
guessing symbols on cards, you will inevitably get bored stiff before
you have done enough tests to satisfy the statisticians.

Telepathy, like any other spontaneous phenomenon, such as an
earthquake or falling in love, only happens when all the conditions
are exactly right. I would have thought that everybody knew that, but
apparently they do not. Professor Mark Hansel, a psychologist at
Swansea University who is regularly consulted by the media as an
expert on parapsychology, gave us these words of wisdom in a 1983
television film: 'If anybody was telepathic, they should be able to
quite easily demonstrate the effect to anybody. I would be completely
satisfied by just talking to the person for a few minutes and asking
him to say what I was thinking of.' The fact that hundreds of people
already have quite easily demonstrated the effect in psychological
laboratories all over the world seems to have escaped him.[9]

Now that we have a model based on the conditions under which
telepathy happens in real life, all the serious and honest critic has to
do is to apply it and look at the statistical results. We can all find out,
in our own homes, whether we are telepathic or not.

'The truth is', say Russell Targ and Keith Harary, 'that most
people are interested in psychic experiences *because they are already
having them*.' A great many people have been having them under
witnessed and controlled conditions in the form of 'remote viewing'
of distant objects devised in 1972 by Targ and Dr Harold Puthoff at
Stanford Research Institute (now SRI International). In these
experiments, subjects sit in an ordinary room, with none of the
trappings of the Ganzfeld environment, and simply give their impressions of the randomly chosen site to which one of the experimenters
has travelled. Whether this is done by direct clairvoyance, telepathy
between subject and experimenter, or the most baffling psi phenomenon of all – precognition – is still unclear.[10]

What is clear is that somehow or other it *is* done. Some of the
fifteen successful published reports (by several independent
researchers) indicate that some people can even describe a target
location before the experimenter gets there, or even before it is
selected. This is some of the best evidence yet obtained for precognition, a part of the psi spectrum that is beyond the scope of this book
but deserves a brief mention.

In 1983, Californian researcher John Gertz published the results
of a particularly imaginative experiment in which he viewed a series
of slides grouped into archetypal concepts such as birth experience,

flight, the underworld, and death. In an adjoining room, his subject was encouraged to enter a hypnagogic state and report his impressions of what Gertz was trying to transmit.

Some of his imagery was right on target; while Gertz was looking at a slide showing Adam and Eve being led out of the Garden of Eden, he said: 'Leaving the garden, me and a girl.'

Again and again, the subject made remarks that fitted exactly with the theme of the group of slides Gertz was watching. During a group devoted to the ambivalence of woman, he said: 'My wife is getting mad over nothing. Suddenly I see her face turning bitter. I say that I have never seen you before like this.'

When the theme was flight, he remarked: 'There was a flying sensation when I jumped. I am looking from a balcony at myself below on a stage dancing.'

On the first day of the three-day experiment, the subject gave a detailed description of a painting showing three very similar-looking girls in a rural setting, with a man watching them. 'They were all the same girls, like triplets,' he said, as indeed they seem to be. What was particularly interesting about this very precise description was that the slide in question was not viewed until some twenty-four hours later. The journal in which Gertz's report was published deleted the paragraph describing this incident, considering it 'irrelevant'.

Gertz made brain-wave recordings of his subject throughout the session, and produced evidence which, though certainly not conclusive, indicates that the springboard-to-sleep moment is one in which telepathic messages are more likely to reach their destination.[11] The Cambridge philosopher Professor C. D. Broad believed that 'paranormal forms of cognition and causation may well be continually operating in the background of our normal lives'. If anything is continually operating in the background of my life, then I want to know more about it. Some climb Mount Everest because it is there; others investigate telepathy for the same reason. It seems a good enough reason to me.

Another philosopher, Professor H. H. Price of Oxford University, reckoned that 'telepathy is something which ought not to happen at all, if the Materialistic theory were true. But it does happen. So there must be something seriously wrong with the Materialistic theory, however numerous and imposing the *normal* facts which support it may be.'[12] This may explain why psi is not more widely investigated. It is a major threat to academic security.

'I don't like to believe in telepathy,' Upton Sinclair confessed after presenting some of the best evidence we have for it, 'because I don't know what to make of it, and I don't know to what view of the universe it will lead me.' Even so, he was not afraid to face the facts and their implications. 'There is new knowledge here, close to the threshold, waiting for us; and we should not let ourselves be repelled by the seeming triviality of the phenomena.' Many major discoveries, such as electricity, had resulted from the pursuit of trivial clues. As for the power of the human mind, to set limits to its potential 'is not to be scientific, it is merely to be foolish'.

He was particularly intrigued by the phenomenon of table-tilting, which he witnessed in his own home and described carefully and objectively. There was enough light in the room for all fourteen people present to be clearly visible, and for him to see a 34-pound table rise four feet from the floor and move slowly over his head. 'Think of the possible importance of faculties like this, locked up in our minds!' he wrote. His wife was ill at the time, and he wondered if 'these faculties might perhaps be used for healing'. Unfortunately, he never pursued that line of enquiry although he considered the investigation of it to be 'a moral obligation'.

Mary Sinclair was bolder and more specific in her speculations. If clairvoyance was real, she wrote, 'then we may have access to all knowledge. We may really be fountains, or outlets of one vast mind.' If telepathy were real, 'then my mind is not my own ... I and the universe of men are *one*'. In such speculations, she is in distinguished company. Jung, for example, believed that our minds contained 'seeds of future consciousness' received from other minds and awaiting their time to grow into conscious expression. Teilhard de Chardin saw the matter that formed his body as 'the totality of the universe possessed by me partially', the universe being held together by what he saw as the crucial factor in evolution – thought.[13]

The idea that all living beings are part of a single conscious organism is very old. It is found, for example, in the complex culture of Polynesia preserved by the *kahunas*, or 'keepers of the secret', and written down for the first time by an American schoolteacher named Max Freedom Long. According to this doctrine, man is a triplicity of lower, middle and higher selves, the first two corresponding to our subconscious and conscious minds and the third to what Long calls the superconscious. Through this *aumakua*, or 'older, parental, utterly trustworthy spirit', all individuals are united.

Telepathy and clairvoyance were no mysteries to the *kahunas*. Just as bodies, whether animate or inanimate, had their 'shadowy bodies', so did thoughts, and once any two bodies had been in contact they remained in potential contact for ever. As for healing, the methods used by the keepers of the secret were remarkably similar to those of Mesmer. They believed in a kind of animal magnetism which they called *mana* (vital force), and in the ability of healers to channel this force from the *aumakua* to an individual in need. According to Long, this doctrine can be traced back to Egypt before the time of Moses. It may be the oldest belief of its kind in existence.[14]

# 7

# I Change His Mind

On 14 June 1955, a welder named Jack Sullivan was working alone in a deep trench near Washington Street in Boston, Mass., when the earth above him suddenly caved in and buried him alive. He shouted for help, but there was nobody around.

Several miles away one of his workmates, Tommy Whitaker, was welding on another job when he spontaneously had the idea that he should go over to Washington Street, just to see if all was well. He had no idea that Jack was there; he just felt he ought to go there, and the feeling became so persistent that he left work early, explaining to a colleague that 'there might be something wrong'.

When he got to Washington Street, he found a company truck with its generator running, but no sign of anybody around. Then he noticed that part of the water-pipe trench had caved in, and looking closer he saw a hand sticking out of the earth. Half an hour later, Jack Sullivan was brought out alive.

This case, unlike nearly all of its kind on record, was thoroughly researched shortly after the event by two experienced parapsychologists: Betty Nicol (Humphrey), one of Rhine's first students at Duke University, and her husband J. Fraser Nicol, a statistician and respected historian of psychical research. They recorded some important details.

Sullivan told them that at the moment he realised he had been buried, a 'vivid picture' of Whitaker had come into his mind along with the thought that he might be able to save him. He reckoned that the fact he was still alive could be due to telepathy, or prayer, or both, but he did not think mere coincidence was a very plausible explanation.

As for Whitaker, curiously enough he reported no feeling of urgency when he received his impulse. It was more like a nagging suggestion, he said. 'He simply felt he ought to go to that place,' the Nicols wrote in their report. 'He didn't know why, but he knew he wouldn't be comfortable until he had.' The message seems to have got through in a rather indirect way, yet it was still powerful enough to make Whitaker do something he would not normally have done. This undoubtedly led to the saving of a life.[1]

Much of the argument and general confusion that still surrounds the subject of telepathy arises from the fact that we still cannot define the mechanisms involved, more than a hundred years after the word was invented. It is all very well, critics have complained, to pile up volume after volume of anecdotal evidence, but these are of no value unless they lead to an explanatory theory and a method of demonstrating telepathy by repeatable controlled experiment. It is still not generally realised that we have had both for some time.

The experimental conditions have been tested and repeatedly confirmed by more than a dozen independent researchers using the Ganzfeld technique described in the last chapter. As for the theory, this was spelled out in detail in 1962 by Andrija Puharich, MD, a neurologist, inventor and maverick independent investigator of unusual people and phenomena. It has been widely ignored ever since.[2]

I mentioned earlier that telepathy, like hypnosis, calls for a very precise state of mind in both parties involved. Puharich was the first to describe these states, as what he calls adrenergia and cholinergia, and to carry out laboratory experiments designed to test his theory and produce telepathy under controlled conditions. His work is an important complement to that of the Ganzfeld researchers and is long overdue for reassessment.

Numerous accounts of telepathy have one feature in common: the sender of the message is in a state of crisis at the time, whereas the receiver tends to be relaxed, doing nothing in particular, or asleep. Adrenergia is the name Puharich gives to the former state, in which the sympathetic nervous system is massively activated to take a dominant role, while cholinergia is a state of dominance by our other nervous system, the parasympathetic.

Together, these two systems form what is called the autonomic nervous system, which looks after our involuntary actions such as heart beat, blood flow and digestion. As with our brains and minds, when nature provides us with two of anything, we can expect them to have complementary but very different functions.

When we 'get the adrenalin flowing', our sympathetic nervous systems have taken charge, speeding up our heart beats, constricting the blood vessels, dilating the pupils of our eyes and generally working us up into a state of ready-for-action excitement. Our kidneys secrete a substance called epinephrine, usually known as adrenalin, because it comes from the adrenal glands. Hence the word adrenergic. This describes the state we are in at times of crisis, panic, great danger or the prospect of imminent death.

The cholinergic state is just the opposite. Activated by a compound called acetylcholine, the parasympathetic nervous system calms us down when it takes charge, by slowing down the heart beat, lowering blood pressure, constricting the pupils and helping the digestion to work smoothly.

Adrenergia, then, is the crisis state of the telepathic sender, and cholinergia is the relaxed state of the receiver.

Obviously, there are degrees of each state. Upton Sinclair's life was not in danger while he was transmitting images to his wife in the next room. Nor was Carl Sargent's during our Ganzfeld experiment. But they were both concentrating on their tasks, and more actively alert, *intending* to send a message. In each case, the receiver was relaxed, in a right-mind mode, and intending to receive. Sender and receiver are, as Puharich has shown, not only in contrasting mental states, but also in contrasting physiological states.

This is the first important step towards sorting out the mystery of telepathy. It will happen only if the two parties involved are each in the right state. This may explain why it does not happen more often than it does.

Puharich quotes the Boston case which I have summarised above in support of his model. Sullivan was obviously the sender on this occasion, he says. He was under extreme stress, facing the fact that he was quite possibly going to die. So he had 'a massive adrenergia'.

Whitaker, on the other hand, was in just the right state of cholinergia to make a good telepathic receiver. True, he was not asleep or resting at the time. In fact, like his mate, he was welding, and as he told the Nicols, 'all sorts of irrelevant things run through your mind, and you hardly know you are working' while doing this. His left mind was concentrating on his job, and so it was not interacting much with his right, which in turn was left open to pick up the message. You do not have to be lying on your back in a Ganzfeld environment to be receptive to telepathy. All you need is to be occupied in a routine task that does not require you to think about what you are doing. Routine physical work, Puharich notes, can be ideal for telepathic reception, especially if it is a hot day and the work is monotonous, as on this occasion.

An incident not unlike that involving the two Boston welders was reported by Upton Sinclair, who had been told of it by the sender, the world-famous conductor Bruno Walter. The musician had suddenly been taken ill during a meal while on tour, whereupon his host had called a taxi for him. The taxi did not arrive, and Walter left to look for another one himself. Out in the street he promptly saw his manager in a car and waved to him, saying what a fortunate accident it was that he should be passing. But it was no accident, the manager said. Half an hour earlier he had felt 'an intense feeling' that Walter was in trouble, and although he did not know where he was, he had got into his car and driven off to look for him, following another impulse – to 'drive in a certain direction'.[3]

After collecting numerous examples of telepathic exchanges between adrenergic senders and cholinergic receivers, including some at first-hand, Puharich took the logical step of trying to create both conditions artificially and see if they would enhance telepathy in his laboratory.

It was not too difficult to make a subject cholinergic. Puharich simply gave one of his colleagues, Harry Stone, a dose of the 'sacred mushroom' *Amanita muscaria*. Then he ran a test of picture-matching along the lines of the Sinclair experiments, and found that Stone got them all right, which he should have done by chance once in a million similar tests. Puharich repeated the experiment with four sceptical journalists as subjects, and numbers generated at random by a specially programmed computer as targets, instead of pictures. This eliminated the 'experimenter effect', since nobody knew what the numbers were until the subjects had made their guesses.

Before chewing up their mushrooms, the subjects scored almost exactly at chance level. About 45 minutes after their sacred mouthfuls, their scores rose to a level of 214 to 1 against chance, which is highly significant. A couple of hours later, when the effects of the mushroom had worn off, scores were back to chance level. (I strongly advise readers not to eat funny mushrooms, and hasten to add that Puharich later got good results using a negative ion generator to induce cholinergia.)

Inducing adrenergia was not so easy, for obvious reasons. You cannot very well put laboratory subjects into real crisis conditions, and an artificial one is not likely to be the same as the real thing. However, Puharich was lucky. One of his regular subjects, Peter

Hurkos, was unusually afraid of electricity. So he set up an experiment for which he asked Hurkos to sit on a metal plate containing 10,000 volts of direct current. Puharich knew the plate was harmless, but Hurkos did not. 'I could see grave doubts and fears written all over his face as the experiment began,' Puharich wrote.

Results were spectacular. While Hurkos, acting as sender, was in this state of artificially induced adrenergia, his subject scored more than twice as many correct guesses as he did when Hurkos was back to his normal state. After running the experiment seven more times and getting similar results, Puharich reckoned he had proved a point: adrenergia could be induced harmlessly, and it improved the performance of the telepathic sender just as induced cholinergia improved that of the receiver.

I have been using the words sender and receiver to describe the people at each end of the telepathic process, but as I think Puharich was the first to point out, the terms are misleading. The act of telepathic 'sending' is not a centrifugal one, like the broadcasting of radio waves. It is a psychological state of concentration that is essentially the opposite – centripetal.

'The sender does not send anything out,' he says, 'but rather serves as a centre of attraction drawing to him the attention of the receiver. It is as though the sender creates a mental vacuum toward which the receiver's mind is drawn. The sender by his need and desire prepares a mental stage; the receiver in turn populates the stage with his own symbols and images.'

Numerous attempts have been made since the 1920s to explain telepathy in terms of radio or electromagnetic waves, but they have all led nowhere. Yet there is a force in nature that can operate over long distances and could well be relevant to telepathy, and it is a very familiar one: gravity.

Gravity can operate only when there are two masses involved, such as a planet and an apple, and here we run into a problem. The mind does not have any mass, as far as we know, so how can it attract anything? I cannot explain how, and nor can anybody else, but I can only point out that it does. Or, at least, it appears to act as if it did, and the idea of telepathy as mental gravity rather than mental radio makes its behaviour slightly less mysterious.

Common sense tells us that if Jack Sullivan, buried in his trench, sends out a distress signal to his friend Tommy on the other side of Boston, some sort of information must have sped across the ether, or air molecules, between them. The simplest analogy seems to be that of radio broadcasting and receiving. It was just a question of Tommy's mind being tuned to the right frequency at the right time. Simple.

Also wrong. Telepathy is *not* any kind of electromagnetic radiation. If it was, we would have no trouble in detecting its waves. It would decrease with distance according to the inverse square law, which it does not. It would be stopped by shielded metal 'Faraday' cages, which stop all known radiation in the electromagnetic spectrum except the very long waves, and there are too many reasons to mention here why the very long waves cannot be carriers of telepathic signals. The idea of telepathy as mental radio may have sounded plausible fifty years ago, but today it just will not do. (This is not to rule out any possibility of interfaces between the electromagnetic spectrum and the psi force, through such exotic concepts as solitons and scalar waves. It merely rules out telepathy as part of the electromagnetic spectrum as presently understood.)

Returning to the idea of mental gravity, we run into another problem. What is even more mysterious than the fact that the telepathic message gets somehow from A to B is the fact that B gets the message, and not C, D, or the rest of the world. Telepathy is *selective*, which gravity is not.

If Jack Sullivan was broadcasting his 'help!' signal all over Boston, how is it that Tommy was the only person to pick it up? Why did Jack's wife and children not come to his rescue? He thought of them during his ordeal, he said, but apparently none of them received his thoughts. Perhaps they were having tea together, chattering away and fully concentrated on what was in front of them, the windows of their right minds firmly shut? Tommy, on the other hand, had his open. He was doing routine physical work, and as he himself put it, 'all sorts of irrelevant things' tended to pop into his mind while he was welding. On this occasion, a very relevant thing also popped in. Why did it pop into his mind and nobody else's?

There must have been hundreds of other Bostonians at that moment in a right-mind or cholinergic state, sitting on their porches or musing in traffic jams on their way home. What was it about Tommy that led him to receive Jack's distress call?

It seems to me that he had two obvious qualifications. One, that he was in the cholinergic state, and the other, *that he knew Jack Sullivan*. The vast majority of all reliably reported instances of useful telepathy take place either between members of the same family or people who know each other fairly well, whether or not any strong emotional ties are involved, as they do not seem to have been either between Jack and Tommy or Bruno Walter and his manager.

Telepathy is not always useful. Sometimes it is trivial to the point of being quite useless. In fact, it comes in a spectrum with life-saving messages like the one I have mentioned at one end, and inconsequential domestic incidents at the other. Here are some examples of useless telepathy at work:

In 1872, a young French hospital doctor named Charles Richet (1850–1935) was visited at work by an American colleague, to whom he decided to give a demonstration of his skill in hypnotism. He used this as a means of helping the patients get to sleep, and he had one particularly susceptible subject, a nineteen-year-old girl named Mariette. He duly put her into a deep trance and then, in his own words:

'A strange idea suddenly entered my head. I had read what the magnetisers of old said about second sight, or lucidity. I thereupon asked Mariette what was the name of the young man with me.'

'How can I know his name?' Mariette asked, with a laugh.

Richet pressed on with his spontaneous experiment. 'Since you cannot speak his name,' he said, 'try and read it. Look!'

There was a pause of thirty seconds, during which time Mariette's eyes were tightly closed. Then she said:

'There are five letters. The first is H, the second is E. I cannot see the third.' She named the others as R and N. The name of the American visitor was Hearn.

This was an example of totally useless telepathy. There was no need for Mariette to know the American's name. If there had been, she only had to ask. It reminds me of those numerous accounts of people who are telephoned by somebody they were just about to call themselves. In these cases all telepathy does – assuming there is any involved – is get a message through a few seconds before the receiver would have got it anyway.[4]

One morning in 1878, Richet was getting dressed when his wife woke in tears. She had just 'seen' his grandfather, she said. He was very ill, and Richet's mother was bending over him. Richet took little notice. He had also seen his grandfather – in the flesh – a few days previously. The old man had been in excellent health, and the Richets were just about to go and spend a few days with him. 'At that time', Richet wrote later, 'I did not believe in veridical dreams.' He did at ten o'clock that morning, however, when a telegram arrived announcing that his grandfather had died suddenly. Time of death was later fixed at about 5 a.m., two hours before Madame Richet's dream. Richet learned that his mother had indeed been at the bedside for a couple of hours before the end.[5]

Here again, telepathy was not particularly useful, although there are one or two points of interest in this case, which is typical of literally thousands of its kind. (The Society for Psychical Research has well over a thousand on file, and the astronomer Flammarion personally collected 1,824 of them.) It was well witnessed, by a man who later won a Nobel Prize, which suggests that he was capable of reporting a simple domestic incident truthfully and accurately. It involved displacement in both time and space, since when Madame Richet received the message, the old man was already dead.

Another interesting point is that Madame Richet received the impression that Grandfather was ill, but still alive. It seems that he sent out his 'help' message when he felt his end was coming, and the message remained dormant in Madame Richet's mind, like one of Jung's 'seeds of consciousness', until she entered the hypnopompic state, the transition between sleep and waking. Then there is the curious detail of Richet's mother bending over the bed, which seems to me to be of special interest in connection with Puharich's theory. This is a detail that Madame Richet had no need to know at all, and it suggests that some part of her consciousness was attracted to the scene so that she could observe it directly, rather than a message being sent out from the deathbed.

These two 'useless' cases have one obvious feature in common: both receivers were in cholinergic states. Mariette was hypnotised, Madame Richet was asleep. The sender in the second case was presumably in an adrenergic state, since he was about to die, but not in the first, surely? We cannot believe that Mr Hearn was desperately trying to communicate his name to Mariette.

I am sure he was not, but he was not the sender. The message came from Richet, not from him, and Richet must have been making some effort to show off his hypnotic skills, so this would have put him into a mildly adrenergic state. This seems to be enough. I am intrigued by the fact that Mariette had difficulty in 'seeing' the third letter of Hearn's name. Could it be that Richet was not sure how to spell it himself?

Richet kept up his interest in hypnosis, telepathy and other 'metapsychic' phenomena, as he called them, throughout his long and active life. Together with his colleague Pierre Janet, one of the pioneers of modern psychology (he coined the word subconscious, by the way, in 1889), he did several extraordinary experiments with a lady known as Léonie B., who was one of the most thoroughly studied hypnotic subjects of her time.

Her speciality was what is called 'travelling clairvoyance' or 'remote viewing', which is similar to telepathy except that there does not have to be a conscious sender of the information. The receiver simply goes out there and picks it up while lying down in a dissociated state.

One day, Janet hypnotised Léonie and sent her 'travelling' to Richet's laboratory, whereupon she announced that it was on fire, which in fact it was at the time. On another occasion, during an otherwise unproductive hypnosis session, Richet happened to mention the name of his laboratory assistant. Léonie promptly said that he had just burned himself while carelessly pouring some red liquid from a bottle. Richet found out later that the man had been pouring bromine – a highly caustic red liquid – and had splashed some on his arm, causing a large red blister.[6]

Richet's most adventurous experiments involved combining hypnosis with travelling clairvoyance in such a way that he could actually interfere with his subject's behaviour, *without her knowledge and at a distance*. This introduces an entirely new feature into the discussion of telepathy: the possibility that not only can information be exchanged at a distance by other than normal means, but that orders can be transmitted and carried out without the receiver knowing anything about it. The implications of this discovery are so alarming that not surprisingly the tendency has been to pretend that the evidence is not there. Yet the evidence is there, and much of it comes from scientists with international reputations such as Janet, Richet, and one or two others to be introduced shortly.

In one elaborate experiment, to which there were eight witnesses, Léonie was hypnotised at a distance and steered across Le Havre by a kind of telepathic remote control, with two investigators tailing her to make sure she came to no harm.[7] On another occasion, Richet carried out one of his spontaneous experiments (which are often the most successful) for his hospital colleagues during a meal, telling them he could make one of his patients go into trance and somnambulate along to the dining-room. He duly sent out his mental instructions, but when nothing had happened for fifteen minutes the experiment was written off as a failure. Then somebody came into the dining-room and said there was a patient out in the corridor looking for Dr Richet. She seemed to be sound asleep.[8]

We have already seen that telepathy and hypnosis have at least one feature in common: the cholinergic state. This is automatically induced in a hypnotic subject, and it is the state the telepathic receiver has to be in if the message is to come through, whether it occurs naturally or is induced deliberately.

Now we have to face the possibility that a third factor, psychokinesis, may also be involved in the process of telepathic transfer under hypnosis. This will be seen by some as such a provocative and wild claim that I hasten to disclaim responsibility for having been the first to make it. That honour belongs to Dr Robert A. McConnell, a physicist at the University of Pittsburgh and a former president of the Parapsychological Association. In 1979, he wrote a paper with the uncompromising title 'Hypnosis as Psychokinesis', and when this had been rejected by six psychology and parapsychology journals, he published it himself in 1983.[9]

Before it is condemned out of hand as outrageous nonsense, it must be borne in mind that if there were any simple explanation for *any* of the mental phenomena I am discussing here, we would have had it by now. But we have not, and when the explanations come they will inevitably seem outrageous in terms of what was generally understood and accepted in 1983. So, rather than dismiss McConnell's claim, let us look at the evidence on which he based it.

This comes from the Soviet Union, and although it has often been summarised before, usually rather sensationally, I will do so again with emphasis not so much on what the early Soviet researchers did, or claim to have done, but on what they said.

The man who started it all was not a scientist, but a circus performer named Vladimir Durov. One of the most popular entertainers in pre-revolutionary Russia, he enthralled audiences with his carefully trained animals, especially his dogs. Although he made use of mechanical aids such as ultrasonic whistles, he gradually became convinced that he had developed direct mind-to-mind contact with his dogs, especially a lively fox terrier called Pikki. Here is his description of an early experiment:

'Suppose we have the following task: to suggest that the dog go to a table and fetch a book lying on it ... I take his head between my hands, as if I am symbolically inculcating in him the thought that he is entirely in my power ... I fix my eyes upon his ...'

With Pikki in what sounds like a mesmeric trance, Durov would then visualise precisely what he wanted the dog to do. Then:

'I fix into his brain what I just before fixed in my own. I mentally put before him the part of the floor leading to the table, then the leg of the table, then the tablecloth and finally the book.' He then only had to issue a *mental* command, and Pikki would spring into action and carry out the task like an automaton.

Durov's work came to the notice of Academician Vladimir M. Bekhterev, an eminent neurologist who became the first head of the huge Brain Research Institute in Leningrad (now headed by his granddaughter Natalia Bekhtereva). Here, in 1922, he set up a special Commission for the Study of Mental Suggestion, for by then he was 'in no doubt concerning the reality of telepathy' as one of his students wrote later. Experiments in his own home with Durov and Pikki satisfied him that it was possible to influence a dog's actions by 'thought suggestion', and he eventually found he could do the same himself both with Pikki and his own dog, Gabish. He took these experiments seriously enough to send three of his colleagues to visit Durov and repeat them independently, which they did successfully.[10]

Bekhterev also did hundreds of experiments in image-transmission similar to those of the Sinclairs, and found that a good telepathic receiver could pick up not only the target picture or object, but also some of the thoughts associated with it by the sender. With a block of cut glass as target, for instance, one receiver described her impressions as 'reflections in water – sugar loaf – snowy summit – iceberg, ice floes in the north illuminated by the sun – rays are broken up'. This is not a very accurate description of a block of glass, but it does describe impressions that could be expected to come into the sender's mind as he looked at it.

On another occasion, while the sender was trying to transmit the image of a framed portrait, he noticed that there was a reflection in its glass from a light bulb that looked like the letter N (H in Cyrillic script). For no apparent reason, this made him think of Napoleon, although the portrait was of a woman. 'Napoleon – the letter N flashed by', he remarked to his assistant. A few moments later the subject (in another room) said: 'I see either Napoleon or Vespasian.' The subject had missed the target altogether, but picked up a thought from the sender's mind (adding an extra emperor for good measure), just as I did when Carl Sargent thought of the moon while looking at an Italian landscape. It is details like this in the Soviet work that I find especially convincing.[11]

It was not long before the Soviets were taking things a stage further. At the All-Russian Congress of Psychoneurology held in 1924, a live demonstration of telepathy was given in public before an audience of professional scientists. The demonstrator was Dr Konstantin I. Platonov, a student of Bekhterev who was to become a distinguished experimental psychologist and professor at the University of Kharkov. Luckily, we have his own account of what happened.

Platonov had not intended to demonstrate telepathy at the meeting, but on his way there he had met one of his patients whom he knew to be highly susceptible to hypnosis. On the spur of the moment, he invited her to come along with him, without telling her what he had in mind. This was a spontaneous experiment, and once again it seems that these tend to be more successful than carefully planned ones. Platonov's certainly was.

He told his audience that he was going to show them that somebody could be sent to sleep by mental command. When he covered his face with his hands, he said, this would mean he had begun the process. His subject, Miss Mikhailova, was then brought in and seated at a table on the stage, while Platonov stood behind a blackboard so that she could not see his face. Then, in his own words, from a letter to a colleague that has fortunately survived:

'Having covered my face, I formed a mental image of the subject M. falling asleep while talking to Professor G. I strenuously concentrated my attention on this for about one minute. The result was perfect: M. fell asleep within a few seconds. Awakening was effected in the same way. This was repeated several times.'

Later, Mikhailova asked Platonov why he had invited her to the congress. 'I don't understand,' she said. 'What happened? I slept, but I don't know why – you did not send me to sleep.' He had, though, and he did it again and again in Bekhterev's laboratory, fully confirming reports from France dating back to at least 1869 of the type of experiment already mentioned involving Janet and Richet.[12] Platonov's work was in turn repeated by a graduate of the Brain Research Institute, Dr Konstantin D. Kotkov. With two colleagues, he carried out what he called 'a small but most interesting piece of work in thought transmission at a distance'. It was indeed most interesting.

The subject was a teenage girl they were repeatedly able to send to sleep and reawaken by unspoken command. (By sleep, I assume they meant deep trance, or left-mind sleep.) Once, she dropped off while standing up and looking at a test-tube. When she came round, she went on looking at the tube, unaware that she had been hypnotised, as in the case with deep-trance subjects. In fact, she never did know what was going on, and kept asking when the experiments she had been told about were going to begin.

'From the very beginning of the experiment to the very last,' Kotkov wrote, 'she did not know whether any experiments had been carried out with her, or what kind of experiments they were.' There were thirty of these altogether, and 'not one was a failure'. The most interesting were those in which, like Léonie in France, she was given orders at a distance to come to the laboratory at a certain time, which she invariably did. 'When asked why she had come, she generally answered, looking embarrassed: "I don't know ... I just did ... I wanted to come."'

Kotkov has left us a very useful account of how he did his telepathic behaviour-induction. There were, he said, three factors that had to be combined. First, he had to get comfortable, relax in silence, and 'mentally murmur' his instructions. Then he had to visualise his subject doing what he wanted 'with the most vivid hallucinatory or hypnagogic intensity'. Finally, and most important of all, came 'the factor of wishing'. He would 'strongly wish' the subject to obey.[13]

This is what Durov and Platonov also did, and it must be clear by now that what made the Russians so successful in this kind of experiment (and, in my opinion, still does) was their intuitive understanding of the experimenter effect, whereby the experimenter is part of the experiment, the outcome of which largely depends on how he plays his part in it. This applies to all experiments in which a human mind is involved, from sending people to sleep and transmitting images to curing diseases like ichthyosis by suggestion. If the experimenter is not totally committed to success, he will probably not succeed. This is hard for scientists trained in objective step-by-step procedures to accept, but as I see it, spontaneous phenomena of any kind should be studied with a view to finding out under what circumstances they happen naturally. Expecting them to happen to order under conditions imposed by the 'objective' experimenter is a complete waste of time.

In his paper on hypnosis as psychokinesis, Dr McConnell concentrated on the most successful and influential of all Soviet psi researchers to date, Leonid L. Vasiliev (1891–1966). He entered the field with a useful qualification: he knew telepathy happened, because it had already happened to him. When he was twelve, he had fallen into a river and nearly drowned, losing his new cap in the process. His parents were eight hundred miles away at the time, and young Leonid begged his aunts, who were looking after him, not to tell his mother when she came home. He seems to have been more worried about being punished for losing his cap than by the fact that he had almost died.

When his mother did return, it was she who told the whole story, in detail. She had 'dreamed' it at the time, and had been so alarmed that she had begged her husband to cable home at once, which he pretended to do just to keep her happy, but in fact had not.[14]

Vasiliev joined Bekhterev in 1921, and took part in some of the Durov dog experiments. His initial interest was more theoretical than practical; he wanted to find a physical mechanism for telepathy, and he spent a lot of time testing the theories of an Italian named Cazzamalli, who claimed to have detected radio waves coming from the brain. Although he failed to prove this, Vasiliev was not inhibited as an experimenter by the lack of a proven mechanism. After all, he argued, vitamins and hormones were in use long before they had been isolated and synthesised. Only by getting down to practical work could he discover what he called 'all those conditions necessary for the unhampered experimental production of mental suggestion phenomena'.

Working in a Leningrad hospital with a hypnotist named Dr Finne, he started in the best scientific tradition by repeating some of the early French experiments of Janet, Richet and others. He chose a suitable patient and had Finne put her into deep trance. Then, standing six feet behind the woman's head so that she could not see him, he would write down the mental order to be given and then transmit it, using methods already described by Durov, Platonov and Kotkov. A good deal of will power was needed, he found, but again and again he was able to make his subject sit up, open her eyes, cross her arms, or scratch a certain part of her body to order.

Like Richet, he believed in the spontaneous, unplanned experiment. Once, he simply raised his right leg and mentally willed the woman to do the same. He noted:

'The subject, almost immediately after the beginning of the

suggestion, bends her right leg, then raises the lower part of her leg. Question from Finne: "Who told you to do that?" Subject: "It was Professor Vasiliev's order." '[15]

Vasiliev was able to keep abreast of the international psi literature throughout most of the 1920s, before Stalin put a stop to that kind of thing. He knew that French and Greek researchers had reported success with telepathy over intercontinental distances, and once again he followed correct scientific procedure and set out to repeat his colleagues' work, only instead of transmitting simple pictures he was transmitting 'the mental suggestion of motor acts'. In other words, motion caused by the mind, which is the definition of psychokinesis.

With Dr I. F. Tomashevsky as hypnotist, he found that one subject, a highly sensitive woman named V. Krot, could be put to sleep in twenty seconds even when the hypnotist was out of her sight. Then he found the same would happen if Tomashevsky was in another room, in another building, or even on the other side of town. V. Krot still dropped off on cue, and Vasiliev notes enigmatically that she also 'responded to sensory and emotionally tinged suggestions'.

The researchers then went for something far more ambitious. Another sensitive subject named Ivanova arrived for her regular 5 p.m. visit to the Leningrad clinic on 13 July 1934, and Tomashevsky prepared to carry out his usual induction routine. On this occasion he was not in Leningrad at all. He was in Sebastopol, more than a thousand miles away.

The experiment was a total failure. Ivanova stayed awake for two hours and then went home. Vasiliev then learned that Tomashevsky had not been feeling well at the prearranged time, so he had not tried to transmit. (I cannot help wondering if in fact Tomashevsky was doing a dummy run to eliminate the possibility that Vasiliev might have been exerting some suggestive effect at close range.) Two days later, they tried again, and this time Ivanova was kept under observation by a man who did not know what kind of experiment was being carried out. Alone on the promenade at Sebastopol, Tomashevsky began transmitting at 10.10 p.m. Ivanova was seen to enter a hypnotic trance one minute later. At 10.40, Tomashevsky sent the 'wake' signal, and at precisely that time according to the observer – whose watch, like Tomashevsky's, had been synchronised with Radio Moscow – she woke up.

Vasiliev did numerous experiments in remote control under hypnosis, though not all were as successful as this one. He was puzzled by the fact that there was often a time-lag before subjects responded, ranging from less than a minute to 21 minutes. Some critics have suggested that the subjects knew they were probably going to be hypnotised sooner or later and it was just a question of waiting until they went into trance, as a result of their own expectation rather than the will of a distant hypnotist. This makes some sense until we read what some of the subjects actually said during the experiments. They might have faked their trances, but they could not have faked their accounts of their own feelings unless they were very sophisticated young ladies, which by all accounts they were not.

Some of the comments indicate that although subjects had perceived the message instantaneously, they did not always want to obey it. 'What's that?' said one. 'I am fed up with him – he won't let me rest in peace.' But whether they wanted to or not, they usually did obey.

Vasiliev makes some very interesting comments on his work, based on what his subjects said during experiments, one of which, held on 20 April 1934, has some intriguing details. The subject, Fedorova, was one of Tomashevsky's regulars, and had never been hypnotised by anybody else. On this occasion, however, Tomashevsky and Vasiliev indulged in a little play-acting to deceive her in the interests of research. Tomashevsky took her from one room in the laboratory to another, while Vasiliev pretended to leave altogether, but in fact returned to the original room and began his hypnotic induction. Tomashevsky stayed with the girl and did nothing at all, and two minutes after Vasiliev had set to work in the other room, she was in trance.

'Who put you to sleep?' Tomashevsky asked.

'You,' Fedorova replied. 'Today he [*sic*] is good at putting to sleep.'

Tomashevsky repeated his question, and received the reply 'Tomashevsky'. He asked her what else came to mind.

'Vasiliev is creeping into my head,' she said. 'he came into my mind, and now he is creeping into my head.'

A few minutes later, Vasiliev tried another of his spontaneous experiments, and visualised a bird. In the other room, the dialogue continued:

Tomashevsky: 'Tell me what comes into your head.'

Fedorova: 'He shows well.'

'Who is he?'

'Vasiliev. His eyes bulge ... A cock. Now I see it, he is sitting at the table, a round one. It was he who took everything from me ...'

'Who hypnotised you?'

'He did. He paralysed me.'

Vasiliev then came into the room and entered a screened area, where he stayed for five minutes before trying to wake the subject. Then Fedorova made an extraordinary remark:

'Stay there for a bit. *He is winding up the reel.* Enough of it. Professor Vasiliev, stop it! I shall have to wake up. I don't want to. Well, enough.' (Emphasis added.) Three minutes later, however, she did wake up.

What interested Vasiliev about this experiment was that Fedorova first assumed that Tomashevsky was doing the hypnotising, but gradually realised that he was not, and that it was Vasiliev. She also seems to have picked up his image of a bird, and correctly stated that he was seated at a round table. In fact, she seemed to be aware of his presence and actions throughout the session. What could she mean by 'winding up the reel'? Vasiliev noted that on another occasion she had mentioned 'winding up the ball', and other subjects had also made references to threads or other symbols of some kind of physical connection with the hypnotist.[16]

These references to threads and reels are particularly interesting in the terms of Puharich's model of telepathy, with its centrifugal and centripetal forces.

Dr McConnell's claim that hypnosis is a form of psychokinesis has some compelling evidence to support it, and it leads him to a startling conclusion. 'We are faced with the possibility,' he writes, 'that hypnosis is an ubiquitous, psi-mediated "brain washing" process that enters, to a greater or lesser extent, into all interpersonal relationships.'

The evidence dates right back to the very first writer on mesmerism after Mesmer himself, the Marquis de Puységur, who has left us several detailed accounts of 'higher phenomena' produced by his peasant subject Victor in 1784. In one of these, Victor has fallen into a deep trance and has begun to talk about his personal problems:

When I thought his ideas might have an adverse effect on him, I stopped them, and sought to inspire more cheerful ones in him, which did not require much effort on my part. Then he looked happy, as he pictured himself winning a prize, dancing at a party, and so on. I fed these ideas into him, and from time to time I forced him to move around on his chair, as if dancing to a tune I was singing (mentally), and making him repeat out loud.

A few pages later, Puységur is even more explicit on the way he is able to wash Victor's brain:

> When he is magnetised, he is no longer a simple peasant who can barely answer a question; he is something I cannot describe. I have no need to speak to him, I think in front of him and he understands and answers me. If somebody comes into the room, he sees him if I want him to, and speaks to him, saying what I want him to say – not always in the same words, but true to their meaning. When he wants to say more than I consider fit to be heard, I stop his ideas and sentences in the middle of a word, and I change his mind completely.[17]

We may not like the idea of having our minds changed for us. It challenges one of our most cherished beliefs: that of freedom of will. Yet if information can be conveyed from one mind to another in such a way that it leads to action on the part of the receiver, then surely we must accept Mary Sinclair's view that our minds may not be entirely our own?

There is good evidence that an exceptionally skilled and evil hypnotist can force an unusually susceptible subject to think and act wholly out of normal character. This is what a German court decided when it sent Franz Walter to prison for ten years in 1936 for extracting large sums of money from a woman, repeatedly raping her, and very nearly succeeding in persuading her to murder her husband on no less than six occasions. This extraordinary case, though exhaustively researched at the time, has received surprisingly little attention.[18]

Fortunately, however, it does not seem generally possible to change the minds of others without a degree of consent. If it were easy to curse people to death by long-distance black magic or hypno-psychokinesis the human race would probably have become extinct long ago. It may have been possible to make a soldier attack an officer by direct suggestion under hypnosis, but this can be seen as a special case of a man doing what he had been trained to do – obey orders and attack enemies.

There are two sides to every coin. If it is possible to harm people without their full conscious consent, it is equally possible to do them a great deal of good when that consent is obtained. When we go to our doctors with mysterious aches and pains, we are hoping for miracles and automatically consenting to their occurrence. We are generally free from resistance to the doctor's wishes. Under such circumstances, it is not surprising that apparently miraculous cures can take place. When the arts of hypnosis, telepathy and psychokinesis are combined, a new health programme can literally be forced into a damaged body. For the body, like the mind, can be changed completely, either by its own mind or by that of somebody else.

# 8

# Will Force

'Electricity', Bertrand Russell wrote, 'is not a thing, like St Paul's Cathedral; it is a way in which things behave. When we have told how things behave when they are electrified, and under what circumstances they are electrified, we have told all there is to tell.'[1]

Electricity, so the legend goes, was discovered by an ancient Greek who rubbed bits of amber together and generated an electrostatic field, which probably made his hair stand on end and scared him out of his wits. Anyway, it took two thousand years to put this discovery to practical use, and today, just a mere hundred years after the opening of the world's first commercial electric power plant (in New York, 1884), electricity is something we take for granted. Its behaviour is predictable and useful, and we use it whether we understand its behaviour or not. We do not need to know why electrons whiz around the nuclei of atoms, jump into different orbits and move along wires. They just do. We have no real need to know why.

Let us see what a tangle we get into if we try to define electricity. All definitions in the following imaginary dialogue are taken unaltered from *The American Heritage Dictionary*.

'What's electricity, Daddy?'

'The class of physical phenomena arising from the existence and interactions of electric charge.'

'Oh. And what's electric charge?'

'The intrinsic property of matter responsible for all electric phenomena ... Well, very briefly, electricity is electrons in motion.'

'What's an electron?'

'It's a subatomic particle. A particle is "a body whose spatial extent and internal motion and structure, if any, are irrelevant in a specific problem". And a subatomic particle is "the hypothesised irreducible component of matter".'

'I see. What's matter, Daddy?'

'"That which occupies space".' And so the dialogue goes on, until the bewildered child goes off to play with something it can understand, like its high-technology computer game.

On the whole, I find Bertrand Russell more helpful than my dictionary. What he says about electricity applies very well to telepathy. This is also a way in which things behave, and when we have told how people behave when they are telepathised, and under what circumstances telepathy happens, we have told all. Electricity is more reliable and predictable than telepathy, but only because we have worked out the laws that govern its behaviour. We still cannot explain it, except in terms of something else. The same applies to telepathy, except that we have not yet worked out the laws involved. We have, however, begun to do so, and made much more progress than is generally realised.

Some of us are so conditioned to the idea that telepathy is beyond the reach of science that we have either rejected it altogether, or rejected science altogether, depending on whether we are left- or right-minded extremists. Neither attitude is very helpful, and surprisingly few people have even tried to describe the behaviour of telepathy, which must be done before we can hope to explain it. Even fewer have noticed that there are similarities between the way in which it behaves and the way in which other things behave.

As I mentioned earlier, it behaves in some ways like gravity, and gravity is an almost total mystery. It is caused by nothing more than the mere existence of two bodies or masses that attract each other according to their size. It is always positive; bodies in space always attract each other, and do not suddenly repel each other. It operates over colossal distances – the planet Pluto reaches distances of more than four billion miles from the sun, but stays where it is thanks mainly to gravity — and yet this is such a weak force that a baby can outpull the entire planet just by picking up a rattle.

There do not seem to be any physical mechanisms involved. A scientist named Joe Weber has spent years down a gold mine in South Dakota hoping to trap gravity waves in a tank of cleaning fluid, but does not seem to have succeeded. Gravity involves both information and action at a distance, and although we have no idea how it operates, it unquestionably does operate, and we have learned to live with it.

Telepathy also involves information at a distance, and sometimes action as well. It is caused by the existence of two mental 'masses' of which one attracts the other under certain well-described conditions. A mental mass in a relaxed state of cholinergia is attracted by a mental mass in a tense state of adrenergia. The forces involved appear to be centrifugal and centripetal.

Centrifugal means 'fleeing from the centre', like the water in a lawn sprinkler; centripetal means 'being drawn towards the centre', like water going down a plug-hole. We have come to think of telepathy as a process whereby the sprinkler sends out a message and the plug-hole draws it in, but according to Puharich's model it is the other way round. The receiver is the sprinkler and the sender is the plug-hole. Let me try to make that clearer.

Think of the mind, or mental mass, of the receiver sweeping the atmosphere like a huge slow-motion sprinkler, and the mind of the sender attracting it by the centripetal force of its vortex-like state. When receivers speak of reels being wound up, they seem to be describing the feeling of being caught in a centripetal force and being drawn into a vortex, rather than just sitting there and passively 'receiving'. In radar terms, the sender is merely a blip on the screen waiting for the receiver to spot it by scanning.

As I have said, telepathy is selective, which gravity is not. Any mass in space attracts any other mass in space, but the telepathic signal somehow gets to the right destination, even when the sender does not know the right address, provided the receiver's mind is in the right state. If it is not, the message is lost, or in some cases delivered somewhere else instead.

In the case of the two Boston welders, it seems that Jack Sullivan's first thoughts when he was buried alive were for his wife and children, naturally enough. Tommy, his workmate, was only his second thought. A picture of him just 'came into his mind', as he put it. Tommy, for his part, simply received an impulse to go to a specific place although he did not know Jack was there. It is as though he received a kind of mental tug, like a mountaineer feeling a tug on his rope indicating that a colleague is in trouble.

This incident suggests a remarkably intelligent unconscious mind at work. Jack's family would not have been able to help him, because they did not know where he was. Tommy did not know where he was either, but he did know the Washington Street site, and the signal he picked up was in the form of an image of the site, not of Jack. Furthermore, it was not just a message, but an order.

This precise selectivity of telepathy leads to another analogy: *recognition of shape*. All our known senses operate by recognising shape or form, and reacting to their relative degrees of probability. Here is an example of each sense at work in this way:

If your neighbour cuts down a large tree while you are away for the weekend, as one of mine once did, you are in for a shock when you get home. At first you cannot explain it; something just seems wrong. Finally you realise that the overall form of the view from your window has changed. One of the familiar shapes in it is not there any longer. When orange-coloured telephone boxes were introduced in London, some people were quite upset. Telephone boxes are supposed to be red. An orange one was an unwelcome improbability.

Our sense of hearing is astonishingly selective and form-dependent, in two contrasting ways. It ignores sound it does not need to hear, yet it reacts sharply to even the faintest improbable sound. If you switch on a tape recorder, let it record 'nothing' for a few minutes, then play it back, you will hear all sorts of noises – your own breathing, your chair creaking, the fridge starting and stopping, traffic passing or birds chirping away outside. You did not notice any of these consciously at the time. They were all accepted as probable.

I once had an impressive demonstration of the effects of an improbability. I was with some friends in Brazil whose dog had recently produced a large number of lively puppies, and about six of us were playing around with them, making a good deal of noise. Suddenly, our hostess rushed out of the room and came back with a wet and frightened animal which she had fished out of her swimming pool in the garden and saved from probable drowning. I had not heard a sound, and nor apparently had the dog's mother, who had been keeping a watchful eye on us and her litter. This may have been an instance of telepathy or of highly selective hearing; there was a lot of happy yelping going on from the other puppies, and if the one in the pool made a sound I certainly did not hear it. Was this a case of telepathy taking over when normal channels were blocked? Mother dog, by the way, showed no reaction at all, possibly because she was concentrating on us and making sure we did not threaten her young. She was not in a cholinergic enough state to pick up a message.

This incident, which will sound familiar to many mothers who 'just happen' to have thought of their children at the moment they were in danger, is the reverse of the 'cocktail party effect', which makes us able to hear what somebody we want to meet on the other side of the room is saying, while ignoring the frightful bore who is yelling in front of our noses.

In 1960, Stephen Black and a BBC research engineer managed to induce selective deafness in six out of six subjects, by giving them direct suggestion under hypnosis that they would not hear a specific musical note at 575 Hz (cycles per second), although they would hear all other notes quite normally. In carefully monitored experiments, they showed that it is possible to induce negative auditory hallucination under hypnosis.[2] Earlier hypnotists had managed to make people partially or totally deaf, but not *selectively* deaf. This was an example of negative selectivity of great precision, and if this can be demonstrated under hypnosis, we can assume that our other senses are capable of exercising equal selectivity, positive or negative. From which it follows that our sixth sense probably can as well.

The form-dependence of our senses of taste and touch is fairly easy to prove. Try giving somebody a gin and tonic without any gin in it, as I once did in a fit of extreme right-mindedness, or reaching for your bedside light switch and grabbing hold of the cat's ear if you want to demonstrate this. As for the sense of smell, it was proved recently that this works by 'pattern analysis of molecular shape', and it is well known how dogs can receive precise information at some distance using only this sense.[3]

Form-dependency applies not only to our senses, but to every cell in our bodies. When an improbable event takes place inside us, our immune systems spot it and do their best to eliminate it. Retaliatory strikes of white blood cells are launched, and if they fail, the whole body can suffer. In the early days of organ transplants, a patient could be given a perfectly good new heart, but his body would reject it and he would die. This was not because the heart was no good, but because it was somebody else's. The form was wrong, and the information derived from this wrong form set up a massive rejection mechanism.

Stephen Black has defined the mind as 'the informational system derived from the sum improbability of form inherent in the material substance of living things'.[4] This is a useful definition, as it helps locate the mind not in some corner of the brain but in every single cell of the whole body right down to the toenails. Yet it leads to another paradox: the autonomic department of the mind rejects improbabilities, but another part of the mind not only welcomes them but needs them. To be suggestible, as most of us are and should be, implies a willingness to accept new ideas, and advertising copywriters exploit this willingness to the full. Our autonomic minds may put up notices saying ALL IMPROBABILITIES WILL BE SHOT ON SIGHT, but there is another sign in a different part of the mind that reads IMPROBABILITIES WELCOME. ENTER WITHOUT KNOCKING. They may be thrown out a few moments later, but all callers are given a chance to say their piece.

Telepathy involves an instant response to an improbable message. The sender says 'help!' or 'I'm just about to phone you', and the receiver reacts accordingly. In the last chapter, I suggested that the reason Tommy got Jack's message was that he literally knew Jack's mind. He recognised the shape of it. There he was, welding away automatically, his mental radar idly scanning space and picking up 'all sorts of irrelevant things', as he put it, when all of a sudden – blip! A signal was picked up indicating that there was something to be done over at the other site. It was not a very precise message, just a single impulse that was strong enough to get results.

In crisis telepathy, the most easily recognisable variety, the message comes through in single bits, or even in one single bit. Certain types of information are much easier to encode and decode than others. The easy ones are strong emotions related to danger or death. The difficult ones are those involving specific words; an odd letter may get through, because a letter has only one form whereas a word needs several different forms all at once, and in telepathy you generally do not get several related forms at once.

Charles Richet was one of the first to point out that telepathic messages were often symbolic. It was, he said, as if the receiver were reconstructing a drama. 'The scene may be more or less veridical, the details more or less erroneous; all the same, the plot is there.'

The receiver, however, tends to interpret fragments of information received in terms of what is already known about the sender. This is known as 'analytical overlay', in which the left mind makes a deduction from the information passed to it by the right, and often gets it wrong. This is what happened when I assumed my long-distance Ganzfeld image to be that of Chairman Mao rather than simply a figure standing on a pedestal.

We would expect crisis messages to be easier to transmit than those in which there is no real emergency, and also easier to interpret correctly. Thus a mother woken in the night by a strong signal from her child will assume, depending on the circumstances, that her baby needs attention, or that her teenage son who took the car out has had an accident. Individuals seem to have their own call-signs, like aircraft, and in some cases the call-sign is a message in itself. No more information is needed.

In planned experiments like those of the Sinclairs, we find again

and again that the receiver will get the form right but the interpretation of it wrong, thanks to analytical overlay, or just to putting the bits
of information together in the wrong order. Upton Sinclair gives
several instances of this. When he drew sixteen crosses in four rows
of four, Mary drew a bunch of stars and then added a crescent moon.
She had picked up the message of a bunch of crosses, interpreted it
(wrongly) as a cluster of stars, and added something she associated
with stars: the moon. On another occasion, he drew an umbrella with
a curved handle, and Mary reproduced the shape of the handle very
accurately. But then she added the word 'snake' to her drawing, and
Upton noted that she had a great fear of snakes and was always
seeing them in the garden, though they were really only bits of
branches and twigs lurking in the shrubbery. That is left-mind
analytical overlay at work.

As for incorrect assembly of bits, a perfect example of this
occurred in one of the earliest well-reported experiments of this
kind, described by a Berlin doctor named Carl Bruck and published
in *Scientific American* in 1924. Dr Bruck drew a pair of scissors, which
in right-mind terms is a pair of circles joined together in a rather
complicated way. The subject drew a pair of dumb-bells, which also
look like two circles joined together. Told to have another go, he
then drew a pair of spectacles! With admirable Teutonic patience,
Bruck told him to keep going, and the third time he got it right.

Bruck's experiments were very interesting in other ways. He
understood the importance of getting his subjects in the right frame
of mind, with 'no intimidation or aggressive scepticism liable to
hamper the subject's psyche'. He noted the existence of a telepathic
time-lag, in which a subject would draw a target picture wrongly,
then go on to another target – and draw the one before correctly. He
also noted that the telepathic subjects had creative periods just like
all artists. 'We should expect success to be capricious,' he wrote, 'and
we find it so.' His most remarkable achievement was to transmit
some pictures very accurately and in great detail, by making use of
hypnosis and prolonging experiments until the target was fully
transmitted. Bruck's unjustly neglected research is the most successful of its kind yet reported.[5]

So far, I have only discussed telepathy in its simplest and most
easily recognisable forms, and mentioned a few examples of some
special cases of it. To summarise; telepathy is a means of conveying
information when other methods are not available, between a mind
in the adrenergic state and another mind in the cholinergic state.

The receiver, not the sender, is the active member of the team. He receives the information by recognition of an improbable signal as identifying a certain person, place, object or emotion. The information is sometimes received in such a way that the receiver takes action as a result. In these instances, psychokinesis is involved as well as telepathy. To a limited extent, telepathy can be induced under controlled laboratory conditions, with or without the aid of hypnosis, provided that the minds of both sender and receiver are in the appropriate states.

So much for special cases of telepathy as reported by research scientists and ordinary individuals. Now I come to the area of general telepathy in nature.

Much of what follows is based on speculation – not mine, but by specialists who, I must emphasise, are speculating on their own specialities. I include this section in a book that is otherwise based on fact rather than on speculation to give an idea of what *might* be happening in nature. I will claim no more than that.

It is often said that great men can be just as silly as anybody else when they are discussing subjects other than those in which they are professionally qualified. In recent years, for example, a Nobel laureate who won his prize for the development of the transistor has become notorious for his views on racial supremacy. Yet when biologists suggest that there may be a psi factor at work in their own subject – biology – they deserve at least a respectful hearing.

The clearest recent statement of this possibility comes from Professor Sir Alister Hardy FRS of Oxford University, whose specialities include those of marine biology, zoology, and ecology – the scientific study of the interactions of living beings viewed as whole systems – in addition to a more recent field to be mentioned in a later chapter. The title of one of the Gifford Lectures he gave at Aberdeen University in 1963–65 on *Evolution and the Spirit of Man* was 'Biology and Telepathy', and after a lengthy survey of the evidence for the latter, he had this to say:

'If it is proved to exist in man, and I believe the evidence is overwhelming, and if we believe that man is one with the stream of life, then it seems that it is most unlikely that so remarkable a phenomenon should be confined to just a few individuals of just one species of animal.' It could be a 'fundamental biological principle' that was operating all the time at a subconscious level, only a few of us being occasionally aware of this.

He had no argument with Darwin, Wallace and Mendel, the pioneers of what he described as 'the greatest contribution that biology has yet made to human enlightenment', namely, the theory of evolution. He welcomed the (then) recent discovery by Crick and Watson of the structure of the DNA molecule, though he was none too happy about Crick's claim that 'the decisive controls of life' were being reduced to 'a matter of the precise order in which the units are arranged in a giant molecule'. Something was missing from such concepts, he felt, and this could be a factor independent of the DNA code that took care of *physical* evolution. There could be 'a psychic side of the animal' that interacted with its own physical system and, indirectly, with the physical systems of all other members of its species.

'If it is established', he went on, 'that impressions of design, form and experience ... can occasionally be transmitted by telepathy from one human individual to another, might it not be possible for there to be in the animal kingdom as a whole not only a telepathic spread of habit changes, but a general *subconscious* sharing of form and behaviour pattern – a sort of psychic "blueprint" – shared between members of a species?'

Professor Hardy made it clear that he was speculating, and made no apology for doing that. 'Hypothesis is the fuel of scientific progress,' he said. 'It is only by the testing and rejection of ideas that we come nearer the truth.'[6]

It may not have seemed easy in the 1960s to put the hypothesis of telepathically induced evolution to the test, but in 1981 another biologist, Dr Rupert Sheldrake of Cambridge University, pointed out that this had already been done fifty years previously, in a long series of experiments later confirmed independently.

Sheldrake's hypothesis, which caused quite a stir in scientific circles, is this. By a process he calls formative causation, the form of all living beings is dictated not only by known physical and energetic processes, but also by a non-energetic organising field which he calls a morphogenetic field, from the Greek *morphe*, form and *genesis*, coming into being. This acts by 'morphic resonance', and is itself formed and modified by the experience of the units it helps to create. In other words, once an acquired experience has been repeated often enough, it becomes part of the morphogenetic field of the species concerned, and eventually all members of the species acquire it.[7]

Part of this process has been popularised by Lyall Watson as 'the hundredth monkey effect', whereby once a hypothetical hundredth monkey has learned to wash food before eating it, suddenly all monkeys everywhere else start doing the same. This has not been proved, as far as I have been able to discover. It was not mentioned in any of the references listed that I was able to find, and Watson admits that much of his story is based on 'personal anecdotes and bits of folklore amongst primate researchers'. Yet there may be some truth in it.[8]

There is much better published evidence for the existence of a '32nd rat-generation effect'. When William McDougall was setting up the parapsychology department at Duke University with the Rhines, he was about half way through an experiment designed to see if a trained group of rats could, over the generations, learn a task progressively more quickly than the untrained control group and its descendants. The experiment took fifteen years and thirty-two generations of rats, and was later repeated in Australia with fifty generations. Neither set of experiments was designed to look for telepathy, but for something even more scientifically disreputable: Lamarck's theory that acquired characteristics are inherited by subsequent generations. This is about as popular nowadays as claiming the earth to be flat or the moon to be made of Gorgonzola.

However, McDougall found that there was a gradual increase in the rate of learning, which is what Sheldrake's hypothesis would predict. There was something else, which seems to lend some support to Hardy's hypothesis: an increase in the control group's learning rate as well. They should not have done this by inheriting the ability from the genes of their ancestors. They should not have done it at all, and I have no doubt the editor of *Nature* would rather they had not. Yet they did, and one possible explanation of how they did it is telepathy.[9]

There was not much evidence to support such an idea in McDougall's day (he died in 1938). There is not a great deal today either, but there is some, thanks mainly to *New Scientist* and to Sheldrake himself, who has repeatedly urged others to test his hypothesis. By the end of 1983, the first results had begun to come in, and although the experiments concerned were somewhat exotic, the results were all positive. One experiment involved the learning of a Japanese nursery rhyme and two control rhymes, one of which was specially written for the test by a Japanese poet, and the other just a string of nonsense syllables. All three rhymes shared the same length, scansion and rhyming scheme. The idea was that non-Japanese subjects should find the real rhyme easiest to learn, because millions of little Japanese tots had already learnt it.

Of the first group to take the test, more than half (51 per cent) found the real rhyme easiest to learn, while a second group found it even easier, 62 per cent of them learning it faster than either of the control rhymes. By chance alone, the percentages should have been around the 33 per cent level.

The other experiment produced even more positive results. Sheldrake sent two high-contrast photographs containing hidden images to colleagues in countries out of range of British television. One of these was then screened in Britain, with the normal-contrast image superimposed. The overseas experimenters tested groups of people before and after the screening, to see how many could identify the images, and how many more could identify them after one of them had hypothetically entered the morphogenetic fields of Britain's TV-addicts, but not, of course, those of the subjects themselves.

In the case of the control picture that was not screened, 9 per cent more of the subjects identified it after the screening of the other one. But the percentage increase for identification of the picture that was shown was 76.[10] What this seems to suggest is that once any member of the human race has acquired any experience, other humans acquire it automatically. This is definitely not always the case; Jewish babies have been circumcised for thousands of years, but they are still born uncircumcised. The zoologist August Weismann chopped the tails off twenty-two generations of rats to see if this would lead to a baby rat with no tail. It did not.

As Arthur Koestler pointed out, Lamarck suggested that acquired characteristics were inherited only when they served some useful purpose. 'And having its tail chopped off can hardly be called a vital need of the rat.'[11] Likewise, learning Japanese nursery rhymes and deciphering televised Rorschach tests serve no useful purpose that I can see. The results of the first tests of Sheldrake's theory are intriguing, but they will need a lot of repeating.

Meanwhile, evidence of a more conventional kind suggesting that telepathy can have survival value has come from Novosibirsk in Siberia, the leading centre for research in many fields in the Soviet Union. It is of special interest for three reasons: it involves one of the few experiments in any paranormal area that any Soviet researcher has reported in detail sufficient to allow others to repeat it; it fully supports the findings of McDougall mentioned above; and the man who did the work was Dr Serguei V. Speransky, a former student of Vasiliev. This is evidence of at least some continuity in Soviet psi research.

The experiment in question was first published in the Soviet science magazine *Khimia i Zhizn* (Chemistry and Life) in 1975. Speransky's original purpose was to study the effects of a chemical poison on living systems by means of a standard test. He began by taking four groups of identical male mice, putting them into separate cages side by side, and giving them all the same amount of food. Then, 'for technical reasons' the experiment was held up, and the mice stayed put without being 'subjected to any purposeful influence' (i.e. poisoned).

One day, while presumably still waiting for his poison to turn up, Speransky noticed that his four 'identical' mouse-groups were not identical any longer. Each cageful had somehow acquired its own pattern of social characteristics. This intrigued him, so he gave up his poison test and decided to explore this new development. He began all over again, and found the same thing happening: after a couple of weeks, a mouse group living in confined territory would develop features that set it apart from the other groups.

Speransky decided to take things a stage further and see if he could get mice of one group to communicate specific information at a distance after being separated from their fellow group-members. So he divided one of his mouse-groups into two sub-groups, taking one up to the fourth floor of the building and leaving the other at ground level. He fed both sub-groups normally for a control period, then he deprived the upstairs lot of food long enough to induce starvation, and watched the downstairs mice to see if they began to eat more when their upstairs colleagues were hungry but unable to eat. This is precisely what did happen, twenty-seven times out of thirty.

Speransky ran the whole experiment again with a new batch of mice, comparing the weight-gain of the ground-floor group during periods in which the fourth-floor group was being fed normally or starved. After twenty-two trials, he found the results as predicted every time: mice would eat more when their distant fellow-mice were being starved, as if sensing their hunger and trying to make up for it. Information of a very specific nature directly related to survival was being transmitted over a distance long enough to rule out any known sensory channel.

Speransky asked a colleague at Leningrad Medical Institute, postgraduate student Ekke Saparmamedov, to repeat his experiment without telling him what the purpose of it was. Saparmamedov's results were statistically even more significant than Speransky's. The phenomenon of 'extraordinary transmission of information' had been established, said Speransky, who has provided enough details to enable anybody to repeat his experiment. Or I should say that he provided all the details except one, which I will mention in a moment.

Speransky's work forms a direct link with that of Vasiliev who seems to have devoted much of his time to studying ways in which humans can influence animals, both normally and paranormally. It was, he found, possible to affect animal muscle movements at a close range by the direct action of electrical impulses from contracting human muscles. Shortly before Vasiliev's death in 1966, he and Speransky worked together to see if they could influence mouse muscular activity by their state of mind, whether calm (cholinergic) or tense (adrenergic). Results were not significant, but Speransky tried again in 1969, using children aged seven to nine as fellow-experimenters. It seems to have worked to some extent, some children being able to make the animals speed up or slow down their running activity – this time not by any electrical muscular action on the part of the children, but by telepathy.

In another series of experiments, published in a 1974 Soviet textbook of pathology, Speransky reported an increase in the weight of the adrenal glands of mice while fellow-members of their former colony were being subjected to stress at a distance. He noted that the effect only occurred between groups of mice that had previously lived together for at least three days, and after twenty-one experiments he reckoned that he had established 'extraordinary transmission of information' as 'one of the manifestations of "preventive" adaptation of animals to the possible influence of extremely deleterious factors'.[12,13]

The missing detail I mentioned above, perhaps the crucial one, was mentioned by an East European scientist with whom I discussed Speransky's work in 1984.

'These experiments only work', he told me, 'if you run them on one day only and then let the animals settle down for one or two weeks before you try another experiment. You need to surprise them.'

At first, I did not understand, partly because the two of us had only about half a language in common. But later that day, after some consulting of dictionaries, the coin dropped and I suddenly felt I had been given an important clue to the mystery of why telepathy operates as it does in real life, and why so often it refuses to operate in laboratory experiments.

The clue was the single word *surprise*.

Speransky's mice, taken by surprise on their first experience of stress, starvation or other form of crisis, sent out the message and their distant colleagues picked it up in the form of a single bit of information, such as 'Help!' or 'Ouch!'. If the stress-stimulus was repeated too often, the response would become progressively weaker. If you are starved or stressed every day, you learn to live with it. This is Pavlovian conditioning in reverse: the more often the stimulus is repeated, the less you respond.

This fits very well with one of the most important discoveries to have been made at Rhine's laboratory at Duke University. It was made by one of his first PhD students, Betty Humphrey (later Betty Nicol), whom I have already mentioned as co-reporter of the Boston incident, in 1940. Plotting the result of a long series of card-guessing tests on a chart, she found that subjects tended to do well at the beginning of an experiment and at the end of it, whereas in the middle results would drop to around chance level. This produced a U-curve on the chart paper, and it became known as the decline effect. Rhine soon found, when he had a look at his earlier records, that it had been in operation for some time without anybody noticing.[14]

So there are at least two effects to be taken into account in any kind of laboratory experiment involving the mind: the experimenter effect, which I have already mentioned, and the subject effect, whereby results depend on how the person (or mouse) doing the experiment is feeling at the time. There is another effect that could well determine the degree of the other two. This is what I would call the national effect, whereby the occurrence of psi phenomena in any given country corresponds to the level of general belief in their possibility.

In an earlier book, I suggested that the most psychically-oriented country in the world is Brazil, where I lived for fourteen years. There, I found, anyone not believing in reincarnation, poltergeists and exotic African spirit deities is thought rather odd. Sceptical visitors assured me this was due to the high illiteracy rate and generally low level of social development.

I wonder. Subsequent research, based on a large-scale sample, by psychologist Professor Erlendur Haraldsson of the University of Iceland suggests that the honour I awarded to Brazil should belong to his country, one of the oldest in Europe with one of the highest standards of living in the world, where illiteracy is nil.[15]

Close runners-up must be the Slavonic countries; Bulgaria, Poland, Czechoslovakia and the part of the USSR that was formerly Russia. In each of these countries, as I know from first-hand experience, there is widespread acceptance of what we call psychic phenomena, despite mixed attitudes in Party circles on how they should be studied and publicised. By comparison, in Romania, Hungary and East Germany the level of interest is very low.

In Czechoslovakia, hypnosis is regarded as the standard treatment for psychiatric complaints, whereas just across the river Danube in Hungary, it is virtually against the law to hypnotise anybody. Such sharply contrasting national attitudes to the mind are bound to have an effect on individual societies. My impression is that the Slavonic peoples are well ahead of the field in acceptance of the powers of the right mind. How many countries today have a state-run oracle as well as a state-backed parapsychology institute? The only one I know is Bulgaria, which has both. During a week spent there, I failed to meet any Bulgarian who had not been to see Vanga Dimitrova, the blind clairvoyant of Petric who gives callers accounts of their past, present and future; or at least knew someone who had.

If a Nobel Prize is ever awarded for the discovery of the role played by telepathy in evolution, I suspect it will go to a Slav, and I hope the winner will pay tribute to the first scientist of international standing to suggest that a psi factor was at work in biology.

Such an idea was put forward in 1870, by none other than one of the joint authors of the theory of natural selection, Alfred Russel Wallace (1823–1913), who rarely gets the credit he deserves either for arriving at his conclusions long before Darwin arrived at his, or for pointing out the shortcomings of his own theory.

In his *Contributions to the Theory of Natural Selection*, Wallace devoted a whole chapter to some of those 'residual phenomena' that could not be explained by the theory that he and Darwin presented jointly in 1858. These included the distribution of hair on the human body, the perfection of hands, feet and vocal apparatus, and especially the size and early development of the brain. He was baffled by the fact that primitive man had a brain that was far beyond the needs of the time. 'Natural selection could only have endowed savage man with a brain a little superior to that of an ape,' he wrote, 'whereas he actually posseses one very little inferior to that of a philosopher.' He concluded:

The inference I would draw from this class of phenomena is, that a superior intelligence has guided the development of man in a definite direction, and for a special purpose, just as man guides the development of many animal and vegetable forms ... Some more general and fundamental law underlies that of 'natural selection'.

Writing about ten years before the birth of Einstein and long before it became the fashion to talk about the universe as a 'great thought', Wallace had some interesting speculations on the nature of matter, energy and the human will. 'Matter', he wrote, 'is essentially force, and nothing but force', and it was obvious that *some* force at least originated in the human mind. And he argued:

If, therefore, we have traced one force, however minute, to an origin in our own WILL, while we have no knowledge of any other primary cause of force, it does not seem an improbable conclusion that all force may be will-force: and thus that the whole universe is not merely dependent on – but actually *is* the WILL of higher intelligence or of one Supreme Intelligence.

As for the mystery of why living beings are conscious, although they consist of the same ingredients as inanimate objects, he suggested after a lengthy argument that 'Either all matter is conscious, or consciousness is something distinct from matter, and in the latter case, its presence in material forms is a proof of the existence of conscious beings outside of, and independent of, what we term matter.'[16]

Wallace, remember, was one of the men responsible for the greatest revolution in biological history, seen at the time as a deathblow to the belief in divine or 'creationist' ordering of nature. Yet he believed that 'man is a duality, consisting of an organised spiritual form, evolved coincidentally with and permeating the physical body'.

At a more down-to-earth level, one natural phenomenon that particularly intrigued Wallace was that of mimesis, the imitation of one species by another for survival purposes. In his wanderings around the world, he observed several examples, usually of insects imitating their predators, the most striking to him being a caterpillar that managed to look like a poisonous snake. Stephen Black notes that some insects and birds not only camouflage themselves, but hypnotise themselves as well, into catatonic immobility. As examples, he cites the mantis 'stick insect', and a marsh bittern that stands next to a clump of reeds and sways with them in the wind so that it can be almost invisible even at close range, and even to a trained gun-dog.

Then there is the lantern-fly *Laternaria servillei*, which Black calls an 'astounding piece of coloured sculpture'. It is about 85 mm long, a third of its length being taken up by its head, most of which is hollow. What is astounding is the way the head has evolved into a perfect miniature model of the head of another animal species twenty to thirty times its own size, namely an alligator. It has a bulging pair of false eyes in addition to its own real ones, and there is even a little white mark on them that imitates light as reflected from a real eye. The jaws are 'open' to reveal a row of false white teeth which, as Black notes, 'are rendered not only in colour, but in bas-relief'.

Presumably, this little insect deceives predatory birds into thinking it is an alligator, bird-brains being thought to be more receptive to information on shape and colour than on size. This is imitation not of a predator, but of its predator's predator. It is all very well to say that it evolves its alligator-like appearance in order to frighten off the birds. It did not work all that out for itself. It cannot have any idea what an alligator really is. Yet the fact remains that its body tissues have been shaped by information originating from an entirely unrelated species and received by a creature that cannot be said to have a conscious mind. If lantern-flies were smart enough to know how to look like alligators, birds should be able to work out that the insect was just trying to fool them and would gobble them up.

This intriguing mini-monster shows to what extent information can be received at an unconscious level and translated into major alterations in a physical body. There are many other examples, some of remarkable ingenuity. Kallima butterflies make themselves look like the fallen leaves they rest on, adapting the mimetic colouring to the seasons and even coming out in spots to imitate fungus on the leaves. There is an American moth that manages to alter both its shape and its colour and impersonate a piece of bird excrement. Some orchids get male bees to spread their pollen around by offering them the use of an artificial female bee. Male flying beetles pick up light signals from crafty fireflies that persuade them to come in to land hoping for a spot of mating, only to get eaten instead.

As Bertrand Russell might have said, once we have described how mimesis occurs in nature and under what circumstances, we have told all. It has been well studied and fairly well understood, and its obvious survival value gives strong support to the Wallace/Darwin theory of natural selection. Living things imitate to survive. But how on earth do they do it? What is the mechanism by which a bit of information gets translated into the alteration of a cell in the body? Stephen Black is very cautious on this crucial question. 'The cybernetic system here has never been precisely proven,' he says. He describes the alligator-like appearance of *Laternaria* as 'a product of the "information field" within a biological system derived from the improbability of the shape and markings of an alligator's head'. This is a good description, but it is no explanation.[17]

At the beginning of this book, I gave some examples of how humans under hypnotic suggestion are able to alter the appearance of their skins, both for better and for worse. When the conditions are right, ichthyosiform erythrodermia can be transformed into nice new skin, burns can be prevented from forming blisters and hurting, warts can be charmed out of existence. Stigmata can be produced by mistake or on purpose, in the form of straight lines that bleed, blobs corresponding to the shape of a 'hot' coin placed on the skin, or marks resembling those that would be expected to occur to one being crucified. In every case information, true or false, has moved living matter, whether the information originates from within or outside the subject's mind. The same can be said of all phenomena of mimicry in nature. The movement of matter, living or not, by information without any known physical mechanism is also a precise definition of psychokinesis.

Before pursuing the implications of that line of thought, I will draw attention to another aspect of natural mimesis, in fact its most obvious one. This is that it is always purposeful and related to survival. Insects do not imitate tree bark or bird droppings just for fun, or to show off in front of television cameras. They do it because it keeps them alive. It is *necessary*.

The same, as I have shown, is true of telepathy in its most widely reported form – that of information transfer in a crisis. It happens because it too is necessary. There is no other way of getting the information through.

When some future Einstein of parapsychology has worked out the Unified Field Theory of hypnosis, telepathy and psychokinesis, it will be possible to translate thoughts into physical action on demand, as to a small extent it already is. I am not about to present such a theory, merely to draw attention to the fact that there must be one.

Having discussed the phenomena of hypnosis and telepathy, I will now move on to psychokinesis (henceforth written as PK). This is such an improbability in itself that I will introduce it by answering the questions I have been asked most frequently about it:

*Does it really happen?* Yes. The mind has real force, as J. B. Rhine put it in 1943. He knew what he was talking about, and he had ten years of laboratory studies to prove it.

*Isn't it all due to trickery?* No. I don't think so, and nor does anybody who has spent time studying it properly. Much of it can be imitated by trickery, but not all of it.

*How can you be sure?* The evidence for it is absolutely consistent, whether it comes from Nobel prize winners or illiterate peasants. The other is that I have witnessed it myself on numerous occasions.

*Is there any scientific evidence for it?* Yes, shelves of it. The evidence has not been generally accepted, but this is not the same as saying that there isn't any evidence.

*Can it be produced to order?* Definitely, under the right conditions, though it is much harder to demonstrate than telepathy.

*Is there any explanation for it?* Not yet. We are still at the description stage, which need not put us off studying it and noting how it behaves. There are any number of more familiar phenomena, such as gravity, for which we have no explanation either.

*Is there any possible explanation for PK?* There must be. If it happens in nature, it is natural. Ground is already being cleared in both the physical and the mental sciences for the eventual construction of testable hypotheses. Some modern physicists accept the fact that it is not 'forbidden' and is therefore possible. In a paper with the delightful title 'S Matrix, Feynman Zigzag and Einstein Correlation', Professor Olivier Costa de Beauregard says that PK and other psi effects are actually predictable. 'Logically, these phenomena should show up, no less than thermodynamical progressing fluctuations – which indeed they are.'[18]

On the psychological side, the American psychoanalyst Dr Jan Ehrenwald has noted the exact symmetry between the functional deficits of the hysterical conversion syndrome (anaesthesia, blindness, paralysis and mutism with no organic cause) and the hyperfunctions of the psi syndrome (telepathy, clairvoyance, precognition and PK). Each group of symptoms is the mirror-image of the other.

Moreover, he shows that psi functions, despite their capricious nature, are governed by the same laws that apply to dreams, neurotic symptoms, and unconscious processes in general. 'In short,' he says, 'they are subject to established psychodynamic principles.'[19,20]

*What use could it be, anyway?* The area in which it will prove most useful is that of healing, once it is accepted that healers of all kinds are already using it, consciously or not.

*And what have the spirits got to do with it?* I don't know.

# 9

# Some Progressing Fluctuations

During twelve years of tropical wanderings between the years 1848 and 1862, occupied in the study of natural history, I heard occasionally of the strange phenomena said to be occurring in America and Europe under the general names of 'table-turning' and 'spirit-rapping'; and being aware, from my own knowledge of Mesmerism, that there were mysteries connected with the human mind which modern science ignored because it could not explain, I determined to seize the first opportunity on my return home to examine into these matters.

Examine into them he did, and many who admired his work as a naturalist wished he had not. Alfred Russel Wallace would be regarded today as a much greater man than he is if he had not, among other things, become a Spiritualist, claimed to have been present when thirty-seven flowers materialised out of thin air, and to have helped levitate the furniture in his own home. In the opinion of many, he spent the second half of his long life doing his best to undo the reputation he had earned by the time he was forty-five and just half way through it.

I am only concerned here, however, with what Wallace was doing in 1865, at which time all the evidence indicates that he was fully in charge of both his brains. This was four years before he announced his conversion to Spiritualism, which came about, he insisted, 'by the force of evidence'. As I have said before, we may reasonably disagree with the conclusion Wallace and many others drew from the facts they observed, but we have no right to reject the facts themselves. In Wallace's case, the facts he reported on his very first examination of 'mysteries connected with the human mind' correspond so closely even to the smallest detail with facts I have witnessed myself that I have no hesitation in quoting them here.

In 1865, Wallace considered himself to have been 'so thorough and confirmed a materialist that I could not at that time find a place in my mind for the conception of spiritual existence, or for any other agencies in the universe than matter and force. Facts, however, are stubborn things ... The facts beat me. They compelled me to accept them *as facts* long before I could accept the spiritual explanation of them.'

Here, then, are the facts as noted at the time by a man with long experience of precise observation of the way nature behaves. The explanation they compel us to accept does not have to be the one chosen by him.

On 22 July 1865, Wallace visited a friend, 'a sceptic, a man of science, and a lawyer' and his family:

Sitting at a good-sized round table, with our hands placed upon it, after a short time slight movements would commence – not often 'turnings' or 'tiltings', but a gentle intermittent movement, like steps, which after a time would bring the table quite across the room. Slight but distinct tapping sounds were also heard. The following notes made at the time were intended to describe exactly what took place:

Sat with my friend, his wife, and two daughters, at a large loo table, by daylight. In about half-an-hour some faint motions were perceived, and some faint taps heard. They gradually increased; the taps became very distinct, and the table moved considerably, obliging us all to shift our chairs. Then a curious vibratory motion of the table commenced, almost like the shivering of a living animal. I could feel it up to my elbows. These phenomena were variously repeated for two hours. On trying afterwards, we found the table could not be voluntarily moved in the same manner without a great exertion of force, and we could discover no possible way of producing the taps when our hands were upon the table.

Wallace and his lawyer friend held about a dozen more sessions at the table. They were not very exciting compared with some to be described later, but they are of great interest as examples of trivial or elementary PK, and as with telepathy the best approach to a complex subject is to start with it in its simplest form and then to observe how it progresses.

This is what Wallace did. One of his first spontaneous experiments involved asking his fellow sitters to leave the table one at a time, to see if taps and movements would continue with less than five people present. They did, with decreasing force, but 'just after the last person had drawn back leaving me alone at the table, there were two dull taps or blows, as with a fist on the pillar or foot of the table, the vibration of which I could feel as well as hear. No one present but myself could have made these, and I certainly did not make them.'

He noted that the taps seemed to come from under the table-top, even when all hands were visible. (You can actually make quite an impressive noise by placing your hands flat on a table and clicking your thumb-nails together, but this does not make a sound like a fist.) As for the way the table moved, he found it was always in curves or zigzags. He pointed out that it would have been quite easy for one of those present to have moved the table, 'but our experiments showed that this could not *always* be the case, and we have therefore no right to conclude that it was *ever* the case'. He concluded: 'These experiments have satisfied me that there is an unknown power developed from the bodies of a number of persons placed in connection by sitting round a table with all their hands on it.'

In September 1865, Wallace went along to see a public medium, Mrs Marshall, and witnessed a number of phenomena in her presence. Whether these were genuine or not, they encouraged him to hold more sessions in his own home with his friends and relatives, and to observe what happened much more closely. His group was soon able to generate a wide variety of noises. 'When these sounds are heard repeatedly in one's own well-lighted room, upon one's own table, and with every hand in the room visible, the ordinary explanations given of them seem utterly untenable,' he wrote. The most common ordinary explanations of the day were 'unconscious muscular activity', suggested by Faraday in 1853 as the explanation for all table-tilting phenomena, and the cracking of joints, which as Wallace pointed out can hardly account for 'tapping, rapping, thumping, slapping, scratching and rubbing' sounds, some of which even beat time while a tune was whistled. Nor could either explanation account for the following episode, which is very similar to one I have witnessed myself:

We stood round a small work-table, whose leaf was about twenty inches across, placing our hands all close together near the centre. After a short time the table would rock about from side to side, and then, appearing to steady itself, would rise vertically from six inches to a foot, and remain suspended often fifteen or twenty seconds. During this time any one or two of the party could strike it or press on it, as it resisted a very considerable force.

To rule out the possibility of some illicit footwork by one of his friends, Wallace then prepared his table before the session by stretching thin strips of tissue paper between the legs, so that nobody could lift it normally with a foot or knee without tearing the paper. 'The table rose up as before, resisted pressure downwards, as if it were resting on the back of some animal, sunk to the floor, and in a short time rose again, and then dropped suddenly down.' Later, he built a cage around the table, making it impossible for it to be lifted by a surreptitious toe. 'This apparatus in no way checked the table's upward motion.'

Wallace witnessed several other intriguing phenomena in his home. On one occasion, a small table moved towards a larger one, at which somebody was seated, 'as if it had gradually got within the sphere of a strong attractive force'. He also saw a heavy armchair sliding along the floor, exactly as I did during the Enfield poltergeist case in 1977.[1]

His first reaction was to ascribe this activity not to the spirits, but to 'some new and unknown power here at work'. Only later, partly as a result of 'messages' received by asking the table to tap an appropriate number of times on the floor for each letter of the alphabet, did he feel compelled to assume that an external agency, or spirit, must be involved. Today, with the benefit of hindsight, we can see the fact that some of the words would be tapped out backwards as highly indicative of the action of a subconscious mind, for it is well known that messages written in automatic writing often appear on the paper in the form of 'mirror-writing'. (For right-handers, writing backwards with the left hand is usually easier than writing forwards with it. Try it and see.)

It is not surprising that what psychologists would now call 'ego-alien activity' of the kind described above was seen by many at the time as the work of the spirits. Spiritualism came into being after the outburst of knockings in the home of the Fox family in Hydesville, New York, in 1848, and communication with the invisible world soon became a popular pastime throughout the United States and Europe. Seances would be held at which tables would tilt and levitate, and messages would be received by various tapping codes, by automatic writing, or with prototypes of the modern Ouija board. The messages were assumed to come from the spirits of the dead for two good reasons: the messages said so themselves, and there was no obvious alternative source in an age in which almost nothing was generally known about either telepathy or the unconscious mind.

Moreover, not all the messages were trivial nonsense, as is often alleged. In Paris, a schoolmaster named Rivail produced several books with the help of automatic-writing mediums and founded a new movement, Spiritism, under his (spirit-dictated) pseudonym, Allan Kardec. It flourishes to this day, chiefly in Latin America and the Philippines as a very practical philosophy and uncompromisingly Christian religion, although firmly based on the assumptions of continuing life after death, reincarnation, and the law of karma.

The rapid growth of the Spiritualist and Spiritist movements, together with the equally rapid appearance of professional and fraudulent 'mediums' led the scientific world to ignore the whole area, rejecting the facts along with the interpretations of them *en bloc*. This is the attitude once described by Kepler as 'throwing out the baby along with the bathwater', and it is still with us today.

At least one early researcher, however, caught a glimpse of the baby. This was Count Agénor de Gasparin (1810–71), who upset scientist and Spiritualist alike by insisting that the tables did tilt, but that not all credit – if any – should go to the spirits. It was he who made the discovery that what we now call PK only takes place when the minds of those involved are in a very precise state, just as we now know to be the case with hypnosis and telepathy.

With a dozen friends, he spent four months in 1853 studying the table-tilting effect in his home in Valleyres, Switzerland, without taking the slightest interest in the spirits. The following year, he reported in a lengthy book that although the phenomenon was genuine, it was due to a *physical* agent directed by the human will. 'It can neither be explained by the mechanical action of our muscles,' he wrote, 'nor by the mysterious action of spirits.'

It could not be explained at all, in fact (as it still cannot), but it could be described in detail, and this is what he did. He found that his table would move around in circles on the floor while he and his friends were touching it and walking around with it – and even when their hands were held above it but not touching it. He got his table to tilt with people sitting on it, or with a 75-kilo tub of sand on board. He was able to get it to move on demand, to a limited extent, and produced interesting evidence for a link between mind and table by asking somebody to think of a single-digit number, then asking the table to tap it out on the floor. The table got it right several times, even when the number was zero, which was greeted with silence.

Gasparin was well aware of the 'unconscious muscular activity' theory, but he did not see how this could account for complete levitations of the table when nobody was touching it at all. He had no idea how this happened. 'When you explain to me how I lift my hand,' he said, 'I will explain to you how I make the table-leg rise from the floor. I "willed" to raise my hand. Yes, and I also willed to raise the table-leg.'

His most important discovery was that the physical effects were closely related to the state of mind of those present. He often found that the table would make a movement as if in direct response to a thought, but only if the thought-instruction was made effortlessly, with no trace of impatience. The way to get the table moving was to approach it 'cheerfully, lightly and deftly, with confidence and authority, but without passion'. Some people were better at this than others, he admitted, though he insisted that no special 'medium' was necessary, but if somebody was tense, tired, or just not feeling well, there would be less activity, or none at all.[2]

Observations like these are of considerable psychological interest, and it is unfortunate that Gasparin, like Wallace, cut short a promising career as a serious PK researcher and turned to other matters, publishing numerous books on politics and religion.

His main findings were however fully confirmed by a member of his original group, Professor Marc Thury, an astronomer and natural historian at the Geneva Academy. In a sixty-page booklet published in 1855, he stated that Gasparin had established the following principles:

1  The will, in a certain state of the human organism, can act at a distance on inert bodies, by a means other than muscular action.
2  Under the same conditions, thought can be communicated directly from one individual to another in an unconscious manner.

Thury went into the question of unconscious muscular activity a good deal more thoroughly than Faraday had done, and included several pages of calculations on the force needed to make a table move by normal means. He too gave up table-tilting, and published nothing more except a history of clocks.[3]

From the brief descriptions of Gasparin and Thury of that 'certain state' needed to get the tables going, it seems that this was very similar to states of consciousness now known to be associated with right-brain activity, alpha brainwave dominance, cholinergia and the 'passive volition' of biofeedback.

Despite Gasparin's claim that no special medium was necessary in order to produce PK, it soon became clear that some people are born with an unusual ability for it. Just as there have been musical or mathematical prodigies like Mozart and Gauss, so there have been PK prodigies such as the Scotsman Daniel D. Home and the illiterate Neapolitan Eusapia Palladino. Home was tested no less than twenty-nine times by one of Britain's leading scientists, William Crookes, FRS, who witnessed an enormous variety and quantity of PK effects and described them in detail. As for Palladino, she was observed more or less continuously from 1888 to 1910 by at least fifty university professors from six countries, including four winners of Nobel Prizes. She was allegedly caught cheating on a number of occasions (which Home never was), but the evidence for PK generated in her presence fills several volumes and would be regarded as conclusive if it were evidence for anything else. Yet, like the evidence for telepathy, it has generally been ignored or rejected *en bloc* by the reflex that operates when we are faced with something we cannot explain.

An interesting feature of Palladino was that she actually had a hole in her skull, the origin of which was never explained, and there is evidence to suggest that 'mediumship' may be an ancient human attribute that can be greatly increased by a severe shock to the brain. Edgar Cayce was hit on the head by a baseball bat shortly before his first display of clairvoyance. Peter Hurkos began his career as a working psychic after falling off a ladder. Chico Xavier, the semi-literate Brazilian who has now written more than two hundred books in an altered state of consciousness (some of them of considerable literary value) was physically maltreated as a child by a foster-parent, once being hit on the head with a saucepan.

Dr Peter Fenwick, a senior lecturer at the Maudsley Hospital in London, has made a study of seventeen mediums and found that 29 per cent had a history of head injury compared to only 6 per cent of a control group of equal size. Another psychiatrist, Dr José C. Ferraz Salles of Brazil, has found interesting correlations between unusual intellectual gifts, including 'mediumship', and blue-baby births, in which he believes oxygen starvation causes normally dormant areas of the brain to be activated. These are promising lines of research, and I hope they are followed up.[4,5]

It could be, however, that PK talent is distributed throughout the population much like any other talent. If, as I discovered in May 1983, I have some myself, I refuse to believe that many others do not also have some. It may be that PK is not something some of us can do, but something many of us deliberately try *not* to do. Anyway, I will now bring the table-tilting story up to date, with an account of the events that led up to my own experience.

On 25th April 1964, four people sat at a table in an isolated country house in Devonshire. None of them was a Spiritualist, and none claimed any mediumistic gifts of any kind. The host was Kenneth J. Batcheldor, principal clinical psychologist for a local group of hospitals, and his guests were two colleagues from work, Pat Coghlan and Bill Chick, with Mrs Chick making up the foursome. It was a normal social evening among friends who knew each other well.

Conversation turned towards the supernatural, and Pat began to recall various spooky experiences from her native Ireland. She was a good storyteller, and Irish ghost stories have a flavour all their own, with their banshee wailings and phantom funerals ... On the spur of the moment, Batcheldor said:

'Let's have a go at table-tipping, just for fun!'

He was fairly sceptical about psychic matters. He had played around with a Ouija board at school, and even formed a Society for Psychical Investigation, which made one brief attempt at table-tipping. However, the very next Sunday, his fellow-members attended a Bible class at which the lecture just happened to be on 'The Dangers of Spiritualism'. That was the end of the Society, and his interest in paranormal matters was eventually largely educated out of him, though he retained 'a sneaking inner interest' in them. On his degree course in psychology, he was trained to regard mental phenomena as by-products of brain activity, and to deal only with observable behaviour, which operated according to the grand law of stimulus and response as explained by Watson and Skinner.

Even so, he wondered if some of the old tales from the Victorian seance rooms might have had some truth in them after all. He knew that the great Faraday was supposed to have debunked table-tipping (in 1853) by explaining that it was all due to 'unconscious muscular activity' (UMA) of the sitters' hands, and he did not expect anything dramatic to happen. 'I expected that the table might tip about,' he recalls today, 'but no more than that.'

I should mention in passing that Faraday never witnessed any table levitations or movements without contact and made no attempt to explain these. All he showed was that the *loose top* of a table could be made to wobble around by UMA. The sceptics seem to have forgotten this.

Nothing happened at Batcheldor's first table-tipping session in 1964, apart from some faint vibration of the table, which he reckoned could easily be ascribed to UMA. Perhaps Faraday was right after all? They all decided to try again a few evenings later, but once again the table refused to leave the floor, although there was one baffling incident during the evening.

Bill Chick placed a large African drum on the table and said, half jokingly, 'Will the spirits beat the drum?' There was a lengthy pause, during which the wind outside seemed to get louder, and Bill said he felt that 'something' had entered the room. They waited for something to happen, becoming rather sleepy, then suddenly there was a powerful BANG from the drum, which seemed to give a small jump.

Bill, who appeared to have fallen asleep, gave a start. 'What was that?' he asked. Batcheldor is still not sure what it was, though he felt at the time that Bill might have accidentally knocked his side of the table as he awoke. It was certainly not the kind of noise he had often heard in the house when the temperature dropped in the evening.

Whatever it was, it was not repeated, and three further sessions were uneventful. Batcheldor felt, however, that he had to give the phenomena time to appear (if there were any) and he persuaded his friends to have another try. During the sixth meeting, the table began to slide around on the floor and tilt up on two legs.

'It felt very curious,' Batcheldor says, 'and we decided to go on with it.' Especially curious was the way the table seemed to resist being pushed back to the floor after a tilt. It was 'like holding an umbrella against the wind'. Batcheldor began to have his doubts about Faraday's UMA theory as the tippings and slidings continued in four more sessions.

Then came the eleventh, during which for the first time the group found itself sitting at the table in total darkness. Previously there had always been some light from a candle, twilight coming through the curtains, or the open fire. Now, the fire had died down, and there was no light at all. Batcheldor will never forget what happened next.

'The room became very dark, and I said "It would be great if this table floated right up off the floor" – and thereupon it did! It rose up several inches, swung from side to side like a pendulum, and settled

down again. We immediately stopped and had an animated discussion for the rest of the evening. We said "My God, there's
something in those Victorian tales after all".'

They might not have seen the table go up, but they had all
definitely felt it rise under their hands, and they were all fully
satisfied that none of the group was deceiving the others with a little
conscious knee or toe activity. They all signed written statements to
this effect, and they all agreed that they had passed the point of no
return. There was something in it after all.

By the end of 1965, Batcheldor had held his two hundredth
session. Nine different tables had vibrated, slid, tilted, overturned
and levitated on numerous occasions. Three of them had been
smashed to bits in the process. Raps of all kinds had sounded not
only from the tables but also from chairs, floorboards and even walls.
Cold-air effects easily distinguishable from normal draughts had
been felt. Chairs had been pulled back sharply, on one occasion
dumping the startled occupant on the floor. The table had been
heard and seen to move without physical contact, even when everybody was standing up and holding hands, or seated and touching
each other's hands and feet. Although the table itself could not be
seen in total darkness, its movement could be witnessed thanks to the
luminous markers usually stuck to its corners and centre.

The table had tilted up four times while Pat Coghlan was sitting
squarely in the middle of it, and once the end on which Batcheldor
was sitting rose up underneath him. He found this more impressive
than being tilted forwards, since he weighed more than thirteen
stone. Faraday's UMA hypothesis, he reckoned, was beginning to
wear rather thin.

Although Batcheldor did not know it at the time, his was not the
first modern group to try and repeat the Victorian table-tilting effect.
Haakon Forwald, a Norwegian engineer working for ASEA,
Sweden's leading electrical company, held sixty-one sessions
between 1948 and 1950, full details of which were only published
eight years after his death, in 1984. His sessions were held in the
light, and he was able to observe his fellow sitters, most of whom
were also engineers, very carefully. Many of the phenomena he
described were identical to those observed independently by Batcheldor, such as the 'umbrella against the wind' effect, which he
described as 'an elastic counterforce'. He also noted that his table
sometimes seemed to be 'held in a firm grip by some kind of guiding
mechanism'.

Forwald continued to study PK, but using dice instead of tables on the suggestion of J. B. Rhine, with whom he collaborated for much of the rest of his life. He made the interesting observation that he found his talent for mental imagery as useful in his PK work as in his profession (he held more than five hundred patents).[6]

In September 1966, the Society for Psychical Research published Batcheldor's eighteen-page 'Report on a case of table levitation and associated phenomena' in its journal. It was a cautious and factual account that omitted any theorising and urged readers 'to suspend disbelief long enough to attempt sustained experimentation for themselves'.

At least one other group had apparently begun to do this independently at about the same time as Batcheldor and his friends. In the March 1967 issue of the SPR's journal, a lady described her own brief series of experiments, which had begun after a dinner party. The eight guests, 'of the type not to be easily convinced', included a company chairman, assorted businessmen and their wives.

In a well-lit London dining-room, they put their hands on the table, which soon began to creak and slide, finally rising completely from the floor. The hostess was certain that her heavy oak table remained in mid-air for several seconds, as she could see a light patch of floor under each leg. She noted that it went on creaking during its levitation, so much so that she was afraid it would fall apart. Her reaction was a delightfully practical one, however disappointing to psychical researchers:

'Requiring it for lunch the next day,' she reported, 'I got down underneath the table and pulled it back to the floor.'

As she did so, she noticed that everybody else was standing up, in order to keep their hands on the table top. The legs, she reckoned, were about eight inches off the floor. She added that her table was of the gateleg type, with folding legs, and if lifted normally while extended to its full size, the leg under the leaf that was being lifted would tend to swing inwards and the leaf itself would drop down.

The writer of this brief report stood to gain nothing by it, and only wrote to the SPR on the urging of a neighbour, the writer Rosalind Heywood, who testified that her friend's attitude was that 'if such a story were told to her, she would not believe it, so why should other people believe her?' One wonders how much evidence of this kind goes unreported for similar reasons.

Mrs Heywood did her best to persuade her neighbour to carry on with her table-work, but after one or two further sessions, one of the participants became upset and decided she did not want to continue. So ended what might have developed into an interesting research programme.

Batcheldor and his friends were made of sterner stuff, and they kept at it. They also persuaded several other groups to try and repeat their findings, in the best tradition of conventional science. Several did so, the best known being the group in Toronto, Canada, founded by Professor George Owen, author of the standard work on poltergeist phenomena, and his wife Iris. They invented a 'ghost' named Philip, whom they persuaded to tap out messages and produce a variety of physical effects, including some lively table movement, which have been fully described in a refreshingly sensible popular book.[7] Another successful group was started by Colin Brookes-Smith, a retired instrument engineer who collaborated closely with Batcheldor and published several detailed papers in the SPR journal describing some ingenious techniques for measuring and recording PK. (He died in 1982.)[8]

It is safe to state that nobody has ever put as much time and thought into table-tilting as Batcheldor, although it was only in the late 1970s that it became generally known just how much he had learned about it. Had it not been for a brief article he published in a very obscure scientific journal in 1979, I would not have known that he was still alive.[9]

In 1982, a large conference was held at Cambridge to mark the hundredth anniversary of the Society for Psychical Research together with the silver jubilee of the Parapsychological Association. A whole morning session was devoted to an international discussion of 'the Batcheldor approach'. It was the first time Batcheldor had travelled more than a few miles from his Devonshire home in several years.[10]

Listening to him speaking calmly and confidently about his long experience with the tables, I felt he knew what he was talking about. I was surprised to learn that he had been holding sessions almost without a break ever since 1964, and even more surprised to realise that he had done what all others had failed to do for more than a hundred years: he had worked out a method of producing that most elusive phenomenon of all – PK – virtually on demand, and had a very detailed psychological theory to support it.

What he had been doing all those years, I found, was much what Charles Honorton, Carl Sargent and others had done for telepathy; instead of sitting around and arguing over whether there was such a thing, they had observed the way it happened in real life, noted the conditions that tended to prevail when it happened, and then recreated those conditions as well as they could in their laboratories. The essential difference between their work and Batcheldor's is that PK is infinitely more elusive and complex a phenomenon than telepathy, and Batcheldor has not yet reached the laboratory stage, although experiments based on his theories have been conducted by Dr John Palmer at the University of Utrecht.

After his first successful table levitation back in 1964, Batcheldor had set out to learn all he could about PK, and to build up what must now be one of the largest libraries in the world devoted to it. He soon found that not only was the evidence documented in the most exhaustive detail, but the best of it was consistent. Independent observers would describe identical incidents, many of which he had also witnessed in his own home, as I was also to do. A glance at some of the titles on his shelves gives an idea why much of the early evidence remains largely unread today. What scientist would even touch books called *Thirty Years of Psychical Research*, *On Miracles and Modern Spiritualism*, or *After Death, What?*, titles surely not worthy of their respective authors Charles Richet, Wallace, and Cesare Lombroso?

The first thing I wanted to know when I went to see Batcheldor in 1983 was why, if there was so much evidence that people could levitate tables by PK, was this not generally accepted as a fact of life? He had a ready and fluent answer, as if he had been waiting for the question:

'There's an awkward antagonism between the scientific, sceptical state of mind, and the state required for the production of PK,' he told me. 'To achieve a PK effect, you have got to believe one hundred per cent that it's going to happen, whereas the characteristic attitude of the scientist is to doubt, and to say "Let's test this thing and see if it really is what it claims to be". But for PK, you must not think "Is it?". You have to think "*It is*". You've got to suspend your scientific attitude if you want it to occur. You can be as critical as you like after you've got it, but not while you're doing it.'

This was not easy for scientists to accept, he admitted, but it was the approach he had found to work, and to make sense. 'If the phenomena are shaped by thought,' he said, 'then doubtful thoughts will obviously create only doubtful phenomena, or maybe none at all.' I was reminded immediately of the passage from the book on medical hypnotism that I quoted in an earlier chapter, in which doctors are told that there must be 'no doubt in the hypnotist's voice (or mind) that the improvement suggested will be achieved'. If the elimination of all doubt from the mind as well as the voice is accepted as an essential part of a medical technique, we have a good precedent for accepting it in another area of research.

Table-tilting may be a frivolous activity, but the study of the factors that make it possible most certainly is not. Faith, we are assured, can move mountains. It can also save lives by reversing the course of 'incurable diseases', and for millennia it has transformed individual quality of life, as it continues to do. Now it seems it can also move tables. Therefore, if we manage to identify ways of achieving enough faith to move a table, we will have learned more about ways to save lives. Faith, after all, is faith – whatever it is applied to. So I asked Batcheldor how we can acquire faith if we have not already got it. There cannot be many people who can sit at a table and not have some doubts as to whether it will leave the ground or not.

'It is almost impossible to acquire sufficient faith by deliberate mental effort,' he replied. 'For instance, it would be useless to place your hands on a table and say to yourself "I believe this table is going to levitate". However hard you tried, you wouldn't succeed because you'd be bound to experience an element of doubt. An adept might succeed, but most people aren't adepts.

'Fortunately,' he went on, 'there's something about table-tipping that enables a group of ordinary people to succeed in generating PK without even trying, provided they are reasonably open-minded. It is this: in most cases, the table will start to move due to UMA. This can give an amazing illusion that the table is moving of its own accord – as if animated by some mysterious force. You get the impression you are already succeeding in generating paranormal movements.

'This has precisely the same impact on you as real success would have. It sweeps your doubts aside and produces total faith – or at least moments of total faith. This happens automatically, involuntarily and without any mental effort on your part. So you get moments of total faith in which you are able to generate real PK. For a while, these are superimposed on the UMA movements, but later they can occur without them. The table movements gradually become stronger and more varied, and in time may lead to movement without contact and levitation.'

This ingenious process of stimulating faith by illusion and immediately reinforcing it is the basis of the principle that Batcheldor calls 'induction by artifact'. He summarised it for me like this:

'All you need is for some set of normal events – artifacts – to be mistaken for paranormal events. This creates sufficiently intense faith to enable you to generate the real thing. Such artifacts can be either accidental or deliberate. In table-tipping, for instance, movements due to UMA arise quite accidentally. But if somebody gives the table a deliberate push, and keeps quiet about it, this will probably have the same effect.'

'You mean that cheating can lead to real PK?' I asked. I felt he was adding yet another boobytrap to an already overcrowded minefield.

'Well,' he replied, 'deliberate artifact-induction is equivalent to cheating, yes. But the development of PK in a group can and should take place entirely on a basis of artifacts of the accidental kind. Cheating would only lead to confusion even if – theoretically – it should work. And of course shamans have known for centuries that it *does* work.'

If Loren Parks is right, the Philippine psychic surgeons still know this and still do it, and it still works. It certainly has led to confusion in their case.

Batcheldor's artifact-induction theory can be applied to many things other than table-tipping, from hypnosis and faith healing to spoon bending and perhaps even poltergeists. It could certainly explain some of the problems that can arise after playing with Ouija boards. As many children and quite a few adults now know, you can start by putting your fingers on an upturned glass, watch in surprise as it moves from letter to letter and begins to spell out intelligent messages, and then find things getting out of control.

'As soon as it spells something a bit strange, you get frightened, and then you're in trouble,' Batcheldor explained. 'The main danger of dabbling with psychic forces is that if you get frightened of them, you shape them into some frightening event – you create what you're frightened of. If you know this, and exercise some control over not getting unduly frightened, by constantly reminding yourself that you're creating this stuff by PK, and it's going to do what you believe, you can keep things under control. I don't allow my sitters to talk about apparitions of the devil or anything like that. We don't know what we might create if we start thinking along those lines.'

As for poltergeist cases, he believes that in some cases the incidents that start them off can be seen as artifacts that arise accidentally. 'I don't go along with the idea that poltergeist outbreaks are the expression of repressed tension and aggression. Mental hospitals are full of people who have tremendous repressed aggression, but they don't explode into poltergeist phenomena. It's a bit naïve to think that aggression gets so strong when it's repressed that it bursts out by throwing cups by PK. I prefer to think that if you have a tense family that interprets an accidental event – like a cup falling off a shelf by accident – as ghostly, then they can use it for the expression of some of their psychological needs. If you *believe* there's going to be hostility, then you probably create it.'

Again we come back to the question of belief and faith, and how to acquire them. Batcheldor has identified another very simple method of acquiring faith in the possibility of PK, and this is to see others do it and promptly imitate them.

Numerous children all over the world have found themselves bending spoons immediately after seeing Uri Geller doing it on television. It is of no importance at all whether Geller is doing it by PK or by sleight-of-hand, as some prefer to believe. What matters is that viewers assume he is doing it by mind-power, and when he tells them they can do the same – right now – they believe him. Instant faith. Children have much less 'ownership resistance', as Batcheldor calls the reluctance to admit that you can do PK yourself. Hence the hordes of 'mini-Gellers' that make news in any country that Geller visits. When he tells them they can bend spoons like him, they do.

Quite a few of these mini-Gellers have found that once they have done this, they learn that it is supposed to be impossible and then find that they cannot do it again. They could do it when they had total faith, plus an instantly implanted 'map-thought' – Batcheldor's term for a visualisation of the task you are trying to achieve – but having lost their faith they resorted to cheating, much to the satisfaction of the left-minded scientists who arrive on the scene too late, after the magic moment has gone, and catch them at it.

The question of fraud and trickery has become such an obsession with some critics of psychic phenomena, and a good many parapsychologists as well, that we might recall the words of the American psychologist William James, himself an experienced psychical researcher: 'If we look at imposture as a historic phenomenon, we find it always imitative. One swindler imitates a previous swindler, but the first swindler of that kind imitated someone who was honest.'[11]

This also applies to people who try to imitate themselves. In 1983 I interviewed a Danish girl named Ayoe, whose mother assured me very convincingly that a fork had bent almost double in her ten-year-old daughter's hand as she held it by the tip and stroked it lightly with one finger after seeing Geller on television. She had never been able to do it again, and was unable to do it for me despite encouragement from her mother. 'It's different now,' she said. It seemed she was unconsciously trying to imitate something with normal force that she knew she had already done without it.

It is quite possible that induction by artifact was responsible for Wallace's success at table-levitation. He describes how the medium Mrs Marshall got her table in the air for his benefit, and from his description of this and several other phenomena, it is quite possible that Mrs Marshall was a genuine PK medium, at least in 1865. Even so, Wallace would have got the same results at home if he had been deceived. Table-lifting is easy to fake. All you need is two accomplices with wooden rulers under their sleeves, which are slid under the table-top to serve as hooks, so that when the hands are lifted, up comes the table. I have done this myself with great effect, though with only one person you can only lift one side of the table. The first time I did this at a party, the effect on my friends was so dramatic that I was tempted to go into business as a fraudulent medium. (I also produced 'messages' by clicking my thumbnails together, one of the many tricks first described by Allan Kardec.) Trickery certainly can induce instant faith.

This is one of many of Batcheldor's theories that were tested independently and fully confirmed by Colin Brookes-Smith, whose technical ingenuity proved an invaluable complement to Batcheldor's psychological insights. Brookes-Smith designed and built a number of special tables (which Batcheldor himself was actually the first to do), wired up in such a way that any normal mechanical force exerted by sitters' hands could be recorded and printed out on chart paper. He then had his sitters draw lots before a session to see who would be 'joker'. The joker was allowed to cheat now and then, and a study of the recording would later reveal exactly when he had. The Rev. Allan Barham, a Church of England clergyman and a very level-headed psychical researcher who had eighty sittings in his own home with Brookes-Smith and three others, reports:

'The interesting thing was that this method of deliberately stimulating an upward force did help to induce a genuine paranormal effect.' The chart recording, he said, showed when the joker had done his joking, and it also showed the table continue to levitate after he had stopped it. 'Our unjustified belief that something paranormal might be taking place released the PK force, which always tended to be repressed by our conscious or unconscious doubts.'[12] Batcheldor's discovery that the paranormal can develop from the normal is an important one, and has many potential implications for the hypnotic process and for healing in general.

Batcheldor reckons that almost anybody can produce PK who really believes and decides that it is possible. Anybody can also inhibit it by believing consciously or subconsciously that it is not possible. This point was made back in 1855 by Robert Hare, the first major scientist to make a serious study of the phenomena of the early Spiritualist movement in the US.[13] He found that even some professed believers in psychic phenomena become very uneasy when faced with the prospect of actually witnessing them and being unable to rationalise them out of existence. Batcheldor recalls an example of such 'witness inhibition', as he calls it, when he held a special session for a visiting committee from the Society for Psychical Research.

'They sat silently watching us,' he told me with some amusement, 'and for most of the time the table refused to budge.' It was one of the least productive sittings he has ever had.

To observe PK, it seems, you have to participate in it, and this obviously makes verification very difficult. The setting up of any kind of control test immediately alters your attitude. You cannot help thinking 'Will it work now?', but not being quite sure, thus losing the necessary total faith. Batcheldor has made numerous attempts to videotape a levitating table, using an infra-red camera and invisible infra-red lighting, but has not yet succeeded conclusively, although some of his sequences are very interesting. One shows the table apparently balanced on two legs while one of the sitters stands up and tries to force it down, leaning on it as hard as he can. Another shows the table rising two or three feet from the floor and floating across the room with only one sitter touching it, but unfortunately it cannot be seen exactly where his hands are.

During one very lively session, I fired off a whole film of still photos, using a flash, in quick succession. While I was doing so, Batcheldor and the other sitter repeatedly assured me the table was rising under their hands, but a fraction of a second before I pressed the shutter, down it would come with a crash, and while some of my photos show the table at unusual angles, none of them caught it in mid-air.

Audio tape, however, has no inhibiting effect at all. This has reinforced Batcheldor's belief that it is not light that inhibits PK, but sight, or the full awareness of the observer. Poltergeist effects frequently take place in light, but usually outside the observer's field of vision. This is one reason why he prefers to work in total darkness.

'In darkness,' he told me, 'the mind can be calm, because you are not witnessing paranormality in a clear-cut form. Also, certain kinds of spontaneous artifacts needed to stimulate belief tend to be prevented in light.' He believes that at some deep level we need a 'loophole' in the evidence, to reassure ourselves that PK might not be taking place after all. An audio tape provides such a loophole, because it only contains part of the record – the sound. A videotape contains a more complete record, and while seeing may be believing, hearing without seeing is not.

'PK seems to cover its tracks whenever it can,' he added, 'even to the extent of sabotaging cameras or video recorders to destroy the evidence, or of making sure that there is a scapegoat on hand to whom apparently paranormal activity can be attributed.'

Anybody who has tried to investigate a poltergeist case will know only too well what he means. You think you have at last got a photo or film sequence that proves you saw what you are trying to persuade others you saw, only to find that it does not. Graham Morris's heroic efforts to record PK on camera during the Enfield case only stirred up endless argument as to whether he had photographed anything more than two girls playing tricks. I believe he did, with his motor-driven sequence showing a curtain twisting into a tight spiral and moving away from a window I knew to be closed, but others have remained unimpressed.

Not surprisingly, critics have complained that the apparent impossibility of catching PK on camera means that there is no PK to catch. They will probably go on feeling this way until they realise that there is now a detailed psychological theory to explain why this elusiveness factor operates in the way it does.

I have given only the barest outline of some features of this theory here. Batcheldor's original 1968 paper runs to 115 pages of manuscript and has yet to be published, although it has been widely circulated among professional parapsychologists and received a good deal of favourable comment. PK is no longer a series of bewildering facts awaiting a theory. It has a theory, which now awaits testing.

# 10

# Turning the Tables

On 20 May 1983 I had a wisdom tooth out. It was an unusually tough one, my dentist said, and although I normally have fillings done without injections, I have not yet had the courage to follow Ainslie Meares's example and have a tooth out without anaesthetic. On this occasion, so much of the stuff was pumped into my jaw that the following evening, when I sat down for the first time at Batcheldor's table, I was still feeling slightly dazed.

A few hours later, I was feeling considerably more dazed. By then, I had witnessed more PK activity in a single session than I had in ten years of investigating poltergeist cases, as described in three earlier books. Many will find the following account hard to believe, as I still do myself. However, all dialogue quoted below comes unaltered from my audio tape, which also recorded all the noises mentioned. As Sir William Crookes once remarked in a similar context, I am not saying all this is possible. I am saying it is true.

There were four of us. Batcheldor sat on my right, the veteran Bill Chick opposite me, and on my left was a relative newcomer to the group, an industrial radiographer named Brian Cosway, who lived just down the road. All three of them struck me as the most normal people imaginable, and the atmosphere was one of a social evening rather than a scientific experiment.

The small table began to move vigorously almost as soon as we put our hands on it. It rocked from side to side on its thin legs, and soon began to vibrate strongly. As Wallace had reported, I could feel it up to my elbows. Unconscious muscular activity? Possibly, I thought at the time, although my own hands were resting lightly on the table top. Perhaps the others were doing a little joking, or artifact-induction, for my benefit? (All of them later emphatically denied this. As Batcheldor said, 'We don't need it.')

The table next began to tilt from side to side with even greater force. Then I felt it slide swiftly to my right.

'Oh, it's pressing into me,' said Batcheldor. 'I can't push it back.'

I tried to pull it towards its original position, but it was absolutely stuck. It was like tugging at a mule that had decided to sit down. Then it suddenly gave a jump, went up at an angle on two legs, and stayed there.

'You can stand up and lean on it if you like,' said Batcheldor.

I did, and felt the same resistance. It was indeed, as Wallace had put it, as if the table were 'resting on the back of some animal'. Then again it suddenly gave way, but instead of returning to its normal position it began to lurch around in all directions, pounding the floor like a mad bull about to charge. It soon became a question not of keeping my hands on the table, but of holding them in front of me in self-defence.

Despite the total darkness, I found a certain amount of observation was possible. From the casual conversation that went on all the time I had a good idea of where the others were. Occasional quick sweeps with my arms or legs satisfied me that no other limb was where it should not have been, and at least one object could be seen directly: the small radioactive luminous marker stuck in the centre of the table. This frequently disappeared from my sight as I felt the table tilting away from me.

Batcheldor suggested we all take our hands off, whereupon the table immediately crashed over on one side as if it had been picked up and flung down. The suddenness and violence of this reminded me, rather uncomfortably, of similar incidents tape-recorded at Enfield during the poltergeist case that Maurice Grosse and I had investigated in 1977 and 1978.

We managed to get it upright again, whereupon the marker disappeared altogether and there was a brief silence.

'It's right up, head · high!' Batcheldor exclaimed. I groped around and found a table leg, the bottom of which was a good two feet from the floor. This seemed to be an example of a normal movement developing into a paranormal one. We had lifted the table to get it upright and it had gone on lifting itself.

At this stage I was making no attempt to look for normal explanations, but just letting things happen. Then came an incident that seemed to have no possible normal explanation. Once again the table lurched to my right and resisted my efforts to bring it back to its original position. So I stood up and tried to pick it up. Then I felt a most extraordinary sensation.

'It's like a magnetic field,' I said. If you try to push the two equal poles of two magnets together, you will find that they seem to bounce off the space of air between them as their fields repel each other. This is precisely what I felt. The table was literally bouncing on air under my hands, and I was satisfied that nobody else was touching it.

This incident, though a minor one compared with what was to come, took on a new significance for me some weeks later, when for the first time I read an account of the series of sessions with Eusapia Palladino held in Paris from 1905 to 1908. One of her investigators, Arsène d'Arsonval, was a pioneer of the study of biological effects of electromagnetism and knew a lot more about magnetic fields than I do. He reported precisely what I had experienced in almost the same words: 'It is just like the resistance of a magnetic field.' He also described trying to move a piece of furniture and finding, as I had done, that 'one would think it nailed to the ground'. Investigators come and go; the phenomena remain the same.[1]

Our table's next trick was to flip right over, with none of us touching it as far as we knew, and start to slide around upside down. Just before this, Batcheldor had fetched a luminous plastic cup and placed it on the table in the hope that we would see it move. It gave off enough light to make any hand in contact with it clearly visible.

As the table went over, the cup fell and rolled towards me on the floor, so I picked it up and put it over one of the upturned legs. I had just taken my hand away when there was a loud plop as the cup shot into the air, rising at least three feet and falling away from me. That, I decided, was not my UMA, and not anybody else's either. As I confirmed later, it was easy to spot a hand or foot that came within six inches of the cup.

Next, Batcheldor placed a luminous plaque six inches square beside the small marker. This was an example of the technique, which he considers essential, of gradually improving the controls only after the action has begun. In the past, he told me, various odd-looking shapes had been seen to pass over this plaque, and as with the cup, no human hand could get within reach of it without being seen. So if the plaque moved at all, or if a shadow passed over it, well ...

It moved. It flapped up and down within a couple of feet of my eyes, making a fluttering sound like that of a moth trapped inside a lampshade. I could not resist the impulse to do some cautious research of my own. If anybody was touching that plaque, I was going to touch them. (It did not occur to me at the time that nobody could have touched it without a hand being seen.) I quickly passed my hands around the surface of the table, and sure enough my left hand collided with what felt very much like human flesh.

'What was that?' I said at once. 'Some piece of human flesh that has disappeared.'

'Human flesh?' Brian repeated. His voice seemed too far away from his hand to have been where I had felt that – whatever it was.

'You'll find you'll run into lumps of the stuff,' Batcheldor remarked casually, as if floating blobs of ectoplasm were quite normal. 'Don't mistake them for human hands.'

'It wasn't my hand,' said Brian, 'because my hands are on my knees, here.' He slapped his knees.

This incident was typical of the kind that makes verification of PK so difficult. I can only say that none of us could find a normal explanation for it, nor could we repeat the fluttering sound the plaque had made without picking it up and shaking it with an easily visible hand.

We stopped for a break, and Batcheldor decided to change tables. The new one was a circular monster four feet in diameter, weighing 46 pounds. It had a wooden top about an inch thick, and stout metal legs that slanted outwards, making it extremely difficult to tilt naturally. Lifting even one side of it required some effort, and I found I was unable to lift it more than an inch off the floor. 'We're not going to get that off the ground,' I said.

Just as the smaller table had done, it began to vibrate a few minutes after the light had been switched off and we had sat with our hands on its top. Then it gave an abrupt slide along the carpet and began to tilt up and down with quite alarming force. My hands were resting lightly on its edge in self-defence. I did not want it crashing into my ribs – which in fact it later did, quite painfully.

'Let's have some raps,' said Batcheldor, as calmly as if he were ordering a round of drinks in the local pub. He knocked with his knuckles on the table top, saying 'This is me' as he did so, for the benefit of the tape-recording. The reply came at once; first, a loud thud as the table did a rapid single tilt, then two taps that sounded like a replay of Batcheldor's, and finally a remarkable succession of noises of all kinds. They seemed to come from all over the place – a kind of scratching noise from the table, assorted raps and thuds from the floor, and one or two unidentifiable sounds from the far corners of the room. Then the table began to vibrate again, this time so strongly that the noise can be heard on the tape-recording.

I asked if I could sit on the table. Batcheldor told me to go ahead, and I sat well back from the edge, with both my feet off the floor. The vibration continued.

'It's like sitting on a conveyor belt,' I said, though this is not quite what I meant. It was more like having a vibro-massage, and I found it quite enjoyable. Then the table began to slide around and tilt up on two legs with me still sitting on it. That was less enjoyable. I climbed off and returned to my chair. The table was still wobbling when I put my hands back on it.

'Those are levitations, aren't they?' said Batcheldor. 'It's off the floor, yes, it's coming right off. Don't you agree?' I could not be sure.

Then, with a thunderous crash, the table flung itself over on its side. If my foot had been in the wrong place, it would have been turned to strawberry jam. I decided to get out of the way for a while, and went to sit on the sofa, holding my chair in front of me like a shield. Bill Chick had the same idea, while Brian turned his chair round and sat astride it. A few moments later, after some miscellaneous knocks and bangs, the table gave a violent jump.

Batcheldor was ready for that one. He had his small pocket torch in his hand and switched it on briefly, just long enough for all of us to see that none of us had a hand or a foot within reach of the table. It was a skilful demonstration of Batcheldor's methods of verifying the phenomena discreetly and unexpectedly. It was the first time he had used his torch that evening, and it came on almost at the moment the table hit the floor, to reveal Bill, Brian and me behind our chairs, with Batcheldor himself holding his torch. So who picked up the table?

Things quietened down after this episode, and I came back to my chair and leaned over the table to listen to what sounded like some very faint taps coming from it. Then I was given a demonstration of one of the standard phenomena of the PK repertoire, one that I had never experienced although I had read and heard innumerable accounts of it.

'Oh!' I exclaimed. 'Cool breeze. Thank you!' There was no mistaking it for any kind of normal draught. But breeze is not the right word for it. It was more like a patch of frozen air drifting past my face and brushing against it, quite slowly. Later, I felt it again, this time on the back of my hand.

The next item on the evening's entertainment was another example of a movement evolving from the normal to the not so normal. When the table slid away from me, I reached out, grabbed a leg and pulled it back. I expected some resistance, but the table slid towards me as if on wheels – and went on moving after I had removed my hand, swerving away to one side as if trying to avoid bumping into me.

The knockings and scratchings were still going on, and the others were talking quite loudly and obscuring them, so I leaned forward and put my ear on the table. I then heard a most weird succession of sounds, now considerably amplified. They sounded purposeful, as if somebody was chopping up carrots or doing a spot of carpentry. It was like eavesdropping on another world. For all I know, I was.

I could understand why our Victorian predecessors had decided that this sort of thing was the work of the spirits. The impression was definitely one of an intelligence at work, and an intelligence not governed by our conscious minds. This is the impression I have always had on poltergeist cases, and it has led me to believe that PK can operate like an independent entity. The question of what relation such entities have to fragments of dissociated personalities or what are called 'exteriorisations of co-consciousness' is a much debated one, but I will not discuss it here. I felt that Batcheldor was right to concentrate on observing the way PK behaved in the real world, rather than look for possible causes in some other sphere. According to his reasoning, if we had assumed there were spirits present, we would have been given evidence that reinforced our assumption. He preferred not to assume anything and just see what developed naturally.

What did develop next was a sequence of events I would not believe possible if it had not been clearly recorded on tape. I would not have forgotten it, but it seemed so unreal at the time that I could never be sure today that I had not been dreaming. However, I was certainly not dreaming. This is what happened:

'We haven't had this table in the air yet, have we?' I asked.

None of the others seemed to think this was possible, but the table responded to my challenge at once, and began sliding around as if tensing its muscles for the high jump. Batcheldor told us all to join hands, which we did, the table continuing to slide around under them, an interesting enough effect in itself.

'Take off, table,' Batcheldor ordered, somewhat half-heartedly.

'You must be joking!' said Bill.

'I'd like to see it in mid air,' I insisted. I felt it was time to force the pace and build up some group-expectation dynamics.

The table-top began to vibrate loudly at a rate of about ten beats a second, with our hands still touching. Then the rate slowed, but the beats became louder and louder until the table was rocking back and forth on its legs at a speed that was impressive for an object of that size. There was no way this could be ascribed to UMA, I decided. This was the real stuff, and it was building up to a climax, like the last movement of a symphony

'Now come on, up, once,' I said firmly.

'Right. One levitation for Guy Playfair, please,' Batcheldor added, now sounding more determined.

The vibration and tilting increased.

'Come on,' I said. 'Up in the air.'

'Up! Up! Up!' Batcheldor echoed. It was an order, not a request. All four of us began to cheer and shout like football supporters whose hero has the ball in front of an open goal. The pounding of the table legs on the floor became louder still. Then it suddenly stopped altogether as we felt a sudden surge of pressure under our hands.

Goal!

It was at least a foot off the floor, and it stayed there for about five seconds before falling back with a tremendous thud. 'Thank you,' I said. 'That was all right.'

The reaction of the others, including Batcheldor, was one of astonishment. It was, he said, the first time this table had been completely off the floor. I was delighted that my spontaneous experiment in group dynamics generation had worked, but frustrated at having no better evidence than an audio tape-recording. Could I ever convince anybody else that a 46-pound table had levitated? How could I prove that two of the others had not lifted it in the dark after some prearranged hand-substitution?

There seemed to be only one answer. Even after its impressive levitation, the table was evidently still not through for the night. It went on vibrating and wobbling like a dog waiting to be taken for a walk. I decided that there was only one way we could get it to do something we could not conceivably do by any normal means. We would all sit on it, back to back.

'Oh no, we haven't tried that,' said Batcheldor. 'That's a classic experiment.' We both knew that Gasparin and one or two other investigators had done something similar in the early days, but we knew of no such experiment in this century.[2]

I climbed on first and sat well back, my knees just over the edge and my feet well off the floor. I was promptly given another brief paranormal vibro-massage, and then the table gave a sharp lurch as if trying to twist round in a circle.

'Oh my God!' Batcheldor exclaimed. 'Let's add you on, Bill.'

Bill Chick climbed on behind me, and we sat with our backs touching. At once, there was another slide followed by a sharp tilt. Bill said he was going to get off again, and before I had time to ask him why, a series of knocks sounded from right underneath my bottom and the table began to do some more of its circular twists, with me still firmly planted in the middle of it.

'Get ready to get back on,' said Batcheldor. 'Perhaps we could sort of get on while it's moving.'

'Oh, I see,' said Bill. 'Like running for a bus, you mean?' This was a typical example of the detached amusement he showed towards the whole proceedings, in contrast to Brian's curiosity and excitement, and they both helped keep up the atmosphere of light-hearted relaxation that Batcheldor insists is an ideal one for PK production. For me, it was a welcome contrast to the deadly seriousness of a Spiritualist seance I had attended not long before, at which the sole phenomenon was the movement of a luminous trumpet, which had moved, as promised, shortly after a creaking noise had told me that the 'entranced' medium had got up and picked the thing up. (The medium also trod on my foot.)

'There it goes!' I cried. The table had tilted up behind me, as if trying to tip me off. As it did so, I felt Bill's back pressing against mine. He had caught the bus and climbed on without my knowing. By this time – it was nearly four in the morning – dawn had begun to break, and Batcheldor said he could clearly see Bill's silhouette as he rose into the air, outlined against the window facing him.

The table found its way back to the floor, and there was another long slide. 'It's moving round,' I said. 'I'm being twisted round, clockwise. I'll be passing Brian soon. It's shaking and wobbling. Come on, let's go round in circles! Yes, it's going round again.'

Batcheldor then clambered aboard, but even the addition of his 221-pound frame did not stop the sliding and tilting. 'Come on it, quick!' he called to Brian, the last passenger – or so he thought – to run for the bus.

But Brian had already caught it. I clearly identified one back against my own – Bill's – and two more backs against each of my elbows. Right, I said to myself, if the bus even moves now with all four of us on it, this is all the proof I need for tonight.

It moved. It very definitely moved. It did not leave the ground, as I had hoped it would, but it twisted and slid as before, in a series of brief but powerful motions that ended only when this unbelievable PK-driven passenger vehicle crashed into my chair, forcing it against the sofa, which had its back to the wall. Before it had come to rest, I managed to bang my feet together and call out for the others to do the same, and I then slid forward until my feet touched the floor and tried to get the table to move normally, by grasping the edge with both hands and forcing my feet against the floor. No harm in a little artifact-induction at this stage, I reckoned. The table would not move an inch.

'They'll never believe this back home,' I said. (They didn't.)

'Well,' said Batcheldor, 'we've proved that one pretty well.'

We had indeed. We worked out that our combined weights plus that of the table came to around 760 pounds. That is roughly the weight of seventeen airline suitcases packed to the 20-kilo weight limit.

Any force that can move a weight of this order cannot be considered trivial, and perhaps it was just as well that the session came to an end soon after our table-borne journey. For all I knew, if PK could move more than a third of a ton, it could have knocked the house down.

Coming face to face with the impossible raises a problem: do you accept the evidence of your senses or do you reject it? The natural course is to reject it if you cannot explain it, and 'explain', in science, means to provide a full description of the whole cause-and-effect process that resulted in what you are saying you observed, and to provide enough information to enable anybody else to repeat your findings.

Charles Richet once wrote an essay on 'the conditions of certainty' in which he described his own experiences of witnessing numerous phenomena that he considered genuine at the time, including several table levitations in his own home, only to find himself later losing confidence in his own powers of observation. 'I saw,' he said, 'but did I see aright?'[3]

Hereward Carrington, who probably spent more time with Eusapia Palladino than any other investigator, has described how he and his colleagues would 'lapse back into scepticism' the morning after a session with her, even when they had been fully satisfied at the time that PK was taking place. 'The incidents seemed to roll off our minds,' he wrote in a report of a series of sessions at which forty-seven table levitations and more than four hundred other miscellaneous phenomena were observed, some under conditions they considered to be ideal.[4]

I saw an unidentified flying object in December 1974. It came tearing over my house in Rio de Janeiro and alarmed quite a few of my neighbours as well as me. It was identified within minutes on the radio as a Soviet satellite, which had left its orbit and returned to earth prematurely. Orbiting satellites were quite a novelty in those days, and we could be forgiven for mistaking one thing for another.

But you cannot mistake a solid table on which you are sitting for anything else, especially when you have three witnesses also sitting on it and describing what is happening, with all the action being recorded on tape. That is one incident that did not roll off my mind, and unlike my encounter with the Soviet IFO (identified flying object), it has yet to be explained.

In July 1983 I was able to attend a second session with the Batcheldor group. This was less dramatic than the first, but equally convincing. In between my two sessions, I had attended the 5th International Conference on Psychotronic Research, a biennial event held since 1973, when an east–west research association was started jointly by psychologists Dr Zdenek Rejdák of Czechoslovakia and Dr Stanley Krippner of the USA. The word 'psychotronics' was chosen as being acceptable to all ideologies, meaning the science and technology of mind in action, on the lines of electronics – the study and application of electrons in action.

The handsome new headquarters of the Trades Union Congress in Bratislava, Czechoslovakia, was an unusual location for a lecture on table-tilting, but there was one given there and the speaker was me, fresh from my experiences described above. I outlined the early research I mentioned in the previous chapter, and went out of my way to emphasise that I was concerned with the phenomena associated with the early Spiritualist movement and not the explanations for them. I ended with these words:

> The moving of tables, like the bending of spoons, is not a very useful social activity. Yet it is a simple and effective method of training ordinary people in the generation of psychotronic effects, like the practice of scales by the music student. We can reasonably disagree today with the beliefs of the mesmerists, the Spiritualists and the early table-movers (some of them, anyway), but we should

not reject their methods, because there is good evidence that they were successful. A closer study of both the formal and informal research of the nineteenth century will be of great value to the science of both this century and the next.[5]

After my talk, I was besieged by delegates from at least four East European countries wanting to know more. Like most of the people at the conference, they were professionally qualified engineers, doctors and psychologists and one of them had managed to visit Batcheldor and attend a session himself. On this occasion, as Batcheldor later confirmed, the table had shot up in the air and right over the heads of the sitters, landing on the video recorder and giving it a sizeable dent.

Later that evening, my colleagues persuaded our hotel manager to find us a small room for 'a scientific meeting', at which I was rather embarrassed to find that I was to take the chair and show them how to get the table going. I explained that this was not possible for several reasons: the only available table was far too heavy, the room was too light and there were too many of us. I might have added that one or two were highly sceptical, and preoccupied with immediate tight control conditions. Also, I said, we would not start to move the table until we had built up group rapport, which might take several sessions.

Anyway, I showed them how to go about it, and we removed the heavy marble slab and sat around the table-frame with our hands on it.

'The physical part is easy,' I said. 'All you need is a table, darkness, and a minimum of two people. The mental part is more complex. You must have total faith in the possibility of generating PK, and a total lack of resistance to the idea of doing this yourself. You must want to do it, and expect that you can. You needn't worry about why you want to do it – anything that exists in nature is worth studying for no other reason than that it exists. And PK does exist, as most of you know very well. But don't take my word for it, and don't listen to the sceptics. Start groups of your own and see for yourselves.'

While I was speaking, a member of the hotel staff opened the door and peered in bewilderment at eight 'scientists' sitting in semi-darkness around a table without a top. I had visions of the immediate arrival of the STB (the Czech KGB) and our detention for what is known over there as 'idealism'. But all went well, and later I learned that groups in three East-bloc countries are already at work, one of them having obtained encouraging results. If the iron curtain is ever to melt, I like to think that a psychotronic effect will have been responsible.

At my second table-tilting session, there were only three of us: Batcheldor, Brian Cosway and me, but the reduction in the number of sitters did not seem to affect the phenomena, many of which were repeated from my first sitting. There was the same cold breeze, or drifting blob of frozen air. The table vibrated as before, and once again I was able to experience the magnetic-field effect as I lifted the table and tried to put it back in its original place. Not having a jaw full of dental anaesthetic on this occasion, I was more alert than previously, and was able to satisfy myself by some rapid foot and arm movements that none of the others was anywhere near the table as it bounced around 'on air' under my hands.

The table had a couple of new tricks to show off for me. One, which I named the Mexican War Dance, involved tilting up on two legs and doing a rapid flip over to the other two while the centre of the table-top stayed in roughly the same position, repeating this at great speed and making a noise like a drum-roll on the floor. Another new stunt reminded me of a dolphin walking on its tail, which I had seen at Brighton. The table went up on one leg and hopped around at the same angle, then balanced itself on two legs with its top at about 45 degrees and began to 'walk' to and fro under our hands.

Even more interesting, however, were the noises. As before, there were regular knocks and thuds from the table in addition to those caused by banging its legs on the floor. Again, with my ear against the surface, I had the impression of eavesdropping on the neighbours. (Batcheldor, I should mention at this point, does not have any neighbours within earshot.) These quieter noises sounded as purposeful as before, and could not possibly be mistaken for settlement creaks caused by temperature changes or rattling water pipes.

We then found that if we beat out a rhythm on the table-top ourselves, it would be played back to us a few seconds later almost identically, though more quietly. Oddly enough, although the table could vibrate audibly and palpably when it felt like it, these knocks caused no vibration at all, unlike the noises we made ourselves. Some were so faint that they were only audible with the ear to the table.

I was reminded of the time I had knocked on the front door of the Enfield poltergeist house and the door had promptly repeated my knocks, although had anybody been behind the door they would have been visible through the glass, and the only person in the house at the time assured me she had been in the kitchen when I knocked.

An even more remarkable example of repetition by PK was given to me personally by Dr Alfred Krantz, a psychiatrist from Pau, France, who is an enthusiastic but very cautious investigator of spontaneous PK phenomena of all kinds. Visiting a poltergeist-infested house in Melun, and hearing raps coming from the wall, he asked the invisible rapper: 'Est-ce que vous m'entendez?' (Can you hear me?). There was a short pause, and then his words were repeated – from the wall.

'It was my voice, with my accent, but at a lower register,' he told me. 'I turned to my colleague and asked if he had spoken. "No," he said, "but I heard it as well." And his hairs were standing on end.'

It is very tempting on such occasions to assume that you are in the presence of the spirits (which, I hasten to add, Dr Krantz has never done). The impression of an independent intelligence at work is very strong, as I said earlier, and it has led me to feel justified in regarding PK-agents as independent entities. Some would call these spirits, and assume that they are driven by the intelligence of somebody who has died.

However, there is excellent evidence against the traditional spirit hypothesis. The Philip group in Toronto certainly conjured up a spirit, but it was one they had invented themselves, complete with portrait and detailed curriculum vitae. Philip had a life of his own, but it was a wholly imaginary one. The fact that this made it no less real in some respects has led some to speculate that reality as we perceive it may to some extent be the result of our imaginations.

As I said earlier, I had the impression, listening to those purpose-ful scrapes, clicks and general clatter coming from our table that I was eavesdropping on somebody doing their domestic chores in another dimension. But the important point is that I did *not* feel that this spiritual somebody was in charge of what was being observed by us – I felt certain that we were, ourselves. Some of the table movements, without doubt, responded to our conscious wishes. At my first session the four of us got the large table in the air by direct order, and on several occasions in both sessions Batcheldor showed it was possible to get immediate response to a direct command. However, he advises beginners not to try this method until they have had results without it; it is more likely to inhibit action than to increase it.

PK tends to behave as if directed from a level of the group mind far beyond any individual's conscious reach. We are still a long way from understanding all the rules for the immediate translation of thought into physical action. I see no prospect at the moment for the dematerialisation of rocket bases by remote-control PK, or for the snarling up of intelligence computers by clairvoyant saboteurs. Such scenarios are still at the science fiction stage, though no longer as impossible in theory as they might seem. However, in this book I am only concerned with what is already happening.

In 1943, J. B. Rhine summed up ten years of work in his laboratory at Duke University on the influencing of dice by PK, and reached some bold conclusions founded on a long series of statistically positive results. He wrote:

> One either has to refuse to accept the PK effect, or else undergo a complete revolution in his mental philosophy. For the PK principle indicates the mind to be a real force, able to go effectively beyond its own physical organism. And, along with ESP [extrasensory perception, or telepathy and clairvoyance] it points to an order of physical causation which by present conceptions is clearly nonphysical, yet one which is capable, as the experimental data show, of really influencing the physical world in a purposively intelligent manner.

Mind is not merely an abstraction, he insisted. It has 'real energy, which does real work, actually influences moving bodies'. It is in fact 'precisely what most people think it is' and always have: a nonphysical component of human beings that exercises 'a causal influence which cannot be otherwise than kinetic'. And all the evidence, both from the laboratory and from real life, showed that PK, like ESP, was not confined by our notions of time or space. Moreover, the two had to be connected. PK was an intelligent force that knew what it was doing, and 'there would have to be an extra-sensory mode of perception to guide the forces that do the work'.[6]

Rhine was not afraid to face the implications of his own discoveries for medicine, psychology and evolution. Writing at a time when there was not much discussion of 'psychosomatic' medicine, he said: 'If a subject can influence the fall of dice by his thinking, he can surely be expected to influence the physiological processes of his tissues, such as the movement of corpuscles and foreign organisms, the functions of healing and growing, and the operation of disease and repair in general.' This claim is fully supported by what little research there has been on possible influences of the mind on physiological processes, of which Stephen Black's inhibition by hypnosis of the 'Mantoux reaction' to tuberculosis infection is a good example.

As for psychology, Rhine felt that a new Copernican revolution of the mind was under way. Copernicus had shown that the centre of the universe was not the earth, but (as far as we were concerned) the sun. The earth was just a planet that obeyed laws dictated from far beyond its frontiers. The ESP/PK hypothesis shifted the centre of the 'personal universe' away from the brain and nervous system and placed it firmly in the mind. It may be 'nervous energy' that directs our muscles, but the nerves are also directed – by thought. And since it takes energy to direct energy, we can assume that there has to be a 'thinking energy'. Dr Howard Miller, as mentioned in chapter 4, made the same point on a basis of his own clinical experience.

Turning to evolution, Rhine pointed out that if 'the mental system of the organism can to some degree dominate the physical world about it, why not suppose that its own bodily processes are within the scope of its influence?'. Wallace, with his speculation that all force might be 'will-force', clearly indicated that there could be what we would now call a PK factor at work in evolution.[7]

To accept the evidence for PK and ESP, we do indeed have to undergo a complete revolution in our mental philosophies. And many of us would rather leave our mental philosophies undisturbed, however incomplete and unable to explain some of the well-established facts of life these may be. The effort required to shift the centre of the personal universe is too much for some, who ignore the evidence for psi altogether or attack it with an intensity often bordering on hysteria, suggesting a subconscious and fiercely suppressed awareness that it is true, and sheer panic at the thought of having to face its implications. This is what lies behind the rage and abuse so often produced by science writers and editors, and by members of 'humanist' vigilante groups such as the Committee for the Scientific Investigation of Claims of the Paranormal (CSICOP).

In this and the preceding chapter, I have mentioned a small sample of the evidence that has satisfied me of the existence of PK, and as with telepathy I have provided a means of ending the arguments over whether it exists by explaining how readers can see for themselves whether it exists or not. Obviously, I cannot guarantee results. No author of a book on, say, guitar-playing, can guarantee that anybody who reads it will be able to sound like Julian Bream. He can show you what you must do if you want to try to imitate the masters, within the limits of your talent and imagination, and he can tell you what the masters themselves did to help them become as good as they were. He cannot guarantee that you will be able to play the guitar at all.

Learning psi is unlike learning to play the guitar in one important respect: it involves not only learning but also *unlearning*. You have to free yourself from the constantly repeated dogma that says it cannot be done because there is no such thing.

There is such a thing, however. It can be done, and it could be very important. There is a lesson to be learned from the ludicrous antics of the poltergeist, the surrealist behaviour of the tilting tables, and the boring but necessary research of the Rhines and their many successors in professional parapsychology, for the PK effect is at work in many more ways than these. To what extent it is at work in the background of our lives, we can only speculate, and the speculations of Kenneth Batcheldor, who has studied the influence of the mind on large objects for twenty years, are worth a hearing.

'I like to think of PK', he told me, 'as being able to produce any effect known to physics. It doesn't have to be motion – it could be chemical change, the creation of a light, an electrical effect, a smell, or a fire. I believe it is not so much a new force as a process underlying all forces, and relating them to mind. What are its limits? It seems that once you get it going, its possible abilities are almost unlimited.'

After what I had witnessed in his house, I was inclined to agree.

'But it is limited,' he went on, 'in the sense that it is difficult to get into the right state of mind to do it. Perhaps fortunately!'

Psi is unlike guitar-playing in another respect: it can happen spontaneously, without any practice, operating according to very precise rules that we are only just beginning to understand.

'I once had the crazy idea', Batcheldor said, 'that everybody in the world is like a giant sitter group ... Why do things apparently behave in an objective way, independently of what I wish? For the same reason that they do in an ordinary small sitter group. The phenomena are a product of the whole group, so they appear to be independent of the wishes of any one sitter. No single person can do much about them, just as in normal life we cannot influence the law of gravity. Yet in both cases the phenomena are probably mental creations.'

I remembered Wallace's speculation that all force may be will force.

'And if,' Batcheldor concluded, 'as most researchers think, PK spreads across time and space, why couldn't everybody who has ever lived, or ever will live, be part of a sitter group creating reality as it is perceived at the moment?

'In a sense, PK may be the fundamental stuff of the universe.'

# Part III

# MAGIC

# Introduction

'Magic', said Paracelsus, 'is a teacher of medicine far preferable to all written books.' 'I have reflected a great deal upon the magical powers of the soul of man, and I have discovered a great many secrets in Nature, and I will tell you that only he who has acquired this power can be a true physician. If our physicians did possess it, their books might be burnt and their medicines thrown into the ocean, and the world would be all the better for it.'[1]

He made it very clear what he meant by magic. He defined it as 'the greatest wisdom', the exercise of which did not require any exotic rituals. 'It only requires a strong faith in the omnipotent power of all good, that can accomplish everything if it acts through a human mind that is in harmony with it.' This could not be obtained 'by merely reasoning logically from external appearances existing on the physical plane' (that is, by left-mind thinking), but only by 'making oneself able to feel and see the things of the spirit', experiencing divine wisdom for oneself rather than repeating the opinions of others about it. 'We should mobilise our inner powers, so that we are not directed by the heavens, but by our wisdom.'

The three fundamental bases of wisdom, he said, were faith, prayer and imagination, and he defined all three with his usual directness. Faith was 'not a mere belief in something that may or may not be true', but 'a luminous star that leads the honest seeker into the mysteries of Nature', a 'power that comes from the source of all good'. He made a clear distinction between 'belief based on mere opinions and creeds' and true faith, which is 'spiritual consciousness'.

Prayer is 'a strong desire and aspiration for that which is good', effective only when practised from the heart. It is necessary, because the Omnipotent Power is not going to give us anything unless we ask for it, and we have to ask for it in the right way.

As for imagination, this is 'a great factor in medicine. It may produce diseases in man and in animals, and it may cure them.' 'Whatever man thinks will take form in his soul.' 'The imagination is a sun in the soul of a man, acting in its own sphere as the sun of the Earth acts in his. Wherever the latter shines, germs planted in the soil grow and vegetation springs up. The sun of the soul acts in a similar manner, and calls the forms of the soul into existence.'

Paracelsus based his wisdom not on books or academic instruction, but on first-hand experience of nature. 'She knows me, and I know her', he declared. He spent much of his early life wandering round Europe and the Near East, and may even have visited India. 'I went in search of my art,' he said, 'often incurring danger of life. I have not been ashamed to learn that which seemed useful from vagabonds, executioners and barbers.' 'Books are studied by looking at the letters they contain. Nature is studied by examining the contents of her treasure-vaults in every country.' 'Reading never made a physician. Medicine is an art, and requires practice.'

It is one he practised very well, to the envy of his more orthodox contemporaries, who were not ready for what we would now call the holistic approach. He undoubtedly did, as inscribed on his tombstone, cure 'wounds, leprosy, gout, dropsy and other incurable diseases of the body with wonderful knowledge'. There is documentary evidence that he cured nine of the fifteen inmates of the Nuremberg prison hospital in 1529, some of whom are thought to have been lepers.

It may be that his faith in his methods, some of which are not taken seriously even by his modern admirers, was the factor that led to his success, and not the herbs he used or the planetary positions that determined the precise time at which he used them. Although he knew that the power of faith in itself was sufficient to bring about miracles whether based on something true or false, he was well aware of the difference between true and false faith. The latter was supported by evil, and led to the practice of sorcery or 'black' magic, whereas 'true faith can only come from the source of all good'.

Eric J. Dingwall has written:

Magic is not, as so many wrongly believe, merely a collection of rites, ceremonies and supernatural feats. It is much more than that. In a few words, it is *a way of looking at the world*. In its very essence, it implies a *mental state*. However many times it may be subdivided; however much we may speak of natural, artificial, sympathetic or diabolic magic, the basic principle is always there. In magic a wide application of the association of ideas is employed. The magician does not attempt to analyse the mental processes upon which he bases his art. He holds certain things, based on his own practical experience, to be true, and does not try to reason about them or consider alternatives ... Once the belief in a supernatural world is established and the conviction that, by appropriate methods, this world can be explored and brought into a kind of subjection to the operator's wishes, then magic follows as night follows day.[2]

Before giving instances of the use of true magic in modern medicine, I will summarise the story so far.

As Dr Puccetti said, there are two of us here in the same cranium. He was not talking about schizophrenia (a brain disease that leads to withdrawal from reality), but about our normal and natural condition. We are driven by two brains, each with its own specialities and ways of handling information. Each of these brains has its own mind-mode; I have called them left and right for convenience rather than geographical accuracy. The left mind, as Liébeault put it, is the 'reasonable and deliberative' one, while the right is 'emotional and instinctive'. To what extent these qualities coincide with the constituent matter of the two brain hemispheres is not important here.

Presumably, our two minds should work as a team, like two well-matched horses pulling a heavy cart. Often they do not. We have tended to become extremists of both left and right; those of the far left-mind tendency being the noisiest and most intolerant. Right-mind abilities tend to be censored or suppressed altogether by the left. Sometimes this is necessary, as when counteracting excessive credulity. Some left minds censor every right-mind impulse on principle, without attempting to understand what they are suppressing or realising that it could be of practical use to them.

In Part One, I concentrated on hypnosis, a word that covers a wide range of techniques that obtain a wide range of results, from the magical to none at all. I have chosen the simplest model, according to which the hypnotist communicates directly with the patient's right mind (or rather, the conscious part of it, which is only the tip of an iceberg) after subduing, bypassing or deceiving the left, and inserts a specific suggestion. This is immediately accepted and acted upon provided there is no opposition to it. As for mesmerism, I showed this to be something quite different, much harder to define, and considerably more magical than hypnosis. As will be seen from the examples to be quoted below, it can lead to an expansion of consciousness rather than a mere alteration of it, as under hypnosis. Mesmerism is not the primitive forerunner of hypnosis, as claimed in the textbooks, but a process whereby the mind is regressed and reprogrammed, in a silent charismatic crisis directed as much by itself as by the mesmeriser.

In Part Two, I showed how telepathy, clairvoyance and psycho-kinesis can be predicted to occur when the minds concerned are in the proper states. Usually, this means states of right-mind dominance, and when these are obtained they achieve specific results, from the receiving of information of any kind at any distance to interfering with physical objects including tables, spoons and physical bodies of oneself or of others.

No useful discussion of relations between mind and medicine can leave magic out of account, and I will now look at ways in which this has been used for medical purposes in many different cultures, including our own. I will introduce this subject with some cases from the early days of mesmerism in which human consciousness was made to expand with positive results.

None of the writers quoted gives a very clear description of what he actually did to get his mind into the right state. Since they all described almost everything else in great detail, this omission may be due to the fact that there is not much to say about it. Indeed, the nearest to any kind of full description of the mesmerist's preparation that I have been able to find comes from Dr Joseph Deleuze, who listed the essential requirements as will power, capacity of attention, control of the will, belief, self-confidence, benevolent intention and good health in himself.

Will power, he explained, was not just a matter of saying to yourself *I will*. 'It must arise naturally from the soul, born of a strong desire to succeed, and it must not be upset by any obstacle. The attention must be free from both constraint and effort; nothing should distract it, though it should not become fatiguing. The control of the will should be kept constant, uniform and calm. There must be nothing vague or uncertain about it; one should not seek to produce curious phenomena, but only to do good by supporting nature's efforts.'

It was belief, said Deleuze, that strengthened the will, together with the self-confidence that inevitably resulted from belief. 'As for intention,' he went on, 'the magnetiser only produces salutary effects when he is imbued with a feeling of benevolence, a tender interest in the patient and a sincere, disinterested desire to do him good. This is what leads to that gentle, peaceful and uniform action that makes itself felt little by little and eases pains.' To work medical magic, it seems, you just decide what you want to do, and then do it. It could be as simple as that.[3,4]

As mentioned earlier, it was the Marquis de Puységur who was the first to state that animal magnetism was 'the action of thought on the body's vital principle', and to describe the abnormal phenomena of the deep trance or 'somnambulistic' state. This was discovered spontaneously by his peasant patient Victor, who simply fell into it one day while being magnetised, and immediately showed signs of a greatly expanded consciousness at work. Several other patients were also able to enter a clairvoyant state quite easily, and produce detailed diagnoses and prognoses of their ailments, and sometimes also those of others. A forty-five-year-old woman whose body was covered with sores dictated her own prescription while in trance, telling Puységur to boil thirty grains of nightshade in some red wine. When he protested that this was a dangerous dose, she replied: 'That's all right. I'll take it. It won't do me any harm, and I'll be cured in ten days.' And, the Marquis reported, so she was, remaining free from body sores for the following twenty years.

Another patient made a curious remark during a magnetic trance: 'You must send me to sleep at eight o'clock tonight, so that I can see how the disease is going, and what medicine I will need tomorrow.' When magnetised, it seems, the Marquis's patients became their own doctors.[5]

Victor, while being treated for a headache caused by a fall, announced that he would be cured between noon and one p.m. the following day, after bleeding from only one nostril. This is exactly what happened, according to Puységur, whose writings convey the impression of an honest and intelligent man (he was an Army officer with a distinguished active service career) with a real concern for the sufferings of others. He wrote up his cases in great detail in several books, and had nothing to gain by making up anecdotes such as these.[6]

The same can be said of two other mesmerisers who have left us important evidence in support of Puységur's claims. One was Epes Sargent (1813–80), an American writer who became editor of the Boston *Transcript*, and was introduced to mesmerism when he took lodgings in a New York doctor's house in 1840. Becoming

acquainted with a regular patient, an actress and writer named Mrs
Mowatt, Sargent decided to see for himself if 'operations of will
without contact' really worked. Sitting in a room with the doctor and
Mrs Mowatt, he hid his face behind a pamphlet and began to
concentrate.

> The effect upon Mrs Mowatt was almost instantaneous. The balls
> of her eyes rolled up, and her eyelids drooped; whereupon I
> suspended the action of my will, and she was herself again. I tried
> this several times till I satisfied myself there was a positive effect
> from my volition, unaided by any sign, look or movement visible to
> the subject. At last, Dr C., looking up from his reading, detected
> from the appearance of her eyes what was going on, and charged
> me with it. I had to plead guilty.

Sargent studied Mrs Mowatt almost daily for two years (her
husband usually being present) and was able to put her through the
whole gamut of abnormal phenomena, from community of taste,
heat, cold or specific mood to self-diagnosis and self-prescription.
While she was in trance, he noted, she would refer to her waking self
in the third person. It was as if she possessed a 'second and higher
self ... In her abnormal state there was that perfect self-poise,
intelligence and self-control, which made the idea of a merely
morbid development ridiculous. She seemed able to look down upon
all the contents of her normal memory as from a superior position.'[7]

Sargent's experiments were repeated independently at about the
same time by the Rev. C. Hare Townshend, a graduate of Cambridge University and author of one of the finest books on mesmerism (1844), which reveals him as a man of great intelligence, culture
and common sense. He, too, testified to the whole range of abnormal
phenomena with two regular subjects, named as Anna M. and E. A.

'There is in mesmeric sleepwalking', he wrote, 'a natural elevation
of the mind above what is base and sensual.' He insisted, however,
that 'Mesmerism is no miracle, but a development of faculties
inherent in man', and he asked a question that all modern hypnotists
might do well to repeat: 'Would it be consistent with the goodness of
Providence to tantalise us by imperfect glimpses of that which we
shall never be permitted to realise?'

Some of Townshend's observations are of great psychological
interest. Early in his career, he noticed that his subjects seemed to
acquire a remarkable level of knowledge when in trance that they did

not have in their normal states. Then he made an important discovery:

> When I first began to mesmerise, I used to consult my sleepwalkers on dark and dubious points, with something of the blind faith of a novice in a new and wondrous science. Their answers to such inquiries were calculated to bewilder me by the pure influence of astonishment; for the simple had become theorists – the uneducated were turned into philosophers. At length I was awakened from my dream of somnambulic knowledge by finding that my patient's ideas shifted so visibly with my own, and were so plainly the echo of my own thoughts, that not to have perceived the source whence they originated, would have been pertinacious blindness indeed. I was but taking back my own, and receiving coin issued from my own treasury.

There was, it seems, a kind of feedback loop between him and his subject, and he was quick to realise that this could be put to good effect. Nearly a century and a half before Dr McConnell startled his colleagues by suggesting that hypnosis was a form of PK, Townshend made essentially the same point in the plainest possible terms:

> We have seen that, in cases of mesmeric sympathy, the actual sensation of one person is transferred accurately to another: so also the mental action of the mesmeriser can – so to speak – perform motion in another ... The connection between particular acts of will and intention, originating with the mesmeriser, and particular motions occurring simultaneously in the patient, is marked and decisive. The inference is irresistible. *One mind originates motion in two bodies ... Whatever be the force which has moved the muscles of the one, precisely the same degree of that force is meted out to the muscles of the other.* [emphasis added]

Townshend knew what he was talking about. His book includes numerous accounts of his experiments in the transfer of taste, sensations and emotions, the inducing of sleep at long distance and even blindfold reading. (Among the many men of professional standing who testified to his abilities was the naturalist Louis Agassiz, who was himself mesmerised by him.) Half a century before Janet, Myers and Freud, he appeared to be on the verge of discovering the subconscious mind.[8]

Indeed, some of the foundations of modern psychology seemed to have been laid as early as 1836, in the first major book in English on animal magnetism, by a lawyer named J. C. Colquhoun. He wrote:

The name of *Animal Magnetism* has been given to the organic susceptibility which renders the nervous system of one individual capable of being affected, in various ways, by particular processes performed by another, especially when accompanied by faith, or at least a certain abandonment, in the patient, and with an energetic effort of volition on the part of the operator ...

The discoveries of Animal Magnetism ... have experimentally proved that there is something more elevated in the nature of man than appears to common observation in the ordinary state of our existence; and, from the interesting and consolatory truths they have unfolded, there has been developed, as the flower from the bud, that delightful faith in the expansive and imperishable character of our spiritual being which, while it exalts us beyond the narrow limits of time and space, and teaches us to aspire to a brighter, a purer and a loftier destiny, seems calculated to produce an eternal reconciliation and harmonious concord between Religion and Philosophy.

He quoted his contemporary Wordsworth, some of whose 'Lines Composed a Few Miles above Tintern Abbey' are remarkably accurate as a description of the state of consciousness of somebody in a mesmeric trance:

> ... we are laid asleep
> In body, and become a living soul:
> While with an eye made quiet by the power
> Of harmony, and the deep power of joy,
> We see into the life of things.[9]

The relatively sudden disappearance of mesmerism from the medical scene by the mid nineteenth century led to the assumption that it was obsolete, having been replaced by hypnotism. Yet mesmerism is alive and well, at least in Canada, where clinical psychologist Dr Lee Pulos of the University of British Columbia (Vancouver) has carried out a study of the comparison of the two therapies, using a total of 102 subjects. His results are indeed, as he described them to a 1978 conference of the American Society for Clinical Hypnosis, 'provocative'.

More than three-quarters of his subjects reported total or partial analgesia after only fifteen minutes of traditional hand-passes, with no physical contact and without a word being spoken: 84 per cent finding the mesmeric trance to be deeper and more effective than the hypnotic one, 22 per cent describing 'the deepest state of relaxation ever'. Almost a quarter felt they were partially or totally out of their bodies, and 9 per cent reported spontaneous healings of minor ailments.

Dr Pulos found the experience of being mesmerised of therapeutic value in itself. 'I experienced the deepest trance of my life,' he told me. 'I felt I was but a pin-point of consciousness, and it was the most relaxing experience I ever had, as muscles "let go" that I never realised I had.'[10]

Townshend, after describing some of his experiments in the transfer of sensations and facial expressions, wrote: 'These things may appear ludicrous – to those who view but the outside of things they are purely so; but to the thoughtful inquirer every trifle connected with a grave subject is of importance.'

To the thoughtful detective, every speck of dust found at the scene of a crime is potentially important. If in our search for clues to the workings of the mind we have to examine such trivia as telepathic parlour-games, table-tilting and the utterances of entranced peasants, so be it. Paracelsus learned his wisdom in the open-air university of nature, and although I am not about to offer any evidence from 'vagabonds, executioners and barbers', I will be trying to discover what can still be learned from his favourite teacher of medicine: magic. For this is not a mere relic of a dark age of superstition, but a potentially useful adjunct to *orthodox* medicine, as many practitioners from Paracelsus to this day have been, and still are, well aware.

# 11

# The Magic Moment

To practise magic, or 'the greatest wisdom' in the words of Paracelsus, calls for a combination of three things: faith, prayer and imagination. Each of these will now be examined separately, beginning with imagination, the most familiar of the three components. It may be a 'luminous star' that leads us to enlightenment, but unfortunately it can also lead us in the opposite direction, as the following imaginary experiment shows:

Take an ordinary plank and put it flat on the ground, then walk along it from end to end. Having done that without difficulty, take the same plank and fix it securely between the tops of two tall buildings. Now walk along it again. There is no logical reason why you cannot, assuming there is no wind and that the plank does not wobble. You have just walked safely along it on the ground.

Émile Coué, who developed Liébeault's healing methods into his own technique of 'autosuggestion', used this example to illustrate a typical conflict between the will and the imagination, or what I have been calling the left and right minds. He explained why most people cannot walk along planks high in the air.

'Before you had taken two steps, you would begin to tremble, and in spite of every effort of your will, you would be certain to fall to the ground ... In the first case [on the ground] you *imagine* that it is easy to go to the end of the plank, while in the second you imagine that you *cannot* do so.' Vertigo, he added, is 'entirely caused by the picture we make in our minds that we are going to fall'.

In 1976, seventy-year-old Karl Wallenda walked across Victoria Street, London, on a tightrope stretched between the tops of two office buildings. Half way across, he stopped and did a headstand for good measure, reminding the world that he was a member of one of the great circus families. How did he do it?

Most of us would ascribe this feat to 'a wonderful sense of balance'. We would be wrong: Wallenda's sense of balance is no more wonderful than anybody else's. Balance is a very precise state; you either have it or you do not. You are either on the tightrope or on the ground. What really guided Wallenda across Victoria Street was a perfect balance of two minds, not of one body. His unusually courageous will and his well-controlled imagination were exactly in phase with each other.

As Coué pointed out, whenever the will and the imagination are in conflict, the imagination has an annoying way of prevailing just when we do not want it to. On such occasions, 'will power' is no use at all. In fact, when the will struggles to overcome the imagination, what he called 'the law of reversed effect' comes into force: the harder we try, the more likely we are to fail. If we try to make ourselves sleep by will power, for example, we probably take longer than we would if we just lie in bed and wait, imagining that we will drop off eventually but not particularly caring when. Likewise, struggling to remember a name 'on the tip of my tongue' is less effective than implanting the positive suggestion 'I shall remember in a minute' and then simply waiting.

'Thus,' Coué concludes, 'we who are so proud of our will, who believe that we are free to act as we like, are in reality nothing but wretched puppets, of which our imagination holds all the strings. We only cease to be puppets when we have learned to guide our imagination.'

Coué, like Paracelsus, was a graduate of the university of nature. He learned his wisdom while working as a pharmacist and noticing that the state of mind of his customers seemed to have more to do with whether they got better or not than the pills and medicines he dispensed. He also learned a good deal from first-hand study of Liébeault, and although he used hypnotism for a time, he abandoned it for the full-time practice of suggestion and nothing else. With the help of his pupil Charles Baudouin, he formulated laws of suggestion that go a good deal further than his well-known phrase 'Every day, in every way, I am getting better and better' might indicate.

Suggestion, he said, could be both general and specific, and each had to be administered in a very different way. Specific suggestions were better repeated quickly. 'The beneficent thought must not allow the maleficent thought to get a word in edgeways,' as Baudouin puts it. Try this next time you hurt yourself. Repeat 'the pain

is going' at top speed without letting your imagination assert the idea
that the pain is not going.

General suggestions, on the other hand, should be repeated
slowly. Coué told Baudouin that his famous 'Every day, in every way
...' mantra should be repeated 'piously' with each word stressed
separately, and special emphasis on 'in every way'. This gave the
imagination a chance to fill in the gaps in between repetitions with
images of individual things getting better and better. Coué noticed
that when his patients repeated this blanket general suggestion twice
daily in the proper way, they would find their specific physical
problems getting better even when they had not mentioned them to
him. They were literally curing themselves by the correct use of the
guided imagination.

Coué's rules for the use of autosuggestion can be summed up as
follows, slightly rephrased from Baudouin's own summary:

1 Every morning, on waking, and every evening before going to
sleep, repeat the 'every day' phrase twenty times, murmuring it
like a litany and not paying too much conscious attention to it, and
leaving a short pause in between each repetition. To help you keep
count, you can tie twenty knots in a piece of string and 'tell' them,
like the beads on a rosary.

2 If a specific problem arises during the day, use the specific
form of suggestion and repeat 'It is going away' quickly, as often as
possible.

3 Whenever possible, have a period of total relaxation (of the
kind recommended by Ainslie Meares, in which you 'meditate' on
absolutely nothing) and conjure up during it an intense image of
the kind of improvement you are looking for.

4 Develop the habit of giving your total concentration to
whatever you are doing. Learning poems by heart is a good way to
practise this. On a wider level, Paracelsus tells us that faith is only
effective if it has a single objective in view. It needs sharp focusing,
like a telephoto lens.

Baudouin admits that Coué's rules were simple to the point of
being 'puerile', but insists that they work. The problem for most of
us is that we need to start the ball rolling, and this is not easy to do on
our own. We need to come into contact with somebody like Coué,
who was by all accounts a man of remarkable charisma. Like Shaw's
doctor, he seems to have healed people 'by the mere incompatibility

of disease or anxiety with his welcome presence'. Although there are no reports of broken bones uniting at the sound of his voice, there are eye-witness accounts of the effects his presence could have when he sought to persuade patients that it was their idea to get well, not his. Here is one, from a visiting journalist:

'He said: "Learn to cure yourselves, you can do so; I have never cured anyone. The power is within you yourselves; call upon your spirit, make it act for your spiritual and mental good, and it will come, it will cure you, you will be strong and happy." Having spoken, Coué approached the paralytic: "You heard what I said. Do you believe that you will walk?" "Yes." "Very well, then, get up!" The woman got up, she walked, and went round the garden. The miracle was accomplished.'

Many such instant cures have been witnessed at public healing sessions, and journalists have often reported that patients collapsed soon afterwards, taking this as proof that such cures were 'all in the mind', as if that somehow made them of no value. Yet for any relief at all, however temporary, to result from a mental act is the clearest possible proof of the power of the positively motivated imagination. This simple truth is often overlooked.

Coué knew perfectly well that the power of the imagination is usually a limited one. That is why he insisted on twice-daily reinforcement in the form of his general-suggestion 'every day ...' litany. Regularly repeated ritual is a standard feature of most religions, and as any charismatic leader knows, conversion cannot be made to last without constant reinforcement. In a recent study of 262 former members of forty-eight different cults, it was found that an average of 54.5 hours a week had been spent in ritual and indoctrination. This is longer than the working week in many countries. It was also found that the more time ex-cult members had spent being indoctrinated, the longer it took to deprogramme them.[1,2,3]

The magic moment is the point at which conscious effort stops and miraculous nature takes over. One of my favourite childhood memories is of bicycling home from the village up a very steep hill which gradually levelled off and then sloped down towards our house. With the right surveying equipment, I could mark the exact spot at which my aching muscles could rest and let gravity take charge of me. It was indeed a magic moment, and it was never the same if I got off my bicycle and pushed it up the hill. I needed to be exhausted in order to appreciate it.

A certain amount of directed effort is necessary for any kind of magic, but it is equally important to know when to stop pedalling. To make a magic moment likely to occur, there are two essential conditions:

1 When a suggestion is fully accepted by the imagination (or right mind) with no resistance from the will (left mind), it will be carried out if it is believed to be theoretically possible and not counteracted by a negative suggestion. Suggestions can be accepted either after constant repetition and reinforcement, or by a single statement that bypasses the left mind and takes the right by surprise.
2 Whoever makes the suggestion (oneself included) must be in a state of total faith, whether this is deliberate or accidental.

Before I look at ways in which magic moments can lead to healing, I should mention some ways in which ordinary suggestion can produce negative results in our daily lives, whether at a trivial level or a more serious one. As Stephen Black noted, 'the informational environment can be just as important to physical health as the physical environment'. The former includes information of any kind, and much information has an element of suggestion attached to it.

The advertising and public relations industries are largely based on the principle of suggestion, positive and ethical or otherwise. A particularly effective and dishonest form of negative advertising makes clever use of the 'taking by surprise' technique, in which two PR agents stand at bus-stops or in crowded trains and gossip casually (but loudly) about so-and-so's product. They do not state directly that they think it is a rotten product, but they agree with each other that *other people* think it is.

In 1983, it was publicly alleged that persons unknown had been carrying out a smear-by-suggestion campaign against the Ford Motor Company, shortly after the launch of its Sierra model. Pairs of them, posing as Ford dealers, would remark to each other, in the hearing of as many people as possible, that their customers just hadn't taken to the Sierra's advanced styling and technology. It was all too futuristic, and so on.

This was an ingenious way of denigrating a very popular and successful car, and it may have been quite effective before it was mentioned on the BBC news programme *The World at One*. It is hard to reject an opinion, however bizarre, if it purportedly comes from somebody other than the speaker. It carries with it the suggestion of established fact, and since eavesdroppers cannot argue with the original source of the idea, their left minds do nothing to stop it penetrating their right minds. When these are idling in neutral, as in a rush-hour train journey, or during the often very long wait at a London bus-stop, they are defenceless.

Suggestion by constant repetition is frequently used by politicians. British Prime Minister Margaret Thatcher's 'There is no alternative', known in media circles as TINA, is a recent example. A reporter covering a campaign by Nelson Rockefeller coined the word BOMFOG to save him writing 'Brotherhood of man and fellowship of God' every other minute.

The most widespread form of suggestion is applied to millions of people every day in their own homes, coupled with electronically-induced hypnosis. It is ironic that it is illegal in many countries to show hypnotic induction on television, when television itself *is* a form of hypnotic induction. One form of this, described in 1843 by James Braid, is 'induced by a fixed and abstracted attention of the mental and visual eye, on one object'. A more modern form is known as the confusion technique, in which the subject is bombarded with contra-dictory instructions, to the point where he surrenders instantly to the first order he can assimilate and process, such as 'Go to sleep'.

Television reproduces both methods very successfully. The viewer's attention is fixed on a small flickering screen, which bombards him to confusion point with constantly changing images. Thirty seconds of techno-dazzle followed by a clear message will sell *anything*, not only soap powder but an idea of any kind, if this is not contra-indicated as is luckily the case with party political broadcasts. Even these make use of dirty tricks. Both commerical television and the BBC (which, in its own words, is under obligation 'not to broadcast a programme which exploits the possibility of conveying a message to, or influencing the minds of the audience without them being fully aware of what has been done') were caught screening a broadcast on behalf of the Labour Party on 8 April 1970 that included three 'subliminal' messages. These were spotted by the late Ross McWhirter, a tireless champion of personal freedom who was murdered for his uncompromising views, who took the matter to the Court of Appeal, the reactions of which, recorded by his twin brother Norris, make horrifying reading.[4]

'All the principles of ritual magic are incorporated in television production, of both commercials and the carefully orchestrated programmes,' writes Michael Bentine, who knows a good deal about both magic and television, and gives numerous examples of ways in which the minds of TV viewers are influenced all the time without their conscious knowledge.[5]

Jerry Mander, an American advertising man, has collected more than two thousand statements from the public on the effects of TV watching. Some examples:

> I feel hypnotised when I watch television.
> I feel mesmerised by it.
> I feel like it's brainwashing me.
> If a television is on, I just can't keep my eyes off it.
> Television is turning my mind to mush.

His small son told him: 'I don't want to watch television as much as I do but I can't help it. *It makes me watch it.*'[6]

In 1982, I was given a remarkable demonstration of the power of hypnotic suggestion by television. On 9 May, I took part in the BBC programme *Choices*, in which propositions supplied by the public were debated by a team of experts. Mine was 'Television rots your brain. We need less of it, not more.'

I described the pleasures of not having a TV set, and some of my experiences during the brief period in my life in which I owned one.

'I began to feel that my TV set was taking me over,' I said. 'Whenever it was on, I would feel my brain going numb as if I was being hypnotised ... Instead of doing things myself, things were being done to me. I didn't want to live in a brave new world of standardised force-feeding of the mind, so I got rid of my set. My quality of life improved at once, that very day ... I have regained control of my mind, and that's something I'm not going to give up again.'

I was vigorously supported by former TV executive Milton Shulman, though I received some blank stares from members of the studio audience, one of whom wanted to know what I was doing appearing on the medium I was denouncing.

'Where else would I be?' I replied. 'You don't preach to the converted, do you?'

A few days later, on the LBC Radio *Night Line* programme, a woman phoned in to say she had just disposed of her TV set, using several whole phrases from my contribution to *Choices*. It is no use telling me you cannot induce suggestion by television. I have done it myself. There was no need for Orwell's Big Brother to watch over our thoughts by 1984. Television was doing his job for him.

Turning from the mass rape of the mind to a more worthwhile subject: the curing of the sick body, I will compare three healers already mentioned: Coué, Harry Edwards, and Dr Mason.

Edwards, a Spiritualist, had complete faith in his spirit guides, and his patients came to him in the belief that something was going to be done to them by a mysterious power, although Edwards himself, a very intelligent man, was well aware of the fact that 'the bodily intelligence is stimulated to cooperate in all spiritual healing processes', as he put it in one of his many excellent books. Coué had total faith in his patients, and made them believe that something was going to be done, not to them, but *by* them. Mason had total faith in conventional medical hypnosis. All three of these men were able to induce magic moments, in their respective ways, and obtain cures of major organic diseases.

Coué did not publish detailed case histories. Edwards did, and was treated very shabbily for his pains. At the 1960 conference of the British Medical Association in Torquay, a film was shown of six cases of 'supernormal' cure, two of whom, unknown to the medical audience, were patients of his. 'This situation has its lighter side,' he noted generously, 'for whereas at the same conference a resolution was passed to deny healers the permission to visit the sick in our hospitals, the conference was marvelling at recoveries from incurable diseases which were the outcome of spiritual healing.'[7]

Mason's 1951 ichthyosis cure was fully documented at the time and cannot be ascribed to anything other than a single session of hypnosis. Let me summarise the sequence of events:

1 'John' was born with an incurable disease.
2 All conventional methods of treatment, including plastic surgery, had failed.
3 He was given a single suggestion under hypnosis.
4 His cure began immediately.
5 Six other doctors, including Dr Wink, produced similar cures by identical methods.
6 Dr Mason failed to produce cures on eight other patients.
7 Dr Mason was unable to hypnotise John four years later.

Thirty years after this extraordinary series of events, I have been unable to find a single serious attempt to explain *any* of them. The whole episode has been swept under the carpet, and even omitted from more than one textbook on medical hypnosis. Dr Bettley's call for 'a revision of current concepts of the relation between mind and body' went unheard by all, with the notable exception of Stephen Black who, like Mason, has since emigrated.

Let us see how this case fits into the scheme of things I am proposing in this book, and look at the sequence of events as follows:

1 Dr Mason did not know that John had ichthyosis, or that this was incurable. He thought it was a case of warts, which he knew he could cure.

2 Dr Mason was put on the spot by his surgeon colleague and virtually challenged to cure the patient himself. He accepted this powerful positive suggestion because he considered it plausible, and set to work in a state of both adrenergia and total faith. He had, in effect, hypnotised himself into believing he could do what he was about to do.

3 The simple suggestion, to grow a new arm of skin *right now* went in like a six-inch nail given a single whack by a professional. It was acted upon at once.

4 Only then did Mason learn what the disease was, and that it was supposed to be incurable. This sowed a seed of doubt in his mind, which luckily took time to germinate, during which he went on with his treatment successfully. But the seed grew, as seeds will, and his doubts overcame his faith to the point where they were finally able to sabotage the programme.

5 Dr Wink acquired instant faith simply by reading Mason's original case report, and he cured his two cases before knowing anything about Mason's subsequent failures.

6 Coué's law of reversed effect came into operation when Mason tried to repeat his cure on eight other patients. His imagination had let him down. No matter how hard he tried, he could not regain his original state of total faith. The conditions were wrong, so there were no magic moments and no cures.

This case is a perfect example of Paracelsus's claim that it makes no difference if you believe in something true or false. Mason originally believed in something false, yet he still got results. This is real faith healing as it should be practised far more often than it is, at least openly, by orthodox doctors. Just how often it is practised secretly, I have no way of knowing. I only learned about Dr Newman's cases mentioned in chapter 4 quite by chance, and another doctor has personally described to me a number of remarkable cures that have not been published, including one of the remission of no less than six tumours for the same patient.

Real faith healing has, of course, been practised by self-taught lay healers for centuries, and still is. I will give just one recent example of it, chosen because it was medically witnessed both before and after the magic moment, and also because I was present myself.

The setting was the ultramodern conference hall of the Swiss Industries Fair in Basle, where a three-day conference in November 1983 on all aspects of 'mind over matter' was coming to an end. The final session was a discussion of healing by twelve practitioners from five countries. One of these, a very calm lady named Joan Reid, had come at the last minute as a replacement, and had very little to say. She told the 700-plus audience that she had been a Spiritualist healer for twenty-four years and was 'very grateful to serve God'. As to what she actually did, she could only remark: 'One is directed.'

At the request of conference organiser Alex Schneider, one of the French translators then emerged from his glass booth at the back of the hall and went to the microphone. He had, he told us, arrived at the meeting under heavy sedation for what two specialists had diagnosed as viral neuritis (inflammation of nerves), which had caused him severe pain in his back. The specialists had been unable to do anything for him except prescribe morphine to enable him to get to sleep, and to carry out his demanding job of simultaneous translation.

A special private hour-long session with Joan Reid was arranged for him, after which all pain ceased. 'I felt she had a tremendous fluid of force,' he said, 'and I felt great warmth. She has an extraordinary gift.'

Joan Reid promptly corrected him, mildly. 'No, I haven't,' she said. 'I am an instrument of God.'

The translator's own doctor then came to the microphone to confirm what his patient had just said. Then, somewhat nervously, he went on to tell us that the same healer had also healed *him*, of a long-standing eye problem. He made it quite clear that he had been given plenty to think about in the previous few days.[8]

It is incidents like this one, of which I could list dozens, that lead me to suspect that we only occasionally catch glimpses of a gigantic iceberg, kept under the surface by the combined weight of the ignorance, prejudice and indifference that has smothered an invaluable and natural phenomenon throughout history, and continues to do so.

This absurd state of affairs will continue until it is generally realised that the orthodox medical profession has already been practising real faith healing for two hundred years, with varying degrees of success, and could practise it far more widely and far more successfully if it were taught properly.

Hypnosis is a creative art form, and it can be taught like any other creative art form, such as painting or music. At present it has become rationalised into a science, and a very inadequate one at that. It is taught, to a very limited extent, as a science, and yet every successful practitioner of it knows very well that he is practising an art, usually self-taught, and not a science.

With the greatest respect to Joan Reid's religious beliefs, I see no reason to suppose that what she did to that French interpreter was any different from what Dr Mason did to John, or what doctors from Mesmer to Meares have been doing to their patients for two centuries, what innumerable lay healers all over the world do every day to all comers – sometimes successfully, sometimes not – and what some individuals are able to do to themselves. With the help of the conference organisers, the interpreter was set up to the critical level of expectancy, the single suggestion of immediate cure was planted in his right mind, and the cure followed at once. It succeeded thanks to the necessary combination of the healer's total faith and the patient's total lack of resistance to suggestion.

There is more to it than that. It would be very neat and tidy if there were no more to faith healing than skilful use of suggestion and overcoming of resistance, but there must be another factor to account for the mechanical side of the process. It is all very well to say that suggestion removes aches, pains, tumours or whatever, but what actually goes on inside the body concerned? What brings on the positive crisis that transforms a sick person into a well one?

I see no logical objection to bringing in the psi factor here, by which I mean telepathy, clairvoyance and PK, or a combination of all three. If a patient is healed without being given any medicine or surgery at all, we cannot expect to find any conventional physical factor, can we? So what are we left with?

For the benefit of any rational left-minded doctors who have read this far without giving up in despair, let me say that I am not about to propose anything that cannot be fully tested, and that I will give specific examples of ways in which this can be done.

First, I will state the following assumption which, if true, explains why phenomena associated with the mind take place as they do, although it does not explain how they do.

The factor common to the hypnotic process, telepathy, and PK is the critical level of faith reached by at least one of the parties involved. Therefore, it follows that it is the state of faith itself that activates the psi factor automatically, to a degree that corresponds to the level of faith involved.

Faith, in this context, can be either active or passive – an intense and unqualified belief or a total lack of disbelief. These are not quite the same thing; you can have the second without the first, although obviously you cannot have the first without the second, and since we do not have a word for passive faith, I must use the word faith to mean either active or passive faith. I would define the latter as 'a state of confident but disinterested expectancy'. It is active faith that generates psi effects, and passive faith that enables them to be received.

The two states are clearly seen at work in hypnosis, where the hypnotist must have active faith, and passive faith is the ideal state for the patient. The same applies to experiments in telepathy such as those of the Sinclairs, where the sender is active and the receiver is passive. PK, on the other hand, needs a delicate balance of both active and passive faith.

This may all sound academic and obscure, yet there is one practice that millions of people indulge in every day which is based on the assumption that mental effort can generate both telepathy and PK. This is the ritual of prayer, which would be a pointless waste of time were it not for the implicit assumption that it is supposed to get results. It would not have survived if it never did get results, and I do not see any way of explaining such results in terms of physical cause and effect. Once again, what are we left with?

Leslie Weatherhead has given an excellent description of the conditions needed to make prayer for the sick get results. There is no point, he says, in just praying and 'hoping for the best'. We have to mean what we are saying. The efficacy of prayer is governed by laws. 'If the patient is known, is loved, is named; if those who pray really care; if they clearly understand what they are doing and why; if a word-picture is painted which helps them imaginatively to enter the sick room and see the patient and enter into his needs ... ', then prayer is more potent than merely mumbling 'Lord, bless all those who are sick and make them better.' He calls for serious scientific research into the nature of prayer, both public and private, and specifically mentions telepathy as a factor that might be involved.

What we need, he says, is 'a faith in prayer which is projected from knowing, not from half-superstitious credulity', and he gives several examples of 'miracle cures' that followed intense prayer of the kind he advocates, and were medically witnessed.[9]

Dr Weatherhead's mention of a 'word-picture' or visualisation that helps 'enter' the patient's environment, and the patient himself, brings to mind what used to be known in the early days of mesmerism as 'community of sensation', or a blending of the consciousnesses of patient and mesmerist, a logical extension of Mesmer's rapport, or 'agreement between two wills'.

Wallace demonstrated this to his own satisfaction in 1844, when he was a twenty-one-year-old schoolmaster. He mesmerised some of his pupils, and found that they reacted appropriately when he was pinched or pricked on a certain part of his body, and could also identify substances that he put into his mouth such as salt or sugar. 'The sympathy of sensation between my patient and myself was to me the most mysterious phenomenon I had ever encountered,' he said.[10]

This was one of the first phenomena to be researched in the early days of the Society for Psychical Research, in a long series of experiments conducted by Edmund Gurney. He apparently fully confirmed Wallace's findings, although it is quite possible that he was deceived some or even all of the time by his subjects, who may have been using simple signalling methods rather than clairvoyance to identify the substances he tasted.[11]

More recently, however, some good evidence for community of sensation has been obtained under laboratory conditions. In Czechoslovakia, psychologist Dr Zdenek Rejdák has filmed an experiment involving the transfer of the sensation of taste between hypnotised identical twins. This was done on behalf of the Czech Army (why, I have no idea) and Dr Rejdák has told me that it was entirely successful.

Quite the most remarkable experiment of this kind was carried out in 1962 by Dr Charles Tart, a psychologist at the University of California (Davis). Looking for a way of increasing both rapport and depth of hypnotic trance, he hit on the idea of having two subjects hypnotise each other, with himself acting as a kind of master of ceremonies, and persuade each other to go into deeper and deeper states. (Milton Erickson had tried something similar thirty years previously, but Tart did not know this at the time.) The experiment was done three times with the same subjects, psychology graduates in their twenties named as Anne and Bill.

The first thing Tart found was that although each subject was reasonably susceptible to hypnosis, each became considerably more so when hypnotised by the other. That was far from all he found. Bill and Anne were able to share a dreamlike hallucinatory experience in which they explored a tunnel in a mountain together, giving suggestions to each other, some of them unspoken, and reaching the point at which they were scarcely aware of Tart's presence. Indeed, Tart began to feel he was intruding.

Anne and Bill's tunnel experience was, he said, 'as real as any experience in life' to them. They later reported a 'sense of merging identities, ... a partial blending of themselves quite beyond the degree of contact human beings expect to share with others'. This felt good at the time, and Bill and Anne became close friends after their first session of mutual hypnosis, but later each felt a certain threat to their individuality, and Bill refused to go on with the experiments.

Tart was mainly interested at the time in seeing to what extent hallucinations of the type associated with drugs such as LSD–25 could be induced safely by hypnosis. He found that in some respects mutual hypnosis was far more powerful as a means of creating an alternative reality. What particularly interests me is that his subjects felt 'so much rapport with each other that it seemed telepathic', and found when listening to the tapes of their sessions that they had shared experiences 'for which there were no verbal stimuli on the tapes'. In other words, either they had been communicating telepathically or they had actually been together in a real (though non-physical) tunnel. Fantasy was in danger of becoming real.

The dangers of such experiments have been explored in a novel, *Links*, by Charles Panati, in which fantasy becomes more real than ordinary life, with fatal consequences. This book is based on Tart's work, and is alarmingly plausible most of the time. It is hardly surprising that Tart did not pursue this line of research.[12]

If sensations and emotions can be communicated telepathically to hypnotised subjects, these must include such constructive feelings as love and the desire to heal. Laboratory experiments have shown that the transmission of these feelings can have a measurable effect on the behaviour of enzymes and even on the structure of water molecules. This has been demonstrated most recently by the healer Matthew Manning and biophysicist Glen Rein, whose work seems to provide easily repeatable evidence for a direct physical effect by a healer on a physical substance. More evidence is provided by chemist Douglas Dean, who measured differences in the absorption spectrum of water that had been held by healer Rose Gladden.[13]

In a series of experiments too complex to summarise here in detail, Gerald F. Solfvin at the University of Utrecht in the Netherlands discovered a 'healing expectancy effect' on mice injected with a parasite, although nobody was consciously trying to heal them. He told the students handling the animals that half the mice were to receive 'distant healing' by an absent healer, which in fact they did not. However, analysis of the animals' blood showed significant effects on the spread of the parasite in the mice that the students *thought* were receiving 'healing'. This is an extraordinary demonstration of the effects not of faith but of nothing more than expectation of a positive result.[14]

Long before such evidence began to appear, it was felt instinctively by many that such positive states as faith, love and prayer can have biological effects on oneself or on others. In 1932, lay hypnotist Alex Erskine published an account of a kind of non-religious prayer used for healing purposes on a well-known patient, the writer Arnold Bennett.

Bennett was suffering from overwork, and came to Erskine wanting something done about it there and then, though for reasons of his own he refused to be 'put to sleep'. Instead, he sent himself into a state of suspended animation, after stipulating that Erskine should not speak a word, but should simply help him get his mind and body coordinated.

'Without speaking,' Erskine wrote, 'I concentrated my thoughts on him, and tried by sheer force of will to communicate with his subconscious mind, trying to convey to it the command to control his nerves and give him rest.'

After an hour of silence, Bennett jumped to his feet and said: 'I feel a new man; as though I'd had all the rest in the world. You kept your word. You didn't speak. But I know just what you tried to will me to believe as soon as you thought I had gone off, for I could read every thought in your mind. It was good advice, and I've taken it.' And he came back for more, several times, saying that he got more peace and rest from Erskine than any doctor or medicine could give him.

'There is no doubt about the accuracy with which Bennett was able to read my mind,' Erskine reported. 'Had he told me the general trend of my thoughts about him while he was in the chair, there would have been nothing noteworthy in it. But his thought-reading went far deeper than that. He repeated to me what my thoughts had been, using in several instances my own little pet phrases which he could not have known, and generally repeating so accurately the suggestions I had "thought at him" that there was no room for doubt that he had really read my mind.'[15]

It seems that Erskine was also able to induce travelling clairvoyance in some of his subjects, sending them out like astral detectives to locate people and describe where they were and what they were doing. Such accounts are easier to believe now that techniques of 'remote viewing' have been developed by Russell Targ and Dr Harold Puthoff at SRI International in California, and repeated independently by several other researchers. There is also some recent evidence suggesting that useful information can be obtained under hypnosis involving the use of not only telepathy or clairvoyance, but also one of the phenomena most difficult for some of us to accept – precognition.

Dr Richard Newman, whom I mentioned in Chapter 4, published a case report in a medical journal in 1978 that makes an interesting comparison with some of those of the early mesmerists. His patient, a girl of fifteen, was in an emotional turmoil because of difficult relations with her parents, and had completely lost her voice. She was a good hypnotic subject, and had been treated previously with hypnosis for muscular co-ordination problems that had followed a head injury, a detail that may be of significance.

Once the girl was in deep trance, Dr Newman told her to float out of her body up to the ceiling and to raise her right arm when she had got there. This she did.

'Now that you are out of your body, you can talk,' said the hypnotist. 'Your body cannot talk. But you can talk. Can you see the two of us?' The girl said yes, she could.

'Why were you not able to talk before?' Dr Newman asked.

'Because I was bad. Everybody hates me,' was the reply.

'That is only how you feel. There is a reason for that. In two minutes you will know what the reason is ... What is the reason?'

'My father tells me I am ungrateful. I should do more at home. I cause them to row about me. They don't love me.'

The doctor said he did not think that was true. Then, without warning, he induced what he calls clairvoyant transfer, in these words:

'We will go and see them and ask them. Feel yourself rising higher ... you are above the house ... it is cold ... now go ... go to [name of town] to your parents' hotel ... go ... go ... raise your hand when you are there ...'

The girl raised her right hand, and when asked where she was, replied 'In the back room behind the bar.'

'Who is there?'

'Daddy. He has the 'flu. He is watching the television. Mum is in the Reception.'

'What is on the television?'

'A war film, I think. Yes.'

'What time is it?'

'I don't know. It's dark outside.' It was in fact three in the afternoon and light outside the doctor's surgery.

Dr Newman told the girl to ask her father if he thought she was ungrateful and to repeat his reply.

'Of course I don't. I just wish you would smile and help more,' came the message.

'Ask him if he loves you ... What does he say?'

'Why do you think I drove a hundred and fifty miles to see you last Tuesday if I don't love you?'

The doctor then explained that the girl's worries were unfounded, and that she could now come back calm, happy and confident, and would be able to talk normally. He then eased her gently out of her trance, and promptly telephoned her father to ask what he was doing.

He was not watching television, but counting the bar takings. He did have 'flu and was planning to take the rest of the day off, put his feet up and watch some TV. Dr Newman asked him to look in the paper and tell him what he was intending to watch later that evening, and the first programme named was 'Enemy at the Door' – a war film – at seven o'clock. By then it would of course be dark outside.[16]

It might be argued that most of the British public spend most of their time staring at television, which is more than likely to be offering them yet another war film. However, this could not apply to a landlord who spent every evening at work behind his bar. Incidentally, neither the girl nor the doctor knew that the man had 'flu.

I give this case, exactly as reported, as an example of the kind of evidence of which there might be more if doctors looked for it more often.

One who did was Dr Frederick Knowles, an Englishman who spent much of his early career in India, where he learned a traditional yoga healing technique involving the storing and channelling of 'prana', a vital substance that supposedly permeates everything and sounds remarkably similar to Mesmer's animal magnetism. Like Mesmer, Knowles had immediate success, but also found early on that he could relieve pain without going through the rituals he had been taught. All he had to do was simply to decide to relieve it, and he soon earned a reputation as something of a miracle worker.

He wondered if this was due merely to his patients' expectations, and tried an experiment. Standing outside a patient's field of vision, he did nothing at all for 'much longer than the duration of a usual treatment'. The patient complained that the 'treatment' was not doing him any good. 'After that, a brief spell of the usual mental effort brought the usual relief, however.'

Knowles used no verbal suggestion. For a time, he used mesmeric passes, but soon abandoned these as well, using nothing but 'the effort of my will'. He found this to be ineffective when the patient was not aware of his intention. 'It seemed that by themselves, neither the patient's expectation, nor my mental effort were adequately effective. Both together were needed for the high proportion of successes to which I was accustomed.' He had rediscovered the 'agreement between two wills', and became convinced that there was a psi factor at work.

'My hypothesis, in brief,' he wrote, 'is that a physician's thoughts can affect a patient by a parapsychological process.' He reckoned that this might be happening all the time. Ordinary medicine, for instance, was likely to be more effective if the doctor gave it to the patient 'with the confident expectation of remarkable benefit' than if he thought to himself 'This stuff isn't the slightest use, but what else can I do?'. It was well known, he said, that some doctors got good results with their own pet remedy, while other doctors used the same remedy but found it worthless. (As mentioned earlier, it is also well known that some new medicines work wonders for a time, until 'proved' to be worthless.)

Knowles's most interesting observation is that he admits having gained his original confidence in his own methods on the basis of a technique in which he no longer believed – the prana manipulation he had learned in India. 'When experience showed the secret part of it to be without intrinsic value, I had seen enough remarkable results to maintain confidence.' Here is further proof of Paracelsus' claim that it makes no difference if we believe in something true or false.[17]

Another latter-day mesmerist of considerable interest was a layman named C. M. Barrows, who practised his own form of 'silent suggestion' in Brookline, Massachusetts, at the turn of the century.

Thanks to Dr Richard Hodgson of the Society for Psychical Research, we have a good deal of independent testimony to his extraordinary technique. 'Mr Barrows did not hypnotise me or do anything which I could see or feel,' wrote Mrs Agnes Lynch. 'He sat down beside me for about fifteen minutes, and the pain was gone.'

Mrs James Honey described how Barrows had examined her painful finger joint and asked her questions about it. 'He did nothing to the finger, but was quiet for not longer than three minutes, I should say, when all pain stopped, and I have had none of it since.' (She was writing ten months later.) An illiterate Irishman dictated his account of a visit to Barrows eighteen months previously, when he had been 'so lame that it hurt me to sit down'. Barrows sat several feet away and questioned him. 'Then he stopped talking for two or three minutes, and I don't know what he did, but the pain all left me.'

Barrows was not sure what he did, either. 'Mine is a silent suggestion,' he wrote. 'I use neither voice nor other means to convey its import to the patient through sensory adits.' (An adit is a nice old word meaning entrance – the opposite to an exit.) 'The conclusion seems wellnigh irresistible that therapeutic suggestion, as I use it, is not sensory but telepathic, that the communication does not require an act of thinking or willing to send it forth.' Having done some experiments in telepathy himself, he noticed that he was most successful when he made 'no thought effort, no conscious effort of any kind'.[18]

One begins to understand why Puységur, Townshend, Sargent and their successors said so little about their own states of mind. There was really very little to say. It was not so much what they did, but the kind of people they were. The same probably applies to those who were unable to obtain any of the higher phenomena. They were the kind of people who did not obtain them because they did not expect them. James Braid was one of these, and he went to some lengths to explain not only that such phenomena did not occur, in his experience, but that if they did in the experience of others then there was probably an alternative explanation, such as misreporting or malobservation. This was also the impression given by Dr E. J. Dingwall and his colleagues in the four-volume collection devoted to the abnormal hypnotic phenomena of the nineteenth century in several countries which he edited.[19]

Whom are we supposed to believe? Braid, who insisted there were no abnormal or higher phenomena, or his equally distinguished contemporary Professor William Gregory of Edinburgh

University, who insisted there were? Dr Milne Bramwell, an eminent medical hypnotist with rooms in Wimpole Street, who agreed with Braid, or Dr Bernard Hollander (also of Wimpole Street) who sided with Gregory? I suspect the Scylla-Charybdis factor to be at work here; the higher phenomena only exist for the right-minded. To the left-minded they cannot logically exist, therefore they do not appear. The only way to settle the argument is the same as for telepathy and PK: see for yourself if the higher phenomena exist by trying to get them.

The evidence for clairvoyant diagnosis is more consistent and convincing than that for unusual healing, mainly because it is free from the bewildering paradoxes that make the healing process so difficult to study. Two outstanding nineteenth-century clair-voyants were the Frenchman Alexis Didier, whose career is well described by Dingwall in the collection already referred to; and the American Andrew Jackson Davis (1826–1910).

Davis, son of an illiterate shoemaker from Orange County, NY, was 'magnetised' by the local tailor after an itinerant mesmerist named Grimes had visited his home town of Pough-keepsie and shown the tailor how to do it. Davis immediately showed an extraordinarily expanded consciousness and ability for travelling clairvoyance, being able to produce detailed diagnoses just by looking at the patients.

He was the forerunner of one of the best documented clair-voyants in history, Edgar Cayce, who produced almost fifteen thousand 'readings' in an altered state that he could produce on his own virtually on demand. He did this nearly every day for forty years up to his death in 1945, often producing descriptions of people's insides from a distance of several hundred miles and dictating precise prescriptions for them. One of his sons, the late Hugh Lynn Cayce, personally assured me he was convinced it was one of those that saved his eyesight after a childhood accident had left him temporarily blinded.

If ordinary people could be trained to become clairvoyant diag-nosticians and work alongside doctors, the potential benefits to both doctor and patient would be enormous. Just imagine if you walked into your doctor's consulting-room to find that he knew what was wrong with you before you opened your mouth? Many doctors would agree that an accurate diagnosis can be as elusive as a cure, and they cannot expect to cure something unless they know exactly what it is. They can only make a guess, pumping the pills and injections, and hope for the best.

Clairvoyant diagnosis is in fact already being practised in the US by at least two people with orthodox medical qualifications. In 1967, Dr Shafica Karagulla described the 'higher sense perceptions' of a number of women who were able to give diagnoses 'as accurate as that of an X-ray machine', some of which were immediately confirmed by surgery. One of her clairvoyants, named in her book as 'Kay', is Frances Farrelly, a graduate of the Northwest Institute of Medical Technology in Minneapolis, who later held a senior post in the city administration of Sarasota, Florida.[20,21]

Farrelly developed her higher sense perception skills after working with 'black box' operator Dr Ruth Drown, and coming to realise that it was the operators of these controversial 'radionic' devices that did the work, and not the boxes themselves. This impression was confirmed after a visit to George and Marjorie De la Warr in Oxford, pioneers in Britain of the radionic ('black box') diagnostic technique. Her first attempt at clairvoyant diagnosis was supervised by Dr Michael Ash, one of the first British orthodox doctors to introduce hand-healing into his normal practice. She was so accurate that he told her: 'You are the instrument, not those devices you've been working with.'

She later set herself up as a full-time medical clairvoyant, working with orthodox doctors. She reached the point where she no longer needed to see her patients, but could produce a diagnosis from a blood sample. 'I just focus my attention on the blood sample,' she said in 1975, 'and data start coming in about the person.' Seventy doctors were using her services, she said, and some had been doing so for ten years.[22]

Another American clairvoyant diagnostician is a fully qualified physician, Dr Robert Leichtman, who likewise has no need to see his patients. The name, age, sex and address are enough. This is how he describes what he does with this limited information:

'I read it, then just sort of get quiet and tune into the subject ... When I think about this person, it's not like thinking about where I'm going out to eat dinner tonight. It's more like trying to recall a distant memory. Then all of a sudden I start to get impressions. It really is that simple.'

It really works, too. Dr Norman Shealy of La Crosse, Wisconsin, rates Leichtman's diagnosis of twenty-five of his own patients as better than 90 per cent accurate. Psychiatrist Dr Ralph Allison of Davis, California, has consulted Leichtman on some two hundred cases and has testified publicly: 'He's never been wrong. Not once. I'm convinced he can do better analyses with his psychic technique than any psychiatrist.'[23]

To ignore evidence of this kind is unforgivable, especially since there is every reason to suppose that clairvoyance can be taught, like anything else. It is taught, for instance, at the College of Psychic Studies in London by experienced instructors like Elizabeth Farrell, Janet Orman and Ivy Northage, and as I have seen for myself some students make rapid progress right from the start. One simple training method is for clients to put their hands on trays of sand for a few minutes, then withdraw them, leaving a pair of handprints on which trainees then place their own hands and describe the impressions that come to them.

There are three possible ways of becoming clairvoyant:

1 By swallowing, at your own risk, substances such as mescaline, yagé, LSD–25 or *Amanita muscaria* mushroom. These will certainly open the doors of perception, but there is no guarantee that you will be able to shut them again.

2 By having a hard bang on the head, preferably when young.

3 By being taught properly by an expert.

The third method is the only one I recommend. When more is known about why the second can be effective, it may be possible to stimulate the appropriate areas of the brain safely, without needing to whack children with baseball bats or drop them off ladders. Meanwhile, parents whose children suffer damage to the head must face the possibility that the children will develop strange abilities. Dr Newman's ostensibly clairvoyant patient mentioned earlier may be an example of this.

Many children, of course, show strange abilities without suffering head injuries. Dr Ernesto Spinelli, a psychologist at Richmond College, has found that psi ability peaks at the age of three, then declines year by year, bottoming out between the eighth and ninth birthdays. He also found an inverse correlation between intellectual development and use of psi – the more backward a child is, the more it will tend to have flashes of telepathy or clairvoyance. (This does not apply to PK, which is perhaps most common around the age of puberty.)[24]

While I was writing this chapter, a friend mentioned to me that her four-year-old son had suddenly announced 'We can't go out today, because the Hammonds are coming to see us.' They were planning to go out for the day, and the Hammonds were not expected, in fact they lived the other side of the Atlantic. But sure enough, without any warning apart from the little boy's telepathic news flash, they turned up on the doorstep that afternoon.

Instances of spontaneous psi in children often pass unnoticed, and they may be far more frequent than might be supposed. An American psychiatrist, Dr Berthold E. Schwarz, took the trouble to note down every instance of possible telepathy or clairvoyance between himself, his wife and their two children. By the time these were aged fourteen and twelve, he had amassed more than fifteen hundred such instances.[25]

Although children's left brains grow faster than their right ones, their left minds are not fully developed until around the age of eight, whereas their right minds are fully active from the moment of birth. This fact alone suggests that relations between brain and mind may not be quite as direct as we think. Babies respond to shapes, colours, sounds and emotions long before they are able to think sequentially. Small children draw and paint with a spontaneity some artists spend a lifetime trying to recapture. They soon learn, however, that ours is a left-minded world. Education becomes a process of cramming facts into the brain rather than of drawing out what is already in it, which is what the word education really means. It is ironic that young job applicants are expected to have such right-mind qualities as imagination, initiative, creativity and foresight, yet these are rarely taught and are often actively suppressed.

With more emphasis on right-mind education of the inner-sports type I mentioned in chapter 3, the medical profession could only benefit. If faith can heal, then faith should be taught at medical schools like any other medical technique. It should not be left, as it is, to a few adventurous individuals to practise almost in secret.

Dr Lawrence LeShan, the New York psychologist mentioned in chapter 4, has put his theories into practice by training himself to become a healer. He has also passed on his self-acquired knowledge to others, and by the end of 1984 he had trained more than four hundred people. His methods, and the rationale behind them, cannot be summarised in brief, but fortunately he has described them very well himself.[26,27,28]

He argues for the need for both 'mechanics' and 'gardeners' in the medical profession. It is not a question of one or the other, he says, but of both. Medical mechanics and body-gardening are not the same thing at all; if we drive our car into a lamp-post, it needs immediate surgery and perhaps an engine transplant, but if our faithful old vehicle starts to rattle and conk out on steep hills, a more subtle approach is called for. So it is with bodies.

Medicine does a fine job, on the whole, in repairing body-crashes. In the field of maintenance and treatment of invisible damage, the position is very different. Here, the panacea is the pill or the operation, neither of which has a record free from major blemishes. Iatrogenic disease, or disease *caused* by doctors, has unfortunately become a field of study in its own right. Molière's claim that 'nearly all men die of their remedies and not of their illnesses' is less of an exaggeration than it should be.

Even suggestion has come to be used negatively as often as positively. To be told you have three months to live is a negative suggestion of such power that few can resist it. Curses of this kind (that is what they amount to) can even be given accidentally; there are several reports of patients whose conditions deteriorated rapidly after operations, later recalling under hypnosis that they had heard the surgeon say something like 'This one isn't going to make it' while under general anaesthetic. (Since the right mind can hear while we are asleep, it is not surprising that it can also hear while we are anaesthetised. Surgeons and nurses should be careful of what they say in the operating theatre.)

Dr Elizabeth Whipp, who objected so strongly to Prince Charles's visit to the Bristol Cancer Centre, admitted with startling candour in a 1984 radio interview that 'I've had patients commit suicide because I've told them too much.'[29] Even assuming, as I am sure we must, that she only gave her opinion because her patients insisted on their right to know it, what better evidence could we have for the need for a place like the Bristol Centre, where patients are given powerful *positive* suggestions that they can prolong or improve their lives?

A vicious circle surrounds much of the medical profession, consisting of restricted faith, negative suggestion and a predominantly left-minded approach to the job. Each of these components continuously supports and reinforces the others. This circle should be replaced with one formed by unrestricted faith, positive suggestion, and an understanding of the value of the right-mind approach.

The successful healer, said Joseph Deleuze in 1825, 'must have in himself, as it were, two persons, who must not exist together, but successively; *one to act and the other to reason*' (emphasis added). While on the job, he should have nothing in his mind except the will to do good and an unbounded confidence. The time for logical reasoning was later, once the healing phenomenon had 'presented and developed itself'. Then, and only then, the healer should be 'distrustful, doubtful of everything, and admit no fact except upon incontestable evidence'. Deleuze, a trained natural scientist, admitted that people of 'simplicity of character and little knowledge of the subject' made better healers than 'those who are versed in the sciences'. Many 'rustics and matrons', he said, often made good healers, but 'if they were more enlightened, they might not succeed so well'.[30]

'I began my mesmeric studies by knowing and confessing my total ignorance of the subject, humbly questioning Nature and trying to understand her replies,' wrote James Esdaile. 'But when I did not, I preferred the positive evidence of my senses to the weak uncertain light of the understanding.'[31] It seems that, like Paracelsus, he knew Nature and she knew him.

# 12

# How to Work Miracles

It has for the last few centuries in Europe been the fashion to minimise the power of the human psyche over the phenomena of external nature. Modern research, however, has gone a long way towards proving the phenomena connected with the exteriorisation of physical energy, though there are not many among us who are now able to control them. It is, moreover, almost certain that primitive people with relatively undifferentiated egos are in touch with collective powers to a far greater extent than modern man, and that native magicians ... develop and foster them *by means of a definite technique.*

This was the opinion (with emphasis added) of a Cambridge University psychologist, Dr John Layard, who spent much of his professional life on Malekula in the New Hebrides Islands. He was no armchair academic, but a determined explorer of both the human mind and the physical world, and his personal experience led him to conclude:

Having lived among primitive peoples, I have no doubt at all that magic is true, although just as in the case of mediumship in this country, when the true source runs dry, fraud takes its place. It may even be said that the great majority of so-called magical acts seen and recorded in these degenerate days (for we in Europe today are in the trough between the two poles, having lost the old power of magic and only tentatively reaching out towards the new) *are* frauds if not based on pure superstition.

Nevertheless, that true magic has played an enormous role in the development of civilisation, *and will do so once more when its laws are properly understood,* I have no doubt. For magic is, after all, only a word used for a manifestation of those forces which we do not understand, but which when understood will be found to have as exact a scientific basis as chemistry or physics. (Emphasis added.)[1]

Since this was written, in 1943, there has been some progress in the search for the scientific basis of that 'definite technique' by which the shaman, medicine man, witch doctor or medium gets in touch with the collective powers. As we shall see in this chapter, magic has laws, and many of them are already well understood. They are even being taught at graduate level by anthropologist Dr Michael Harner, a member of the New York Academy of Sciences, of whom more in due course.

There is scarcely a culture anywhere in the world without its tradition of what is generally called shamanism. The shaman (the word comes from the Sanskrit *sramanas*, meaning ascetic) is the common ancestor of the witch doctor, the faith healer, the medium and the charismatic leader. He is, in Jerome Rothenberg's words, a 'technician of the sacred', and he has a number of jobs to do. He must control the weather, locate food sources, cure disease, and act as psychological counsellor to the individual and the social group alike. He must have 'one foot in the present and the other in the eternal', and this is hard work. 'A shaman's practice is very, very fatiguing,' a Siberian shaman once told a visiting scientist. 'It is much harder than felling trees.'[2,3,4]

Traditionally, shamanism is a vocation often taken up spontaneously after a severe illness or accident in early life. In his book *Lightning Bird*, Lyall Watson has described the brief career of a modern British-born shaman, Adrian Boshier, an epileptic who became initiated as a *sangoma* in a South African tribe. But you do not have to be born into shamanism or mediumship, or to have it thrust upon you, as in an epileptic attack. You can study it like any other definite technique.

There are many standard initiation methods, some involving no more than a period of solitude and starvation, as described in the Book of Deuteronomy (8:3): 'And he humbled thee, and suffered thee to hunger ... that he might make thee know that man doth not live by bread only, but by every word that proceedeth out of the mouth of the Lord ...'

Other methods are even more physically demanding. In Manchuria, a novice shaman was dropped down a hole cut in the ice of a frozen lake, and made to swim to another hole, the ordeal being repeated eight times.[5] The central feature of shamanic initiation is a form of what I have called the charismatic encounter, which need not involve another human, physical hardship, shock, or even a known source of inspiration. Any means of becoming aware of those invisible 'collective powers' seems to have the same effect. An Iglulik Eskimo described his magic moment of enlightenment like this:

'I sought solitude, and here I became very melancholy. I would sometimes fall to weeping, and feel unhappy without knowing why. Then, for no reason, all would suddenly be changed, and I felt a great, inexplicable joy ... And then in the midst of such a fit of mysterious and overwhelming delight I became a shaman, not knowing myself how it came about.' From then on, he was in contact with 'all the spirits of earth and sky and sea' and 'able to see and hear in a totally different way'.[6]

The shaman is the intermediary between ordinary mortals and that dimension we have long known to exist, but cannot define except as supreme power, great spirit, gods, or God. He is not always successful, and I suspect that the word 'sham', the origin of which is unknown, may first have been used to describe a technician whose powers have faded. Modern shamans, such as the Philippine psychic surgeons, know all about what Batcheldor calls induction by artifact and the need for it to induce instant faith. If they are caught practising sleight of hand they are denounced as frauds, or shams.

Mircea Eliade, author of the classic study of shamanism, subtitled it 'Archaic techniques of ecstasy', implying that the tradition has died. This is not so; what has almost died out is the breed of anthropologists adventurous enough to go and look for it. Shamanism survives today both in its original and in more sophisticated and urbanised forms, and nowhere is this more evident than in the land of its origin: the Soviet Union.

In 1978, the Soviet Academy of Sciences published a dictionary of traditional shamanic terms collected in the Buryat Republic, a region that lies between Mongolia and Lake Baikal and has one of the oldest traditions of shamanism in the world. According to this, there were originally fifty-five white gods and forty-four evil ones led by the fearsome Erlen Khan, who spread disease and death all over the world until the good gods produced the first shaman to combat them.

In his introduction, social scientist Ivan A. Manzhigeyev explains that Buryat shamanism died out soon after the 1917 revolution in accordance with Lenin's claim that 'our programme is wholly based upon science ... and inevitably includes atheistic propaganda and the explanation of the real historical and economic origins of the fog of religion' (my literal translation). However, Manzhigeyev did a good job of research, and his book, which is subtitled *The Success of the Atheistic Interpretation* (of shamanism), contains more than a thousand terms with more space given to traditional explanations than to the author's somewhat half-hearted atheistic ones. These are based on the assumption that shamans are, or rather were, a primitive bunch of madmen, and one cannot but wonder why, if this is so, it should still be necessary to study in such detail something that died out sixty years ago. The reason may be that the shaman's programme, unlike Lenin's, really is 'wholly based on science' and is still practised in the land of its origin, as the following eye-witness account indicates:[7]

In 1960, the director of the Palace of Culture in Magadan in eastern Siberia, a lady named Yana Ilieva, caught an unexpected glimpse of a surviving tradition. The fiancé of a friend of hers, a young construction worker, fell from a building two days before the planned wedding and suffered severe internal injuries. He was taken to hospital and X-rayed, after which his bride-to-be was told there was nothing to be done for him. He was not expected to live more than a few hours.

The girl refused to accept this, and when her mother, who had spent twenty years in a local labour camp, mentioned having heard of a great Chukchee shaman in a nearby village, they decided to go and see him as a last resort. Yana Ilieva went with them, and about four hours after the accident they arrived, without any previous warning, together with the patient, at a village of skin-covered huts.

Their first surprise was to find the shaman waiting for them, although he had no communication link with Magadan (apart from telepathy, of course). He promised to do what he could, adding ominously: 'If, in four hours after I have finished, he wakes up, he will never be ill throughout his lifetime and will live to a very old age.' He then asked for the price of five dogs, though he would accept no further payment. Then he set to work.

The three women sat and watched in silence as the shaman undressed the patient and rubbed his body with what smelled like blubber oil. Then – I apologise to animal lovers, who are not going to like this – he took the first dog, killed it, ripped out its organs and placed the kidneys, spleen and lungs on the corresponding areas of the man's body, which he then wrapped in a bearskin. He removed this about three quarters of an hour later to reveal what Ilieva described as 'something like thin oil-paper' where the dog's organs had been. She had the impression that 'some kind of exchange between these organs and the patient's body' had taken place.

The shaman went through this grisly ritual four more times, and each time it seemed that the dog's organs had undergone less of a change, until after the fifth application they remained almost unaltered. Mercifully, the patient was still unconscious.

Next, the village healer poured some kind of mushroom soup into the man's mouth and drank some himself. Then he rubbed more blubbery stuff into the patient's skin, wrapped him up once more in the bearskin, and announced that he would sleep for four hours. He then repeated that *if* the patient woke up, he would be all right. But he would never know what had happened, and should not be told.

It must have been a painful vigil for the women. Yet the patient did wake up, looking refreshed and feeling perfectly normal. Although by now it was six o'clock on a Sunday morning, the women had the presence of mind to take him straight back to the hospital where he had been seen the previous day. There, he was X-rayed again and pronounced fully cured.

Although the women did not tell the doctors what had happened, the case eventually became public knowledge in Magadan and was mentioned in the local paper, *Magadanskaya Pravda*. The young couple married and lived happily ever after, at least up to the time several years later when Ilieva emigrated to Israel and gave her account to Larissa Vilenskaya. It may raise some eyebrows in addition to churning stomachs, yet it will not come as a surprise to anybody with a knowledge of traditional shamanic use of sympathetic magic.[8]

One of the Soviet publishing surprises of 1979 was a reissue of selected works by the explorer and mystic Nicholas Roerich, who spent much time in search of the ancient wisdom and the mythical kingdom of Shambala in the Altai mountains of southern central Siberia. In 1980, a popular Soviet magazine published an article by a Moscow psychologist, Elena Andreyevna, who drew attention to the fact that 'we often come across facts that indicate that a system of secret or esoteric knowledge of the laws of Nature has existed since ancient times'. She gives a sympathetic account of Roerich's quest for Shambala, 'the cosmic centre of esoteric knowledge', and while admitting that there was no hard evidence for the existence of such a place, she concluded: 'Who knows? Perhaps here is the second Troy, and the legend will become reality?'

If we accept Shambala not as a physical kingdom, but as an association of enlightened minds, then the legend already has become reality. In 1980 an account of the activities of one of its citizens turned up in a rather unexpected source: the Soviet magazine of the building trade, *Stroitel'naya Gazeta*, in the form of an interview with a Moscow engineer named Vladimir Safonov on his spare-time activity – healing.

Safonov claims he can heal people in three ways: by touch, by passing his hands close to the body, or by long distance. He can diagnose disease by holding a photograph of the patient and 'feeling the bio-field' which he then examines with his hands as if it were physically present, tuning into it by a process he sees as analogous to that of holography, whereby the whole appearance of an object can be reconstructed from a part of it.

A Soviet academician has publicly testified that Safonov was able to determine the cause of a man's death by examining a plaster death mask. In a less publicised experiment, he was shown photographs of Chinese leaders and asked to describe their state of health. He even diagnoses and heals by telephone, a method also used by Barbara Ivanova, of Moscow, who told me in 1982 that she was receiving up to twenty calls a day including some from the US. Czechoslovakia also had its dial-a-healer, Roman Catholic priest František Ferda, now retired, whose work was described in detail by Dr Rejdák at an international conference in 1979.[9]

Engineer Safonov takes an objective approach to his hobby. He does not believe in miracles, he says, but looks for scientific explanations for what he does. He reckons he can cure any organic disease except certain skin ailments, multiple sclerosis and hereditary or genetic abnormalities, and his listing of a successful healer's requirements will sound familiar to his western counterparts. First, he says, the healer must be in good shape himself. He is donating energy, which must be of good quality, and he must have enough to spare. Then he must overcome 'the inner barrier of disbelief' in his own ability, and should also 'lack respect for an "opposing" authority'. He must be honest and altruistic, and share the results of his research into his own abilities with all.[10]

Safonov is one of several Soviet healers who have repeatedly been tested successfully in laboratories. (Others include Red Army colonel Alexei Krivorotov and the exotic Georgian healer Dzhuna Davitashvili.) In no other country is there so much research into paranormal human abilities, or so much effort to study them rationally and fit them into an expanded model of man.

Edgar Cayce frequently forecast in his trances that the next major religious and spiritual revival would come from the Soviet Union. 'Through Russia', he said, 'comes the hope of the world.' He saw the emergence of a society in which 'each man will live for his fellow man'. The principle had already been born, he said in 1944, but it would take 'years to crystallise'. It now seems that it has.

In 1981, a psychology journal published by the Soviet Academy of Sciences disclosed that after interviewing five thousand people aged seventeen to twenty-five, it was found that about a quarter either believed in God or were fellow travellers in that direction. 'The changing nature of religiosity among young believers must unquestionably lead to corrective action within the system of atheist education to bring it as closely as possible into line with the task of producing young Communists', the journal concluded.[11]

One healer and teacher of psi that no amount of 'corrective action' has managed to silence is Barbara Ivanova, who sees the main aim of parapsychology as 'to help people accept facts and realities known all over the world for thousands of years' and to learn from them. She says:

Since ancient times these have been linked to religious sentiment and used as a basis for understanding the need for moral uplift, and to help people contact the cosmic sphere – Jung's 'collective unconscious', Vernadsky's 'neosphere', or whatever we like to call it. The age of pragmatism interrupted this process, but now we are going back to the old traditions. Those who can feel the real significance of parapsychology are on the way towards this internal uplift.

It is well known, she goes on, that psi abilities tend to disappear when they are misused. 'Many sensitives feel they should not take part in laboratory experiments just to demonstrate their abilities, and without helping others.' The true yogi, she reminds us, rarely shows off his powers in public.

'Anybody seriously interested in parapsychology, even if he has no psi abilities, begins to enter a new world of ideas, or rather an ancient world rediscovered. This helps raise his own moral and ethical code, elevate his interests above the average level, and make both his inner and outer lives more human and richer in meaning.'[12]

Barbara Ivanova is not a dissident. She has no intention of emigrating, although as a Jew she could probably get to Israel. She is a prominent member of a new Soviet group whose members see themselves as 'transformationalists', and whom I see as the builders of the new Shambala, a kingdom without frontiers. These include scientists, artists, intellectuals and 'extrasensers' (as the Soviets call mediums) like her who despite their disillusionment with Marxism are determined to stay in the country they love and try to improve it. The size and influence of this group was described in a rare and surprising magazine interview in 1982 with veteran American transformationalist Michael Murphy, co-founder of the Esalen Institute in Big Sur, California.

Described in 1975 by *Time* magazine as one of the '200 Leaders of the Future', Murphy and his colleague James Hickman have made several trips to the Soviet Union and set up an exchange programme with their Soviet counterparts. Unnoticed by the US media and the professional Soviet-watchers, Murphy says, there are 'certain profound changes' going on in Soviet society, amounting to a 'cultural awakening' not unlike that of America in the 1960s. Interest in psi, alternative medicine, yoga, meditation and esoteric teachings had led to the formation of a 'growing subculture' that was making an impact even on official circles. 'We know for certain that many top officials are involved in these activities themselves,' he said.

The USSR, he believes, has more gifted psychics than any other country simply because Russians have traditionally tried harder than anybody else at whatever they are doing and thrown more of themselves into their literature, music, sport and now psi development, especially healing. Psi is not a mere hobby or topic for academic debate, as in much of the West. It is a real part of real life, vigorously discussed, attacked, defended and practised in public and private. *Komsomolskaya Pravda* (circulation 11 million) calls for the setting up of a National Healing Institute. The Soviet Health Ministry has actually ordered the building of a special clinic to study healing, while Dzhuna Davitashvili has made a considerable impact on official bodies, both figuratively and literally. (British photographer Tom Blau asked her outright in 1980 if it was true she had helped the ailing Leonid Brezhnev extend his lease of life, and was told 'that was something she could not discuss'. To any journalist, that invariably means yes.)[13]

Michael Murphy has expressed his views on East–West social transformation in a novel, *An End to Ordinary History*, which he insists is based on real events. It features an institution in Tashkent where initiates learn to transform their minds and bodies and experience broader realities. The American hero, whose background is similar to Murphy's, is invited there by a man from the KGB who is determined to use psi to help the human race evolve. 'We owe the world our collaboration', he tells his US colleague.

The revolutionary mission of the transformationalists of both east and west was made clear in Murphy's interview. 'It's not enough to talk about transforming a particular body,' he said, 'Because changes of this magnitude change the whole world around you. What happens in such bodily transformation, I believe, is that we inhabit more of the space we are given to inhabit. We grow into a "larger earth".'[14]

Fiction? Utopian fantasy? I am not so sure. Murphy's Tashkent institution sounds to me much like the enormous biophysics laboratory at the Kazakh State University in Alma-Ata headed by Dr Viktor M. Inyushin, where some interesting research on the transformation of both body and mind is known to be going on. A first-hand account of some of it was given in my book *The Cycles of Heaven*, my co-author Scott Hill being one of the few Western visitors ever to get into the place. Here, useful ways of improving athletic performance are studied by the leading Soviet authority on yoga, Dr Alexander S. Romen, and some fairly conventional research into the use of lasers in medicine is carried out. And there are reports that Inyushin and his colleagues are moving into less conventional areas.

One such report comes from Soviet emigrant Mark Popovsky, who described a 1972 meeting at which Inyushin announced his plans to design and build 'psychogenerators' to influence people's feelings and emotions at a distance without their conscious knowledge. A respected American brain researcher, Professor W. Ross Adey, has witnessed a demonstration in which an entire hall of people was put to sleep in a few minutes by having low-frequency electromagnetic waves pulsed at them. Direct intervention in the brains of others is undoubtedly considered a serious possibility in some Soviet circles.[15,16]

Whatever is going on in Inyushin's Alma-Ata laboratory, a certain amount of apparent collaboration between east and west mind-researchers is on public record. Georgi Arbatov, KGB North American affairs specialist and a close associate of the late Yuri Andropov, has visited Esalen, while Werner Erhard, founder of the wealthy and influential *est* (Erhard Seminars Training) organisation, has made a number of trips to the Soviet Union. What type of social transformation they and others are working for remains to be seen.

The negative approach was touched on in an interesting essay written by Edgar Cayce in 1931, in which he gave an example of his own ability to interfere with the minds of others. One day, working in his photographic studio, he told his assistant that he could make a specific person come and see him just by using his mental powers. He asked her to suggest a candidate for the experiment, and she told him to try her brother, who was very sceptical about Cayce's talents.

Cayce duly sat down and meditated for half an hour, 'just thinking about the boy', whereupon to his sister's surprise he walked into the studio for no reason that he knew of. As everybody always does on these occasions, the girl asked Cayce to do it again, and suggested that he try it on a man who particularly disliked him. Cayce agreed, did his meditation, and then left the building. He would be out when the man called, he said, and the man would not know why he had come.

The man arrived about an hour later, and as predicted he told Cayce's assistant that he had no idea why he was there. 'I just came up,' he explained as he left.

Cayce described these demonstrations as examples of 'forcing yourself upon someone else' which, he said, should never be done unless we are very sure of our motives. Once we have learned to control our own minds, he added, it is relatively easy to control the minds of others. If we do so for our own purposes, the process will backfire and destroy us. Mind control is only justified if we use it 'to serve the Creative Forces and God' through prayer, to persuade our target person to do 'God's bidding'. He insisted that 'the force that changes must be from the Divine Source'. This is a clear description of prayer as a combination of telepathy and PK: a process that begins with mental effort and ends with the application of a force that changes the mind of another.[17]

Echoes of Cayce's philosophy are to be found in the Soviet Union today. Vladimir Safonov has described how he diagnoses and heals at long distance, by using powerful concentration to 'conjure up' his patient. 'It is essential,' he writes, 'to forget for the moment that you are diagnosing an empty space in which you are imagining the subject, but rather to think that you are diagnosing the actual person.' While doing this, he sometimes picks up information about his distant patients as if he had taken a shamanic flight and seen them for himself. Cayce often did the same, and was as likely to comment on the colour of his client's pyjamas as on the state of his guts, while Safonov is clearly aware that both telepathy and PK can be projected and focused on specific targets.

His patients have described feelings of warmth, cool breezes, heaviness in the affected organs, even slight pains while being treated at long distance. Safonov is convinced that he can influence people physically by remote control, and the most encouraging part of the interview mentioned above is its title: 'Never Wish Evil on Anybody'.

I have heard the same sentiment expressed so often by Soviets and East Europeans that it seems likely that some Communist authorities have tried to do just that, and at least three books dealing with 'psychic warfare' appeared in 1984. There is, however, one good reason why psi wars are not likely to break out: the potential warriors are simply not going to cooperate.

Throughout the history of mesmerism and hypnotism, practitioners have become instinctively aware of the workings of a powerful natural law, any violation of which is its own punishment. Dr van Pelt, for example, described hypnosis as the 'invoking of a natural law' that can lead to 'an irresistible power of dominant thought which brooks no opposition'.

If such power is harmonised with the greater powers of the 'larger earth', it gets the desired result. If used in opposition to them, it returns to its source and destroys it. Our minds are our own, but the power they can mobilise is not. In the psi arms race, collaboration between potential enemies can only benefit both sides. This is not a matter of ethics, morality or obedience to any particular religion or political system, but one of common sense. According to reporter Ron McRae, the US Army already has a semi-official First Earth Battalion, headed by Lt. Col. Jim Channon and trained to perform 'evolutionary breakthrough actions on behalf of people and planet'. This sounds like a promising development.[18]

The founders of several religions seem to have been aware that all paths lead to Shambala, the kingdom of the enlightened where the Law operates unhindered. Madame Blavatsky, a founder of the theosophical movement, wrote in *The Secret Doctrine* that her aim was 'to rescue from degradation the archaic truths which are the basis of all religions; and to uncover, to some extent, the fundamental unity from which they all spring'. Christian Scientists, the direct descendants of the mesmerists, speak of 'the infinite order of a harmony of the universe created, maintained and beheld by divine Mind'.

However many new religions we invent, we may never be able to define the Natural Law precisely, though we can still believe in a system that works, however elusive and mysterious its behaviour may be. As will be shown shortly, when the system is appealed to in a certain way, it tends to deliver the desired result. The most common form of such an appeal is prayer, the practice of which implies a state of faith in the person doing the praying. Faith and prayer should therefore be studied as practical features of everyday life.

'Man cannot live by bread alone. Neither can he be cured by drugs alone,' writes Dr William A. R. Thomson, a former editor of *The Practitioner* and the compiler of *Black's Medical Dictionary*. 'They have their part to play, but only in collaboration with treatment of the mind and spirit. They are no substitute for those many faiths that heal.'

Faith, he adds, has healed man since the beginning of time. It still does, and it always will, and he has assembled a formidable anthology of quotations from men at the top of all branches of the medical profession to show that he is not alone in his faith in the value of faith itself. Resisting the temptation to quote thirty or forty of them, I will give just one example, from Dr Elmer Hess, president of the American Medical Association: 'The doctor who lacks faith in a supreme being has no right to practise medicine.'[19]

In the opinion of the 1912 winner of the Nobel Prize for medicine, Alexis Carrel, 'the influence of prayer on the human mind and body is as demonstrable as that of the secreting glands'. Prayer, he said, is 'a force as real as terrestrial gravity'. William James saw it as 'no vain exercise of words, no mere repetition of certain sacred formulae, but the very movement itself of the soul, putting itself in a personal relation of contact with the mysterious power of which it feels the presence'. To Frederic Myers, prayer was 'a real increase in intensity of absorption of spiritual power', and it did not really matter to whom or what one prayed so long as the 'attitude of open and earnest expectancy' was there. If it was, then 'grace flows in from the spiritual world'.

The modern scientist is uneasy with such nebulous terms as 'supreme being', 'mysterious power', or 'spiritual world'. Such things cannot be laid out on the laboratory bench and analysed. What *can* be studied is the effect they have on people who believe in them, and we are forced to assume their existence on a basis of their effects.

If prayer is answered, somebody or something out there (or perhaps in here) must answer it. I see no need to complicate things further.

If you take some substance X, add some substance Y, heat it to exactly N degrees, shake and stir, you are sure to get a result in the form of some substance Z. That is how chemistry behaves, provided you get the ingredients and the methods exactly right.

Prayer behaves in precisely the same way. The ingredients and methods required have been described throughout this book, and can be summarised like this:

1 An attitude of open and earnest expectancy and total commitment to the job in hand.
2 Total lack of resistance or doubt.
3 Clear visualisation of what is being prayed for.
4 General consensus that what is being prayed for is both theoretically possible and in the common interest.

There is no reason to suppose that the same general principle does not operate whether you are playing a telepathic parlour game, levitating a table, or saving a life. Let us see how it has been seen to work in practice.

Editors of professional magazines tend to let their hair down at Christmas time, and in 1983 the *British Medical Journal* published some seasonal fare in the form of a special section on the relations between faith and medicine. This included an eight-page article the title of which indicated that its author considered the subject to be of more than academic interest: 'Miracles of healing in Anglo-Celtic Northumbria as recorded by the Venerable Bede and his contemporaries: a reappraisal in the light of twentieth century experience.'

Miracles are not often mentioned in the *BMJ*, and it is not often claimed that there is any modern evidence of them in the light of which to reappraise them. Yet there is, and a good sample of it was given by the author, Dr Rex Gardner, a Fellow of the Royal College of Obstetricians and Gynaecologists and the 1982 president of the Newcastle and Northern Counties Medical Society.

The seventh-century Celtic church in northern England, dominated by the figure of St Cuthbert (*c.*635–87), Bishop of Lindisfarne, was thoroughly documented by the historian known as the Venerable Bede (673–735), who devoted most of his *Vita S. Cuthberti* to accounts of healing miracles wrought by the Celtic saint. These were considered at the time simply as signs of the power of

God, but with the arrival of the Age of Reason, says Dr Gardner, it came to be considered that a belief in miracles was incompatible with serious scholarship, and as recently as 1963 a historian was able to describe faith healing as 'that dangerous field, placed between theology and medicine, that no one has dared thoroughly to explore'.

'It seems to me', writes Dr Gardner, 'that such an exploration is timely', especially if healings similar to those described by Bede are still being reported today. And as he proceeds to show, they are. 'Miraculous healing', he says, 'is a subject that will not go away and has to be considered.' I will summarise very briefly the seven cases he considers in some detail.

1. In 1951, a German nun working on the construction of new premises for the Lutheran Evangelical Sisters of Mary fell from a second storey and was rushed to hospital, where X-rays revealed a compound fracture of the pelvis. Several weeks of traction was prescribed, and the doctor in charge insisted that while prayer might heal mental sickness, 'it will never mend a broken bone'. The nuns thought otherwise. They took the patient home after two days, accepting full responsibility for her, and then got down to some serious praying. The injured sister was on her feet and free from pain in less than a fortnight.

2. In 1963, a Christian missionary named Robin Talbot witnessed the apparent death of a Thai village woman, who had recently been converted, to the dismay of some of the locals. A mere twenty minutes of intense prayer by Mr and Mrs Talbot brought her back to normal, and although evidentially this is the weakest of Gardner's cases, it has three interesting features: a very similar case was recorded by Bede, the cure was sufficiently impressive to convert the local pagan priest on the spot, and during her brief near-death state the woman apparently became clairvoyant – on coming round she displayed an 'accurate and devastating' knowledge of her fellow villagers' secrets.

3. A 1976 case from Nepal also involved an accident while building new premises for church work. The missionary doctor considered that the victim had broken some ribs and ruptured his spleen. No hospital was within reach, so the missionaries held a special ceremony of anointing with oil as described in the Epistle of James (5:14–15), and the man made a full recovery with no medical aid other than an initial injection and an intravenous saline infusion.

4. Wales, 1975. A young woman (a trainee doctor) contracted a form of septicaemia with meningitis of which 'no case had ever

survived' in the hospital to which she was taken. Prayer groups in four Welsh towns held independent but simultaneous meetings for her. An improvement in her condition was noted while these were under way and confirmed by X-rays. One, taken earlier, had shown extensive pneumonia with collapse of the central lobe. The other, taken forty-eight hours later, showed an entirely normal chest. An ophthalmologist examined (and photographed) her left eye, found it severely damaged by internal bleeding, and diagnosed permanent blindness in it. 'You have got to face medical facts,' he told her. After being seen by four consultants, the woman made a full recovery and developed perfect vision. 'Do you realise', one consultant asked, 'you are unique?'

5. An eleven-month-old baby developed fibrosing alveolitis, described by the doctor in charge at the Newcastle-upon-Tyne hospital as 'almost uniformly fatal' for a patient less than a year old. When there had been no response at all to three months of conventional treatment (in fact, he got worse), the child's own GP suggested that his parents should take him to Heaton Pentecostal Church for a healing service, on 26 February 1978. They did; the baby began to recover immediately, and was pronounced perfectly normal in 1983. Both the GP and the hospital doctor are convinced that divine intervention was involved.

6. In 1982, a thirty-five-year old Pakistani woman suffered a massive haemorrhage without clotting following a caesarian section. In the opinion of missionary doctor Dr Ruth Coggan, 'this condition responds only to infusions of triple or quadruple strength plasma and fancy drugs in England'. But 'here, where these things are not available, it responds to the prayer of faith in Jesus's name'. The patient was given one ordinary blood transfusion and some very professional praying, after which she went home with her premature but healthy baby. Dr Coggan's father, incidentally, was 93rd in the line of archbishops and bishops of York, which began with two celebrated seventh-century healers, Wilfrid and Paulinus. He then became Archbishop of Canterbury.

7. In the early 1970s, the captain of the Girl's Brigade at Enon Baptist Church in Monkwearmouth was told by her doctor to give up her activities. The large varicose ulcer on her leg had reached the point where even if it healed it would need a skin transplant. The girl attended the monthly charismatic prayer meeting, and 'by the next morning almost the whole ulcer had dried up, with healthy skin covering'. After one more prayer session, including the laying-on of

hands, healing was complete, Dr Gardner writes. 'This story', he confesses, 'is so bizarre that it would not have been included were I not one of the doctors who examined the patient's leg at the next monthly prayer meeting, and were not all the people who had been present available for interrogation.' Monkwearmouth happens to be the site of the monastery in which the Venerable Bede served, and is not far from where he was born.

'Against the background of such cases one can no longer shrug off the miracles of the sixth and seventh centuries,' says Dr Gardner. As to why they ever were shrugged off, he believes it may be simply that they came to be 'no longer expected or even welcome', and he mentions a delightful example of what can still happen today when miracles are both expected and welcomed.

Some missionaries in Ethiopia left copies of the New Testament in the community where they had been working before they moved elsewhere. Several years later, they returned to find not only a thriving church, but a society in which miracles similar to those reported in the Bible were a part of everyday life. There had, it appears, been 'no missionaries to teach that such things were not to be taken literally'.[20]

Six of Dr Gardner's seven cases mentioned above are supported by evidence from qualified doctors, including Dr Gardner himself, the evidence being very comprehensive in at least four of them. But the one feature they all have in common is that healing took place after prayer *by professionals*. The nuns, missionaries and charismatic groups had all studied that 'definite technique' mentioned at the beginning of this chapter. Like professionals in any other field, they were better at their job than most amateurs. They knew exactly what they were doing and how to do it, and they obtained the predicted result.

Can we conclude, then, that all that is needed for a miraculous healing is total faith in God or Jesus? The evidence suggests that we can, but some of the evidence does not quite fit this model, and to have any explanatory value a theory must account for *all* the facts. It is unlikely that the baby in the Newcastle case had any well-developed religious views. He presumably had instinctive faith in and dependence on his mother, who in turn had faith in the value of the healing service at her church. But how was a mother's faith conveyed to her baby's body? We seem obliged to assume the transfer of a real force. The faith-state of the patient, important though it can be, is not the only factor involved.

There is another complication. In Dr Mason's fish-skin case, a result as striking as any of Dr Gardner's cases was achieved by a fairly standard method of medical hypnosis and suggestion. As far as we know, no prayer at all was involved. Now, if healing by standard hypnosis can get the same results as healing by prayer and faith, then they must have something in common. What could it be?

It cannot be the technique, because many faith cures are performed at long distance without laying-on of hands. Some healers, like some hypnotists, touch their patients while others do not. Some use verbal suggestion, some do not say a word. It cannot be the practitioner's belief system either, because these differ widely. No two healers or hypnotists agree completely as to what they are doing, and some of each have admitted to me that they really do not know.

How about the patient? The one feature all types of healing, normal or paranormal, must have in common is a patient, and there is much evidence to suggest that the patient's state of mind has a good deal to do with the outcome of the disease in question. In any religious context, such as that of each of Dr Gardner's cases, we can assume the patients had faith (or lack of resistance to it), or they would not have been in that context in the first place. In any doctor's surgery, patients must likewise have some faith in standard medicine or they would not have come.

The only hypothesis that seems to fit all the facts is that somebody must have faith in something. It can be the patient, the healer or hypnotist, or even a third party. The faith can be in God, Jesus, the Great Spirit – almost anything imaginable. It can even be simply in the doctor and his pills and nothing else. Miracles, it seems, can be worked by nothing more than a firm belief in their imminent occurrence. When such a belief is implanted in the right mind of a patient, by whatever method – even by deception, outright lying, or as in Dr Mason's classic case, by mistake – the suggested miracle fulfils itself automatically.

It begins to seem, in fact, that the mere act of acknowledging the existence of some power greater than ourselves, or even just assuming this, is enough to activate it.

There are many ways in which real faith healing can be tested under controlled conditions. One would be to apply it to sick animals. (It would make a welcome change to use animals in laboratory experiments designed specifically to help them rather than torment them.) Of course, you cannot verbally implant the idea of a miracle in the mind of an animal, or a baby, but you can still test the hypothesis that the quality of faith in itself can bring about physical effects.

A much more useful experiment would involve terminal cancer patients, of which we unfortunately have a ready supply. Subjects should be selected on a basis of life expectation (assuming a cure) and will to live. The healers themselves should be hypnotised, to make them accept the suggestion that what they are attempting is both plausible and necessary, and to overcome their conditioned negative response to the very idea of trying to break up tumours with hypnosis.

Tumours are ideal targets for this kind of experiment. They can be X-rayed, and are sometimes visible or at least palpable. The rate at which they regress 'spontaneously' is fairly well known, and is very low indeed. The probability of a spontaneous regression in a sample of a hundred patients, or even a thousand, is close to zero.

In 1983, Dr Steven Greer of King's College Hospital (London) gave a lecture to the Royal College of Psychiatrists on 'Cancer and the mind'. 'Most clinicians', he said, 'have seen occasional patients with very advanced cancer whose deep faith or fighting spirit seems to keep them going for unexpected extra weeks or months'. (Let us not forget Dr Newman's patient who survived for two years after being given a few days to live.) He has seen them himself, and published a statistical survey of them in 1979. He made it plain that while the psychological component of the cause of cancer was far from clear, some types being attributable to a virus or to genetic mutation, the potential psychological influence on the course of the disease was a good deal more soundly established. There is now abundant evidence that attempting to cure cancer by treating the mind is a perfectly feasible idea.[21]

I am not calling for the abolition of conventional medicine, nor am I advocating any alternative to it. There is no alternative to medicine, as defined in my dictionary: 'The science of diagnosing, treating or preventing disease and other damage to the body or mind.' This is a profession, and like any other profession it must be practised by professionals. But it needs updating. Its members need to realise what some of them have already been doing in the area of healing by faith, and more of them need to do it more often.

I repeat: if faith is the important factor in healing that countless medical authorities, from Paracelsus to Dr Gardner, have shown it to be, then it should be taught to medical students and studied as thoroughly as anatomy or pathology. Doctors should learn to use it as a standard weapon in the medical armoury, and not as a last resort when all else has failed.

Today's doctor is trying to do two different jobs at once: mechanics and gardening, and it is not reasonable to expect anybody to graduate in two different professions. The mechanical side of medicine is well organised; if you fall downstairs and break some bones, you have a very good chance of receiving prompt and very professional attention. When a crashed body is wheeled into the emergency ward, the medical mechanics know exactly what to do, and in my experience they do a difficult, dangerous and unpleasant job with great efficiency and dedication. It is the other medical profession, body-gardening, that is not being practised as it should be.

Medical students should be given the chance to specialise in this at an early stage. They should be taught the basic facts of mesmerism, hypnotism, suggestion, psychology and religion. They should be given practical courses in telepathy, clairvoyance, psychokinesis and even magic. Let us remember that it was the British Medical Association that named 'healing through religious agencies' as one of the 'main fields which might particularly engage the attention of serious medical research workers' back in 1955. And when such serious researchers appear, they will find that faith healing cannot be studied without taking its paranormal aspects into account.

Deans of medical schools may not care for the idea of teaching magic or miracle-working. Yet once the essential features of each are understood, there remains nothing supernatural about them. 'What we call miraculous,' writes Lama Anagarika Govinda, 'is nothing but a short cut in the interaction of natural forces, i.e., a direct action from mind to mind, without the usual round-about way via the senses and material agents. Faith merely acts as a conductor, which makes this short cut possible.' Like Paracelsus and Myers, he insists that the object of one's faith is relatively unimportant. It can, he says, be in 'a divine power, a human Guru, or in an ideal, or in one's own inner reality'.[22]

'A psychic ability can be trained so that it is actually useful,' says Lawrence LeShan, who has found such an ability to be latent in almost 90 per cent of his trainees. An important feature of his method is to persuade trainees to adopt a 'clairvoyant reality' in which so-called 'paranormal' healing is not only possible but also normal. He has identified two types of healing: one in which the healer visualises a transfer of energy to the patient, the other going right back to Mesmer's 'agreement between two wills'. 'The healer's being', he says, 'should merge into that of the patient, so that both are one.' He uses meditation specifically to alter the healer's state of consciousness, an exercise he has found as effective as a gymnastic one designed to alter the body.[23]

Training of a more colourful kind is provided by Dr Michael Harner, who has made several field trips to isolated communities all over the Americas, and has taken part in 'magical' ceremonies himself. He now teaches shamanism, or 'power and healing', as he calls it, to urban North Americans. His students have included doctors who, he says, 'seem enthusiastic about what they have learned'. Western medicine, he points out, is just as magical to the Amazon Indian as theirs is to us, and just as many Amazon shamans welcome the help of the Western medicine-man with his advanced mechanical skills, so he feels there is a place for shamanism in the sophisticated West.[24]

One has awful visions of New York consultants leaping around in bird feathers, shaking rattles and disembowelling dogs as their assistants bang drums and brew up the *ayahuasca*. Harner, like LeShan, is merely giving instruction in a 'definite technique', one that has been adopted (and adapted) in societies all over the world for centuries. If the exotic rituals of shamanism help people achieve a state of faith, clairvoyant reality, or whatever we want to call it, then they are worth studying.

Paracelsus based some of his faith on beliefs now generally considered false. His was a view of the cosmos in which all things were interdependent, the distant planets influencing our lives, and the 'signatures' of plants (their shapes or colours) curing the diseases of the organs they resembled, while the mind of the alchemist was able to blend with chemical substances and alter them, being altered itself in the process. Astrology, herbal medicine and alchemy may not be quite what Paracelsus thought they were, yet his belief in them helped reinforce his overall faith, which is what mattered.

Mesmer brought magic back into Western medicine, whether by design or by accident. Mesmerism, hypnosis and suggestion are all forms of magic in so far as they obtain results by methods still not fully understood. Doctors use them because they work, but only to a very limited extent. No serious attempt has ever been made to explore their full potential, except by one or two isolated individuals.

One of these was Sir Alexander Cannon, who was a member of both the executive council of the British Medical Association and the Society for Psychical Research. He admitted having used telepathy to transmit 'mind pictures' to his patients, and fifty years ago he wrote: 'Speaking as a medical man, I will prophesy that in ten years' time a complete revolution will have taken place in medicine in regard to hypnotism and mediumship.'[25]

Instead of the revolution, we have had half-hearted calls for revisions of the mind-body concept, textbooks of a pathetically downgraded and restricted form of hypnosis, and only occasional initiatives from enterprising individuals such as Black, Mason, and the specialists mentioned earlier. Elliotson's plea that 'we should lead the public' has long been forgotten. If anybody is leading us today, it is the multinational manufacturers of panacea-pills and of expensive machines.

The mechanics have taken over, pushing the body-gardeners out to the fringes, where lay 'hypnotherapists' may bring some comfort to rich neurotics but are forbidden by law to treat organic disease. If orthodox medicine does not bring simple, direct healing back into its practice, it will leave the field open as so often in the past to the charlatan.

For the resulting state of affairs, it will have only itself to blame.

# Conclusion

'If you leave out the spiritual nature of man,' said Alfred Russel Wallace, 'you are not studying man at all.'[1]

What is this nature, and how can we study it? The answers are surprisingly simple. William James described it as 'the belief that there is an unseen order, and that our supreme good lies in harmoniously adjusting ourselves thereto'. We study it in the same way that we study anything else: by collecting facts, listening to what they tell us, forming hypotheses and testing them.

Colin Wilson, writing a century after Wallace, has described what happens when the study of man's spiritual nature is left out:

> In order to realise his possibilities, man must believe in an *open* future; he must have a vision of something worth doing. And this will not be possible until all the determinism and pessimism that we have inherited from the nineteenth century – and which has infected every department of our culture, from poetry to atomic physics – has been dismissed as fallacious and illogical. Twentieth-century science, philosophy, politics, literature – even music – has been constructed upon a *Weltanschauung* that leaves half of human nature out of account.[2]

The need to complete this *Weltanschauung*, or comprehensive world-view, has been well put by Sir Alister Hardy. 'The science of life, as I see it,' he writes, 'should range from biophysics and biochemistry, at one end of a descriptive "spectrum", to the study of man's emotional behaviour, both sexual and religious, at the other end of it.'

There has been no lack in this century of study and exploitation of man's sexual behaviour, especially its more disagreeable aspects, but the study of his spiritual or religious behaviour has been left out of account by the life scientists. Fortunately, Professor Hardy has now not only defined the problem, but has also begun to work it out, using the accepted materials and methods of the life sciences.

The first method was to assemble the facts, and in 1969 he helped found the Religious Experience Research Unit (RERU) at Manchester College, Oxford, to do just that. He made several appeals to the public for written accounts of personal experience of 'some power, whether they called it God or not, which had appeared to them to be either beyond their individual selves or even entirely within their being'. It was obviously impossible to study somebody else's subjective experience directly, but it was perfectly possible to make an objective study of accounts of them, and the RERU soon amassed a data-base of more than three thousand such accounts.

The second method was to classify the accounts into twelve categories, with numerous sub-categories, and this alone revealed some useful findings. Experiences reported by more than 20 per cent of the respondents included: 'sense of security, protection, peace' (25.3 per cent); 'sense of joy, happiness, well-being' (21.2); and 'sense of presence (not human)' (20.2). But the clear winner was 'initiative felt to lie within the self, but response from beyond; prayers answered' with 32.3 per cent, very nearly one third of the whole sample, and more than two and a half times as many as experiences of grace 'coming out of the blue' or 'initiative felt to be beyond the self'. Thus the RERU has established, on the basis of a large sample, that the most commonly felt aspect of religious experience is that it can actually be generated by oneself and responded to. Religious experience may be something that 'just happens' to some, to others it is something they *make* happen.

Professor Hardy's hypothesis is that 'there is some profound reality behind religion', and he insists that 'like any other hypothesis it must be made the subject of prolonged and thorough research' before being accepted or rejected. One way to do this is to regard prayer as 'a formula for generating religious experience' that can be tested whether one is already 'religious' or not. All the believer or the sceptic has to do is to 'try the experiment of approaching the power we call God in a particular way, not by prayer for the alteration of physical events or for personal safety or material ends, but for strength and guidance for a better way of life' and 'to achieve some worthwhile purpose'. Hardy believes that 'if they make the experiment in the right way, they would find it works. "Ask and ye shall receive".'

It could be, he says, that 'the various separate solutions to our individual problems are always within us if only we could reach them, and that the act of prayer brings them to the surface'. He believes that prayer may in fact be the only way of mobilising a force that can not only solve problems but also heal sick bodies and lead to what William James called 'a faith, a *force* that re-infuses the positive willingness to live' (emphasis added).[3]

Sir Alister has already published a whole book based on a study of the specimens of personal experience provided by his volunteer helpers.[4] This has every right to be considered as a scientific textbook for students of the soul, and even to some extent as a book of instructions for the working of miracles, for as he wrote in an earlier book:

> Improvements in the world are brought about through the actions of men and women and not by miraculous Divine interventions in the course of nature; yet again and again those who have altered the world for the better have declared that they have felt that they have received help from beyond themselves: 'it is God working through me', they have said. God works wonders in the world – but his hands are the hands of men.[5]

Here is just one of about a thousand cases collected by the RERU in its first ten years in which prayer seems to have obtained practical results. The narrator, an anonymous woman, seems to have caused a minor but useful intervention in the course of nature, and somebody seems to have received help from beyond himself in consequence.

The woman was speaking on the telephone to a friend whose problems had brought him close to breakdown point. When he spoke of his misery and distress, she longed to help him but felt unable to do so in person:

> Instead I went on my knees saying 'I know I may not go to him, but if I could go, this is what I'd say' – and I said to God all that was in my heart to give comfort to our friend. Some days later I met him unexpectedly and he said, 'I'm feeling better. If you ever get as low as that, remember this', and he proceeded to tell me, almost word for word, what I said on my knees. I have no doubt that we had met on some different plane and God has used me to bring him the

comfort it would have been entirely wrong to give him in any other way.[6]

This is one of several cases Professor Hardy uses to support his view of faith as something that can be considered experimental in the original sense of the word – based on experience rather than on conjecture or the word of somebody else – as used by John Wesley. I see no reason why we cannot now speak of faith as experimental in the more recent sense of the word – based on experiment – as well, on a basis of the kind of experiment I have already suggested involving 'incurable' patients.

Prayer can also be regarded as an experimental method, in both senses of the word. It has already been used for thousands of years simply because it is known to work, and if it works it can be shown to work like any other experimental method. Detailed instructions for how to do it properly are readily available. Thousands of people already know how to do it properly, including many doctors.

'Even when my patients are under anaesthesia, I'll lay hands on them and speak lovingly,' says Dr Bernard Siegel, a cancer surgeon at Yale University. 'Time and time again I'm made to believe it makes a difference.' Students have reported him as saying to a patient whose heart stopped during an operation: 'Come back! It's not your time yet', an example of spontaneous prayer at a time of crisis.

'I get criticised for telling healing anecdotes – like that was the same as telling lies – but you can imagine how likely it is for me to obtain a grant to do a study on healing,' he laments. 'If I came up with a chemotherapy that made your ears fall off I'd be more likely to get a grant.'[7]

It is becoming more and more difficult to separate what we call religion from what I have been calling psi, the paranormal mental and physical effects of telepathy, clairvoyance and psychokinesis. Forty years ago, reviewing the results of ten years of experimental research in the laboratory, J. B. Rhine wrote:

'The mental system has a determinative influence which produces registrable effects without any conceivable physical intermediation. These effects reveal the stamp of intelligent purpose and do so in a way that is nonetheless physically a cause-effect phenomenon.'[8] This, I suggest, is the basis of an explanation not only of PK, but also of prayer, which need no longer be considered as miraculous or magical, but as a wholly natural and testable phenomenon. The same applies to natural healing, whether this is brought about by hypnosis, mesmerism, suggestion or personal faith.

Throughout this book, I have given examples of how the mental system can be made to produce registrable effects, from the regeneration of skin and the suppression of blisters, pain and tumours to the receiving of information from a distance and the levitation of furniture. Some of these effects are trivial and destructive, others save lives. The methods used to cause them are the same, therefore the process by which they are caused is probably also the same. While we may not understand the real nature of this process, we know enough about the way in which it behaves to make it work for us, as is the case with electricity.

There is no need for me to urge the orthodox medical profession to apply the method. It is already doing so, and has been for two hundred years, though in general only in their most half-hearted manner. It only remains for medical hypnotists to understand what they are really doing, to do it better, and to do it more often. Nature, as Mesmer claimed, does offer us a universal means for curing and preserving mankind. It may not operate in the way he thought, it may not cure or preserve all patients every time it is used, and it may not always be needed. It may be the universal panacea, or it may not. We simply do not know. What we do know is that its potential has been and continues to be greatly underestimated.

We know the rules. We know how to alter a person's state of mind safely and painlessly by the use of mesmerism, suggestion or hypnosis. We know how to induce faith, and how to use prayer in the most effective manner. We know how to facilitate the sending and receiving of telepathy and clairvoyance, and how to generate psychokinesis. All of this knowledge can be tested and verified by anybody who is prepared to obey the rules, and to repeat the conditions under which the various phenomena occur spontaneously. It now remains only to unite the phenomena and apply them for the common good, whether or not this is generally considered possible. The only way to establish the limits of the possible, as Arthur C. Clarke has pointed out, is to attempt the impossible.

Religious interpretations of this knowledge are a matter of personal choice, but it is possible to take a strictly scientific view of matters sometimes considered the sole property of the theologian, as Hardy has shown. The leading scientist of this century, Einstein, was not ashamed to speak of 'the illimitable superior power', or to identify the basis of true religion as the awareness that 'what is impenetrable to us really exists, manifesting itself as the highest wisdom and the most radiant beauty which our dull minds can comprehend only in their most primitive forms.'

Many of us, great and small, have caught glimpses of what a former Communist, Arthur Koestler, called 'the third order of reality' beyond those of our senses and our concepts. One could not read a text written in invisible ink, he wrote, but 'the knowledge that it existed was sufficient to alter the texture of one's existence'.[9] Forty-five years after the experience in a Spanish prison that made him aware of this, he was to leave most of his large fortune to the study, in his own words, of 'parapsychology and parapsychology alone' at university level.

In this book, I have given examples of several ways in which we can explore new orders of reality and make use of a wisdom far higher than our own. As has been said, this appears to be available for human use. For all the complexities of life, it appears that we are able to obtain the support of the Supreme Intelligence, the Biological Organising Model, Morphogenetic Field, *aumakua*, God – whatever we choose to call it – by no more than a conscious decision to ask for it.

History, says psychologist Dr Martin L. Rossman, abounds with cases of 'guidance received when men cried out for help in the darkness of unknowing and suffering', and he concludes: 'It is in this empirical relationship to a higher level of organisation, whether in our own nervous system or in the universe at large, that the great self-care potential of the human imagination may reside.'[10]

This relationship can be discussed in terms of systems theory as well as the language of mysticism. Dr Gary L. Schwartz, another psychologist in tune with changing world-views, points out that once the appropriate connections are made, a system will behave with a sense of purpose, taking on a life of its own as it works to meet specific goals. If we change the connections, he says, we change not only the way the system works but also its purpose, and the human imagination has the power to make or break all kinds of connections, whether at biological, psychological or social levels.[11]

The informational environment, as Stephen Black discovered, 'can be just as important to physical health as the physical environment.'[12] Whether the information comes in the form of a germ or an idea, what is fed into the system dictates what comes out of it. As we have seen, we are able to obtain information from some mysterious source by means of the definite technique known as prayer. We can also transfer information from one mind to another, sometimes causing action in a body as a result. The power to make new connections in the personal, social or global systems appears to be ours for the asking; connections between left and right brains, brains and minds, minds and bodies, bodies and other bodies, perhaps all other bodies.

'Intelligence', said the late Glen Schaefer, Professor of Ecological Physics at Cranfield Institute of Technology, 'dominates the entire universe and the whole of evolution.'[13] This implies the existence of a dominant mind, one that has already made a number of connections. Our own minds can add to them if they wish. The choice is theirs.

# Notes

## 1  Miracle at East Grinstead

1  A. A. Mason, *BMJ*, 23 August 1952, pp. 442–3.
2  Interview with Mason in BBC 2 film 'Hypnosis. Can Your Mind Control Your Body?' by Michael Barnes, 27 September 1982.
3  *BMJ*, 1952, pp. 434, 615, 725, 832, 996, 1043, 1101, 1356 (discussion of Mason, op. cit.).
4  S. Black, *Mind and Body*, London: William Kimber, 1969, p. 130.
5  A. A. Mason, *BMJ*, 7 October 1961, p. 946.
6  C. A. S. Wink, *BMJ*, 16 September 1961, pp. 741–3.
7  A. A. Mason, *Hypnotism for Medical and Dental Practitioners*, London: Secker & Warburg, 1960, pp. 82–3.
8  G. Ambrose and G. Newbold, *A Handbook of Medical Hypnosis*, London: Baillière Tindall, 4th edn, 1980, p. 107.
9  D. M. Ewin, 'Emergency room hypnosis for the burned patient', *American Journal of Clinical Hypnosis*, 26 (1), 5–8, 1983. For independent reports on hypnosis and enhancement of burn healing, see Margolis *et al.*, pp. 9–15 and Moore and Kaplan, pp. 16–19 in the same journal. The quotation is from an interview with Ewin, in the film cited in n. 2.
10  J. Delboeuf, *De l'origine des effets curatifs de l'hypnotisme*, Paris: Alcan, 1887, p. 23 ff.
11  L. Chertok, *Sense and Nonsense in Psychotherapy*, Oxford: Pergamon, 1981, ch. 2.
12  Interview with Chertok, in film cited in n. 2.
13  Black, op. cit., ch. 12.
14  J. Braid, *Neurypnology; or the Rationale of Nervous Sleep*, London: Churchill, 1843, p. 94.
15  Black, op. cit., p. 163.
16  V. M. Bekhterev in L. Satow, *Hypnotism and Suggestion*, London: Allen & Unwin, 1923, p. 27.
17  Interview with G. Maher-Loughnan, in film cited in n. 2.
18  Le LeCron (ed.), *Experimental Hypnosis*, New York: Macmillan, 1952, p. 239.
19  *Daily Telegraph*, 27 August 1986. Ambrose and newbold, op. cit. p. 220.
20  J. Jaynes, *The Origin of Consciousness in the Breakdown of the Bicameral Mind*, Boston: Houghton Mifflin, 1976, p. 379.

2 *Postponed Investigation*

1 S. J. van Pelt, *Hypnotism and the Power Within*, London: Skeffington, 1950, ch. 1.
2 F. A. Mesmer, *Le Magnétisme animal* (ed. R. Amadou), Paris: Payot, 1971, p. 139.
3 Marquis de Puységur, *Du magnétisme animal*, Paris: Dentu, 2nd edn, 1820, ch. 14.
4 W. Sargant, *The Mind Possessed*, London: Heinemann, 1973, ch. 21.
5 W. Sargant, *Battle for the Mind*, London: Heinemann, 1957.
6 R. O. Becker and A. A. Marino, *Electromagnetism and Life*, Albany: State University of New York Press, 1982, pp. ix, 206.
7 E. J. Dingwall (ed.), *Abnormal Hypnotic Phenomena*, London: Churchill, 1967 (4 vols), vol. 1, p. 8.
8 B. MacManaway and J. Turcan, *Healing*, Wellingborough: Thorsons, 1983, p. 42.
9 E. Fromm and R. E. Shor (eds) *Hypnosis. Research Developments and Perspectives* London: Elek, 1973, pp. 20–1.
10 Van Pelt, op. cit.
11 V. Buranelli, *The Wizard from Vienna*, London: Peter Owen, 1976, p. 216.
12 J. Esdaile, *The Introduction of Mesmerism ... into the Public Hospitals of India*, London: W. Kent, 2nd edn, 1856, p. 40.
13 Van Pelt, op. cit.
14 F. Podmore, *Mesmerism and Christian Science*, London: Methuen, 1909, pp. 152, 154.
15 J. Milne Bramwell, *Hypnotism and Treatment by Suggestion*, London: Cassell, 1909, p. 10.
16 L. Satow, *Hypnotism and Suggestion* London: Allen & Unwin, 1923, p. 47.
17 A. Forel, *Hypnotism, or Suggestion and Psychotherapy*, London: Rebman, 1906, pp. 219–20.
18 *BMJ*, 23 April 1955 (Supplement), pp. 190–3.
19 Ibid., 13 September 1958, pp. 682–3.
20 Ibid., 11 August 1962, pp. 371–6.
21 Ibid., 7 October 1978, p. 978.
22 Ibid., 17 March 1979, p. 751.
23 *The Practitioner*, May 1981, p. 746.
24 Van Pelt, op. cit., p. 107 ff.
25 S. Black, *Mind and Body*, London: William Kimber, 1969, p. 172.
26 Ibid., p. 179
27 A. A. Mason, *Hypnotism for Medical and Dental Practitioners*, London: Secker & Warburg, 1960, p. 15
28 Ibid., p. 63.
29 J. Reyher in *Annals of the New York Academy of Sciences*, 296, 1977, p. 84.
30 Black, op. cit., p. 13.
31 A. C. Clarke, *Profiles of the Future*, New York: Harper & Row, 1963, chs 1, 2.
32 J. G. Watkins and P. C. Young in L. LeCron (ed.), *Experimental Hypnosis*, New York: Macmillan, 1952, ch. 16.
33 Forel, op. cit., ch. 12.

34 Interview with Dr Franz Baumann in BBC 2 film 'Hypnosis. Can Your Mind Control Your Body?' by Michael Barnes, 27 September 1982.
35 Paracelsus quoted in Satow, op. cit., pp. 36–7.
36 Sargant, *The Mind Possessed*, op. cit., p. 84.
37 J. Coates, *Human Magnetism*, London: Fowler, 1910, p. 148.
38 B. Hollander, *Hypnotism and Suggestion in Daily Life*, London: Pitman, 1910, p. 195.
39 Van Pelt, op. cit., p. 200.

3  *Scylla and Charybdis*

1  M. S. Gazzaniga and J. E. LeDoux, *The Integrated Mind*, New York: Plenum, 1978, p. 47.
2  J. Oppenheimer in *Annals of the New York Academy of Sciences*, 299, 1977, p. 13.
3  R. Sperry and R. Puccetti in ibid., p. 453.
4  J. Bogen, quoted by Puccetti in ibid.
5  J. Jaynes, *The Origin of Consciousness in the Breakdown of the Bicameral Mind*, Boston: Houghton Mifflin, 1976.
6  T. R. Blakeslee, *The Right Brain*, London: Macmillan, 1980, ch. 8.
7  E. Swedenborg, *The Spiritual Diary of Emmanuel Swedenborg* (1748), London: James Speirs, 1883, pp. 34, 329.
8  E. Swedenborg, *Heaven and Hell* (1758), London: Swedenborg Society, 1966, § 367.
9  F. W. H. Myers, 'Automatic Writing', *Proceedings of the Society for Psychical Research*, 3 (8), 1–63, 1885, pp. 30, 43.
10  C. Lloyd Tuckey, *Treatment by Hypnotism and Suggestion*, London: Baillière Tindall & Cox (1889), 3rd edn, 1891, p. 42.
11  T. J. Hudson, *The Law of Psychic Phenomena*, Chicago: McClurg, 1893.
12  D. L. Pedersen, 'Hypnosis and the right hemisphere', *Proceedings of the British Society for Medical and Dental Hypnosis*, 5 (4), 2–14, 1984.
13  See M. E. Humphrey and O. L. Zangwill, 'Cessation of dreaming after brain injury', *Journal of Neurology, Neurosurgery and Psychiatry*, 14, 322–5, 1951.
14  W. Penfield and R. Lamar, *Speech and Brain Mechanisms*, Princeton University Press, 1959.
15  C. MacLeod-Morgan, 'Hypnosis is a Right-hemisphere task ...', *Svensk Tidskrift for Hypnosis*, 10, 84–90, 1983. See also: *Psychophysiology*, 19, 687–90, 1982; *Australian Journal of Clinical and Experimental Hypnosis*, 10 (2), 99–102, 1982.
16  C. Wilson, *Frankenstein's Castle*, Sevenoaks: Ashgrove Press, 1980, p. 37.
17  R. E. Shor in E. Fromm and R. E. Shor (eds), *Hypnosis. Research Development and Perspectives*, London: Elek, 1973, ch. 2.
18  Einstein, quoted by Blakeslee, op. cit. pp. 45–6.
19  J. D. Watson, *The Double Helix*, Harmondsworth: Penguin, 1970.
20  W. T. Gallwey, *The Inner Game of Tennis*, New York: Random House, 1974, p. 25.
21  Blakeslee, op. cit., ch. 5.

22  D. F. Brown, *New Realities*, 1 (4), 1977, p. 12.
23  *Science in Action*, BBC World Service, 11 July 1982.
24  Quoted by J. Whitmore, 'The Russian Connection', *Human Potential*, Sept./Nov. 1982, pp. 6–7, 16.
25  P. B. Field, quoted in Shor and Fromm, op. cit., p. 483.
26  S. Black, *Mind and Body*, London: William Kimber, 1969, p. 263.
27  A. W. Scheflin and E. M. Opton Jr, *The Mind Manipulators*, London: Paddington Press, 1978, pp. 40–3.
28  Black, op. cit., p. 162.
29  *Sunday Times*, 11 December 1977, p. 5.
30  H. B. Gibson, *Hypnosis. Its Nature and Therapeutic Uses*, London: Peter Owen, 1977, p. 89.

4  *Miss Barber is Cured*

1  J. Elliotson, *The Zoist*, October 1848, pp. 213–37, 312–16.
2  K. S. Bowers in *Annals of the New York Academy of Sciences*, 296, 1977, p. 234.
3  *The Lancet*, 1 October 1983, pp. 773–4.
4  E. Green and A. Green, *Beyond Biofeedback*, New York: Delacorte Press, 1977, pp. 111–12.
5  Ibid., p. 55.
6  Ibid., p. 62.
7  C. Maxwell Cade and N. Coxhead, *The Awakened Mind*, London: Wildwood House, 1979, pp. 197–8.
8  H. Benson *et al.*, 'Body temperature changes during the practice of g Tum–mo yoga'. *Nature*, 295, 234–6, 1982.
9  E. and A. Green, op. cit., p. 209.
10  Ibid., p. 116.
11  D. W. Smithers, 'Cancer: an attack on cytologism', *The Lancet*, 1, 493–7, 1962.
12  B. W. Newton, 'The use of hypnosis in the treatment of cancer patients', *American Journal of Clinical Hypnosis*, 25 (2–3), 104–13, 1982, and personal communication, May 1984.
13  T. C. Everson and W. H. Cole, *A Study and Abstract of Reports in the World Medical Literature and of Personal Communications Concerning Spontaneous Regression of Malign Disease*, London: W. B. Saunders, 1966.
14  B. W. Newton, personal communication, May 1984.
15  A. Meares, 'Cancer, psychosomatic illness and hysteria', *The Lancet*, 7 November 1981, p. 1037.
16  A. Meares, Lecture at the Royal Society of Medicine, 19 January 1981.
17  A. Meares, 'What makes the patient better?', *The Lancet*, 10 June 1961, pp. 1280–1.
18  A. Meares, 'What makes the patient better? Atavistic regression as a basic factor', *The Lancet*, 20 January 1962, pp. 151–3.
19  A. Meares, 'A form of intensive meditation associated with the regression of cancer', *American Journal of Clinical Hypnosis*, 25 (2–3), 114–21, 1982/3.
20  A. Meares, 'What makes the patient better?', *The Lancet*, 10 June 1961, p. 1281.

21 A. Meares, 'Regression of cancer after intensive meditation', *Medical Journal of Australia*, 2, 184, 1976.
22 A. Meares, personal communication, May 1984.
23 O. C. Simonton, S. Matthews-Simonton and J. L. Creighton, *Getting Well Again*, New York: Bantam Books, 1978.
24 L. LeShan, *You Can Fight for Your Life*, Wellingborough: Thorsons, 1984.
25 R. J. Newman, personal communications, November 1983 and February 1984.
26 H. B. Miller, 'Your emotions: can they influence disease?', *Science Digest*, July 1970, pp. 61–4.
27 H. B. Miller, 'The process of thought', *British Journal of Clinical Hypnosis*, 3 (1), 49–53, 1972; and personal communications, November 1983 and May 1984.
28 E. H. Shattock, *Mind Your Body*, Wellingborough: Turnstone Press, 1979.
29 J. Achterberg and G. F. Lawlis in A. A. Sheikh (ed.), *Imagination and Healing*, Farmingdale: Baywood, 1984, p. 42.
30 H. L. Hall in ibid., pp. 159–69, and *American Journal of Clincial Hypnosis*, 25, 92–103, 1983.

## 5  *The Tower of Pisa*

1 *The Times*, 16 December 1982.
2 Bristol Cancer Help Centre, Grove House, Cornwallis Grove, Clifton, Bristol, Avon.
3 P. Pilkington, lecture at the College of Psychic Studies, London, 18 October 1983.
4 *Daily Telegraph*, 16 July 1983.
5 *The Times*, 16 March 1983.
6 B. Kidman, interview with Sarah Jones, *Expansion*, 2, 1983, pp. 22–4.
7 A. Woolley-Hart, lecture at the College of Psychic Studies, London, 29 May 1984.
8 ANAC, c/o The Seekers Trust, The Close, Addington Park, Maidstone, Kent.
9 M. McCausland, personal communication, August 1983.
10 *Harmony*, Spring 1983, pp. 8–9.
11 *Psychology Today*, September 1980, p. 45.
12 I. T. Baldwin and J. C. Schultz, 'Rapid changes in tree leaf chemistry induced by damage: evidence for communication between plants', *Science*, 15, July 1983, pp. 277–9.
13 K. Sabbagh, *World Medicine*, 25 July 1981, p. 69.
14 Quoted in *Harmony*, Spring 1983, p. 4.
15 *British Medical Journal*, 5 January 1980, pp. 1–2.
16 L. LeCron (ed.), *Experimental Hypnosis*, New York: Macmillan, 1952, p. x.
17 *The Lancet*, 1 October 1983, pp. 773–4.
18 *Science Digest*, May 1982, pp. 88–95.
19 L. Rose, *Faith Healing*, Harmondsworth: Penguin Books, 1971.
20 Quoted by L. Satow, *Hypnotism and Suggestion*, London: Allen & Unwin, 1923, p. 21.

21 D. Shapiro, 'Psychological Aspects of Medication', in *The Psychological Basis of Medical Practice* (ed. L. L. Leif), New York: Harper & Row, 1963.
22 A. W. Scheflin and E. M. Opton Jr, *The Mind Manipulators*, London: Paddington Press, 1978, pp. 247–9.
23 G. L. Playfair, *The Flying Cow*, London: Souvenir Press, 1975, Part 2.
24 L. Parks, *Getting Results from Hypnosis*, Psychological Research Foundation Inc., PO Box BB, Beaverton, Oregon 97075, 1979, and personal communications, 1984.
25 P. McKellar, *Experience and Behaviour*, Harmondsworth: Penguin, 1968, pp. 78–81. For current understanding of the left-right brain puzzle, see J. Levy in *Omni* (January 1985) and *Psychology Today* (May 1985).

**II** *Introduction*

1 G. L. Playfair, *The Flying Cow*, *The Indefinite Boundary* and *This House is Haunted*, London: Souvenir Press, 1975, 1976 and 1980.

**6** *Glad Day*

1 F. E. Leaning, 'An introductory study of hypnagogic phenomena', *Proceedings of the Society for Psychical Research*, 35 (94), 289–412, 1925.
2 See T. R. Blakeslee, *The Right Brain*, London: Macmillan, 1980, ch. 9.
3 S. Hampshire, *Susan's Story*, London: Sphere Books, 1983.
4 P. McKellar, *Imagination and Thinking*, London: Cohen & West, 1957, p. 36.
5 E. and A. Green, *Beyond Biofeedback*, New York: Delacorte Press, 1977, p. 17.
6 B. B. Wolman (ed.), *Handbook of Parapsychology*, New York: Van Nostrand Reinhold, 1977, pp. 459–65.
7 *Alpha* 6, January/February 1980, pp. 9–10.
8 U. Sinclair, *Mental Radio* (1930), New York: Collier, 1971, ch. 21 and *passim*.
9 C. E. M. Hansel in 'The Case of ESP', BBC 2 *Horizon* film by Tony Edwards, 26 September 1983.
10 R. Targ and K. Harary, *The Mind Race*, New York: Villard Books, 1984.
11 J. Gertz, 'Hypnagogic fantasy, EEG and psi performance in a single subject', *Journal of the American Society for Psychical Research*, April 1983, pp. 155–70, and personal communication May 1984.
12 Quoted by A. Hardy, *The Living Stream*, London: Collins, 1965, pp. 238–9.
13 Quoted by J. Newson, lecture at the College of Psychic Studies, London, 1 November 1983.
14 M. Freedom Long, *The Secret Science Behind Miracles*, Santa Monica: DeVorss, 1954.

**7** *I Change His Mind*

1 B. Nicol and F. Nicol, 'Buried alive – saved by telepathy', *Tomorrow*, Spring 1957, pp. 9–13.

2  A. Puharich, *Beyond Telepathy*, Garden City: Doubleday, 1962.

3  U. Sinclair, *Mental Radio*, New York: Collier, 1930, p. 160.

4  C. Richet, *Our Sixth Sense*, London: Rider, 1929, pp. 67–8.

5  Ibid., p. 45.

6  C. Richet, *Thirty Years of Psychical Research*, London: Collins, 1923, p. 125.

7  F. W. H. Myers, 'On telepathic hypnotism, and its relation to other forms of hypnotic suggestion', *Proceedings of the Society for Psychical Research*, 4 (10), 127–88, 1886 (pp. 131–7).

8  L. L. Vasiliev, *Experiments in Distant Influence* (1962), London: Wildwood House, 1976, p. 214.

9  R. McConnell, *An Introduction to Parapsychology in the Context of Science*, privately printed, 1983, chs 15, 16.

10  V. M. Bekhterev, 'Direct influence of a person upon the behavior of animals' (1920), *Journal of Parapsychology*, 13, 166–76, 1949.

11  Vasiliev, op. cit., p. 93.

12  Ibid., pp. 214–19.

13  Ibid., pp. 220–2.

14  Ibid., xiii–xiv.

15  Ibid., ch. 4.

16  Ibid., chs 8, 9.

17  Marquis de Puységur, *Mémories pour servir à l'histoire et à l'établissement du magnétisme animal*, Paris: Cellot, 2nd edn, 1809, pp. 42, 49.

18  H. E. Hammerschlag, *Hypnotism and Crime*, London: Rider, 1956, ch. 7.

## 8  Will Force

1  B. Russell, quoted in L. Barnett, *The Universe and Dr. Einstein*, 2nd rev. edn, 1957, p. 15.

2  S. Black, *Mind and Body*, London: William Kimber, 1969, ch. 13.

3  Ibid., p. 60.

4  Ibid., p. 56.

5  A. Gradenwitz, 'Experimental telepathy. Tests by Dr Carl Bruck, MD Berlin, on the transmission of drawings', *Scientific American*, May 1924, pp. 304–5.

6  A. Hardy, *The Living Stream*, London: Collins, 1965, ch. 9.

7  R. Sheldrake, *A New Science of Life*, London: Blond & Briggs, 1981.

8  L. Watson, *Lifetide*, London: Hodder & Stoughton, 1979, ch. 6.

9  W. McDougall, *British Journal of Psychology* 17, 267–304, 1927; 20, 201–18, 1930; 28, 321–45, 1938. Quoted in Sheldrake, op. cit., ch. 11.

10  *Brain Mind Bulletin*, 12 September 1983; *New Scientist*, 27 October 1983.

11  A. Koestler, *Janus. A Summing Up*, London: Hutchinson, 1978, p. 197.

12  S. V. Speransky, 'Extraordinary transmission of information about starvation', *Parapsychology in the USSR* (ed. L. Vilenskaya), Washington Research Center, 3101 Washington St, San Francisco CA 94115 (5 parts), Part 3, pp. 4–11. See also pp. 26–7.

13  S. V. Speransky, 'Extraordinary transmission of information about stress', *Parapsychology in the USSR* op. cit., vol. 4, pp. 16–17.

14  J. B. Rhine and B. M. Humphrey, 'Special evidence from hit patterns ...', *Journal of Parapsychology* 8, 18–60, 1944.

15  E. Haraldsson *et al.*, 'National survey of psychical experiences ... in Iceland' in *Research in Parapsychology 1976* (ed. W. G. Roll, R. L. Morris, J. D. Morris), Metuchen: Scarecrow Press, 1977.

16  A. R. Wallace, *Contributions ...*, London: Macmillan, 2nd edn, 1871, pp. 359–65.

17  Black, op. cit., ch. 15.

18  *Physics Letters* 67a (3), 171–4, 1978.

19  J. Ehrenwald, *The ESP Experience. A Psychiatric Validation*, New York: Basic Books, 1978, ch. 19.

20  J. Ehrenwald, *New Dimensions of Deep Analysis*, London: G. Allen & Unwin, 1954, p. 114.

### 9   Some Progressing Fluctuations

1   A. R. Wallace, *On Miracles and Modern Spiritualism*, London: Burns, 2nd edn, 1874, ch. 10.

2   A. de Gasparin, *Science vs. Modern Spiritualism. A Treatise on Turning Tables* (2 vols), New York: Kiggins & Kellogg, 1857.

3   M. Thury, *Les tables tournantes considérées au point de vue de la question de physique génerale qui s'y rattache*, Geneva: J. Kessmann, 1855, p. 11.

4   P. Fenwick *et al.*, '"Psychic sensitivity", mystical experience, head injury and cognitive change' *Journal of Medical Psychology* (in press).

5   J. C. Ferraz Salles, 'Hipoxemia fetal e superdotados intelectuais', *Revista de Ginecologia e d'Obstetricia*, October 1968, and paper read to congress of Infantile Neurology, Rio de Janeiro, November 1970.

6   D. Robinson, 'The table-tipping experiments of Haakon Forwald', *Theta*, Spring 1984, pp. 7–12.

7   I. Owen and M. Sparrow, *Conjuring Up Philip*, Ontario: Fitzhenry & Whiteside, 1976.

8   C. Brookes-Smith, *Journal of the Society for Psychical Research* 45 (744), 265–81, 1970; 47 (756), 69–89, 1973; 48 (764), 73–86, 1975. See also extensive unpublished MS material in the library of the SPR.

9   K. J. Batcheldor, 'PK in sitter groups', *Psychoenergetic Systems* 3, 77–93, 1979.

10  *Research in Parapsychology 1982* (ed. W. G. Roll, J. Beloff, R. A. White), Metuchen: Scarecrow Press, 1983, pp. 45–61.

11  W. James, *The American Magazine*, October 1909.

12  A. Barham, *Strange to Relate*, Gerrards Cross: Colin Smythe, 1984 (2nd edn), ch. 5.

13  R. Hare, *Experimental Investigations of the Spirit Manifestations*, New York: Partridge & Brittan, 1855.

### 10   Turning the Tables

1   J. Courtier, *Rapport sur les séances d'Eusapia Palladino à l'Institut Général Psychologique en 1905, 1906, 1907 et 1908*, Paris: Institut Général Psychologique, 1908, p. 29. See also C. Flammarion, *Mysterious Psychic Forces*,

London: T. Fisher Unwin, 1907,. p. 415: 'While resting our hands upon it, we have the sensation of a fluid resistance, as if it were in water – the kind of fluid sensation we experience when we bring a piece of iron into the field of force of a magnet.'

2 See also E. Hardinge, *Modern American Spiritualism*, London: James Burns, 1870, p. 81: 'On several occasions a very heavy dining-table was held suspended in the air with several persons seated on it whose feet did not even touch the floor', D. D. Home in *Report on Spiritualism of the London Dialectical Society*, London: 1873, p. 190: 'I have seen a table lifted into the air with eight men standing on it', and 'M.R.C.P.' in *Spiritual Magazine*, April 1860, p. 161: 'a writing table on which the four witnesses seated themselves was twice tilted over with a strange unearthly facility, and they landed on the floor'.

3 C. Richet, *Proceedings of the Society for Psychical Research* 14 (35), 1899, p. 156.

4 E. Feilding, W. W. Baggally and H. Carrington, *Proceedings of the Society for Psychical Research* 23 (59), 309–569, 1909.

5 G. L. Playfair, 'Psychotronics and the Subjective Mind', *Proceedings of the 5th International Conference on Psychotronic Research*, Bratislava, 1983, vol. 3, pp. 177–82.

6 J. B. Rhine, *Journal of Parapsychology*, June 1943, pp. 69–75.

7 Ibid., September 1943, pp. 139–43.

## III  Introduction

1 All quotations from Paracelsus are taken from Franz Hartmann, *The Life of Philippus Theophrastus, Bombast of Hohenheim ...*, London: George Redway, 1887.

2 E. J. Dingwall, 'The slow escape from magic', *International Journal of Parapsychology* 1 (1), 106–11, 1959.

3 J. P. F. Deleuze, *Practical Instructions in Animal Magnetism* (1825), London: H. Baillière, 4th edn, 1850, ch. 10.

4 J. P. F. Deleuze, *Histoire critique du magnétisme animal*, Paris: Belin-Leprieur, 2nd edn, 1819 (2 vols), pp. 132–5.

5 Marquis de Puységur, *Recherches ... dans le somnambulisme*, Paris: Dentu, 1811, pp. 60–1.

6 Marquis de Puységur, *Mémoires pour servir à l'histoire et à l'établissement du magnétisme animal*, Paris: Cellot, 2nd edn, 1809, p. 224.

7 E. Sargent, *The Scientific Basis of Spiritualism*, Boston: Colby & Rich, 1881, ch. 7.

8 C. H. Townshend, *Facts in Mesmerism*, London: H. Baillière, 1844, pp. 323, 343.

9 J. C. Colquhoun, *Isis Revelata*, Edinburgh: Maclachlan & Stewart, 3rd edn, 1836 (2 vols), vol. 1, p. 59; vol. 2, pp. 172–3.

10 L. Pulos, 'Mesmerism revisited: the effectiveness of Esdaile's techniques in the production of deep hypnosis and total body hypnoanaesthesia', *American Journal of Clinical Hypnosis* 20 (4), 206–11, 1980; personal communications July and August 1984.

11  *The Magic Moment*

1   E. Coué, *Self-Mastery Through Conscious Autosuggestion*, London: Allen & Unwin, 1922, pp. 11–14, 82.
2   C. Baudouin, *Suggestion and Autosuggestion*, London: Allen & Unwin, 1920, ch. 6.
3   *Science Digest*, January 1982, pp. 86–92.
4   N. McWhirter, *Ross. The Story of a Shared Life*, London: Churchill, 1976, ch. 14.
5   M. Bentine, *The Door Marked Summer*, London: Granada, 1981, ch. 12.
6   J. Mander, *Four Arguments for the Elimination of Television*, New York: Morrow, 1978.
7   H. Edwards, *The Power of Spiritual Healing*, London: Herbert Jenkins, 1963, p. 98.
8   Enquiries regarding spiritual healers to: National Federation of Spiritual Healers, Old Manor Farm Studio, Church St, Sunbury-on-Thames, Surrey.
9   L. D. Weatherhead, *Psychology, Religion and Healing*, London: Hodder & Stoughton, rev. edn 1963, pp. 442–3.
10  A. R. Wallace, *On Miracles and Modern Spiritualism*, London: Burns, 2nd edn, 1874, ch. 10.
11  *Proceedings of the Society for Psychical Research*, several papers in vols. 1–3, 1882–5.
12  C. T. Tart (ed.), *Altered States of Consciousness*, New York: Wiley, 1969, ch. 19.
13  G. Rein, lecture at the College of Psychic Studies, 1 May 1984, unpublished MS and several personal communications 1982–4.
14  G. F. Solfvin, *European Journal of Parapsychology*, 1982, pp. 159–97.
15  A. Erskine, *A Hypnotist's Case Book*, London: Rider, 1932, pp. 28–31.
16  R. J. Newman, 'A case history using hypnotic clairvoyant transfer in a treatment', *Proceedings of the British Society of Medical & Dental Hypnosis*, 4 (2), 39–41, 1978, and personal communication November 1983.
17  F. W. Knowles, 'Psychic healing in organic disease', *Journal of the American Society for Psychical Research*, 1956, pp. 110–18.
18  C. M. Barrows, 'Suggestion without hypnotism', *Proceedings of the Society for Psychical Research*, 12 (30), 21–44, 1896.
19  E. J. Dingwall (ed.), *Abnormal Hypnotic Phenomena*, London: Churchill, 1976 (4 vols).
20  S. Karagulla, *Breakthrough to Creativity*, Santa Monica: DeVorss, 1967.
21  S. Karagulla, interview by J. G. Bolen, *Psychic*, August 1973, pp. 6–11, 29–31.
22  F. Farrelly, interview by C. Bird, *Psychic*, August 1975, pp. 48–55.
23  R. Leichtman, profile by R. Neubert, *Psychic*, February 1976, pp. 32–6.
24  E. Spinelli, *Human Development and Paranormal Cognition*, unpublished thesis.
25  B. E. Schwarz, *Parent–Child Telepathy*, New York: Garrett, 1971.
26  L. LeShan, *Clairvoyant Reality*, Wellingborough: Turnstone, 1980.
27  L. LeShan, *From Newton to ESP*, Wellingborough: Turnstone, 1984, ch. 11.

28 L. LeShan, *Holistic Health*, Wellingborough: Turnstone, 1984 (former title: *The Mechanic and the Gardener*).

29 E. Whipp, interview with Janet Cohen, BBC Radio 4 *The World Tonight*, 20 February 1984.

30 J. P. F. Deleuze, *Practical Instructions in Animal Magnetism (1825)*, London: H. Baillière, 4th edn, 1850, pp. 231–3.

31 J. Esdaile, *Natural and Mesmeric Clairvoyance*, London: H. Baillière, 1852, p. 129.

12  *How to work Miracles*

 1 J. Layard, 'Psi phenomena and poltergeists', *Proceedings of the Society for Psychical Research*, 47 (168), 237–47, 1943 (pp. 239–40).

 2 J. Rothenberg quoted in J. Halifax, *Shamanic Voices*, Harmondsworth: Penguin, 1980, pp. 4, 121.

 3 A. W. Scheflin and E. M. Opton Jr, *The Mind Manipulators*, London: Paddington Press, 1978.

 4 J. Halifax, op. cit.

 5 M. Eliade, *Shamanism. Archaic Techniques of Ecstasy*, Princeton University Press, 1964, pp. 112–13.

 6 M. Harner, *The Way of the Shaman*, New York: Bantam, 1982, p. 28.

 7 I. A. Manzhigeyev, *Buryatskie shamanisticheskie i doshamanisticheskie terminy*, Moscow: Izd. Nauka, 1978.

 8 *Parapsychology in the USSR* (ed. L. Vilenskaya), San Francisco: Washington Research Center, 3101 Washington St, CA 94115 (5 parts), Part 3, pp. 63–4.

 9 *Proceedings of the IV International Conference on Psychtronic Research*, São Paulo, 1979, vol. 1, pp. 260–5, 272–3; vol. 2, pp. 391.

10 *Parapsychology in the USSR*, op. cit., Part 1, p. 21; Part 3, pp. 42–5.

11 *Sunday Times*, 31 January 1982, p. 14.

12 B. Ivanova in *Gli Arcani*, November 1979. English summary in *Psychic News*, 24 July 1982, pp. 4–5.

13 T. Blau, personal communication, December 1980.

14 M. Murphy, *New Age*, March 1982, pp. 33–9.

15 M. Popovsky, *Manipulated Science*, Garden City: Doubleday, 1979, pp. 189–92 (quoted in *Psi Research*, March 1984, supplement).

16 W. R. Adey in *Magnetic Field Effects on Biological Systems* (ed. T. S. Tenforde), New York: Plenum, 1979, pp. 67–8.

17 E. Cayce in *The Edgar Cayce Reader* (ed. H. L. Cayce), New York: Paperback Library, 1969, pp. 15–19.

18 R. M. McRae, *Mind Wars*, New York: St Martins Press, 1984, ch. 6.

19 W. A. R. Thomson, *Faiths that Heal*, London: Black, 1980.

20 R. Gardner, *BMJ* 24/31 December 1983, pp. 1927–33.

21 S. Greer, lecture in *British Journal of Psychiatry*, December 1983, pp. 535–43; survey in *The Lancet* 2, 785–7, 1979.

22 A. Govinda, *The Way of the White Clouds*, London: Rider, 1984, p. 94.

23 L. LeShan, *Clairvoyant Reality*, Wellingborough: Turnstone, 1980.

24 M. Harner, *The Way of the Shaman*, New York: Bantam, 1982.

25 A. Cannon, *Powers That Be*, London: Francis Mott, 1934, p. 161.

*Conclusion*

1 M. J. Kottler, 'Alfred Russel Wallace, the origin of man, and spiritualism', *Isis* 65 (227), 145–92, 1974, p. 163.
2 C. Wilson, *New Pathways in Psychology*, London: Victor Gollancz, 1972, pp. 219–20.
3 A. Hardy, *The Biology of God*, London: Jonathan Cape, 1975, ch. 12.
4 A. Hardy, *The Spiritual Nature of Man*, Oxford: Clarendon Press, 1979.
5 Hardy, *The Biology of God*, op. cit., p. 231.
6 Hardy, *The Spiritual Nature of Man*, op. cit., p. 45.
7 B. Siegel quoted in *Science Digest*, May 1982, p. 92.
8 J. B. Rhine, *Journal of Parapsychology*, December 1943, p. 225.
9 A. Koestler, *The Invisible Writing*, London: Collins/Hamish Hamilton, 1954, ch. 33.
10 M. L. Rossman in Sheikh (ed.), *Imagination and Healing*, Farmingdale: Baywood, 1984, p. 232.
11 G. L. Schwartz in ibid., p. 42.
12 S. Black *Mind and Body*, London: William Kimber, 1969, p. 281.
13 G. Schaefer, quoted in N. Coxhead, *The Relevance of Bliss*, London: Wildwood House, 1985, p. 132.

*Additional addresses:*

The Alister Hardy Research Centre (incorporating the RERU), Manchester College, Oxford.
The British Society of Medical and Dental Hypnotists (Secretariat), 42 Links Road, Ashtead, Surrey KT21 2HT.

# Index